Breaking Ground

Leaving Certificate

AGRICULTURAL SCIENCE TODAY

Carol Cronin & Sandra Tiernan

*Darina Doody
6th year.*

EDCO

THE EDUCATIONAL COMPANY

First published 2011
The Educational Company of Ireland
Ballymount Road
Walkinstown
Dublin 12
www.edco.ie

A member of the Smurfit Kappa Group plc

ISBN 978-1-84536-369-7

The paper used in this book comes from Managed Forests in Northern Europe For every tree felled, at least one new tree is planted

QUALITY
I.S. EN ISO 9001:2008
NSAI Certified

Editor: Kate Duffy
Design and Layout: Brendan O'Connell
Artwork: Daghda
Indexer: Patricia Carroll
Cover Design: Design Image
Cover Photography: SPL, Alamy
Printed by W&G Baird

Photograph Acknowledgements
Page 136 Sponge courtesy of Pharmplex Ltd., Ram Crayon courtesy of Ritchey.
Page 143 courtesy of Susan Schoenian, Sheep & Goat Specialist, University of Maryland Extension, USA.
All other photos Alamy, Carol Cronin, Corbis, Getty Images, iStockphoto, Sandra Tiernan, Science Photo Library, Shutterstock.

- Free online multiple choice tests are available on *www.edcoexamcentre.ie*
- Solutions available online for teachers on *www.edcoDigital.ie*
- Available in ebook format on *www.edcoDigital.ie* for teachers to use with an IWB or Data Projector

Acknowledgements

We would like to thank everyone at Edco for their support, help and advice from beginning to end: Emer Ryan, Jennifer Powell, Declan Dempsey and Marie Gray. Sincere thanks to our editor Kate Duffy and to Brendan O'Connell for the design and layout of the book.

We would like to thank everyone who gave their time and expert knowledge to us when writing this book: Brian Costello and Lough Gara Farm, Barry Lynch and the Green Veterinary Clinic, Boyle, Frank Buckley and Teagasc Moorepark Dairy Research, James and Martin McNamara, Kieran Gallagher, John and Eoin Purfield, John Foley and Maizetech Ltd, Colm O'Muireagain and Sligo District Veterinary Office, Frank Hynes, William John Fitzmaurice, Ann Mullen, Felix McCabe and Ballyhaise Agricultural College, Pat Greaney, Pius Earley, William Flanagan, Paul Manton, and the Leaving Certificate Agricultural Science Classes 2011 of Castleknock College, Castleknock, Dublin and Abbey Community College, Boyle, Co. Roscommon for their valuable feedback.

We would also like to acknowledge Teagasc and their research centres at Grange, Moorepark and Athenry, Coillte, Department of Agriculture, Fisheries and Food without whose research and information this book would not have been possible.
We would also like to thank the Cronin and Tiernan families for their ongoing support while writing this book.

Contents

Introduction

Breaking Ground is written for the Leaving Certificate Agricultural Science course for both Higher and Ordinary Level students.

As there is no differentiation between Higher and Ordinary Level material in the syllabus, the material is presented in such a way as to facilitate Higher and Ordinary Level students.

The book is divided into colour-coded units to fulfil the requirements of the syllabus, the practical coursework and the written examination. The most up-to-date agricultural practices and research available have been included in the units on crops, grassland and animal production. The early units focus on the scientific concepts underlying the course, while the later units have an agricultural focus. Teachers may choose to teach the units in a different order if preferred.

Each chapter has a concise summary followed by questions suitable for both revision and homework. In addition, examination questions have been included from recent past examination papers at Higher and Ordinary Level.

The textbook has been laid out to begin with units on plant and animal physiology, creating a link between Junior Certificate Science and Leaving Certificate Agricultural Science, allowing students to build on their knowledge and to expand on it in greater detail. Students are initially introduced to topics with which they are familiar, while links between science and agriculture have been created from the beginning. Where possible, agricultural examples are used to explain scientific concepts or theories.

This book includes a large range of diagrams and coloured photographs; these are used throughout the text to aid student understanding. Definitions have been highlighted in the relevant chapters and are also included in a glossary at the end of the book.

A number of case studies have been included in the text to highlight contemporary issues in agriculture that are relevant to the course. In researching and compiling material for the text, many experts in their fields were contacted to ensure that the most recent advances in agriculture have been included in this book. It will also give students a feel for contemporary practices and issues in the Irish agricultural community. Crops that are increasing in popularity and importance in Irish agriculture have been included in the text. These topics have also appeared on the most recent examination papers.

As there is no mandatory list of experiments included in the syllabus, this book includes a wide range of experiments and activities to meet the requirements of the practical coursework assessment and the written examination at both Higher and Ordinary Level. Experiments have been included in the text where relevant to the theory, to complement the material and to improve student learning and understanding. Experiments have been highlighted throughout the text in green panels.

Project links have been included in the relevant sections of the text to guide both teachers and students in the completion of the coursework portfolio. Guidelines are provided for the writing of the crop and animal production projects for the practical coursework assessment.

Teachers can access the *Breaking Ground* e-book and further teacher resources by registering on *www.edcoDigital.ie*. Students can complete multiple choice tests on *www.edcoexamcentre.ie*.

General guidelines

Students should keep a notebook or folder as a written record of all practical activities (experiments, field work, excursions to farms, etc.).

Diagrams should be included wherever possible, and results and conclusions for all investigations should be recorded.

For the animal and crop production projects, students are recommended to take photographs as evidence of their practical experience.

Carol Cronin and Sandra Tiernan

●●●● UNIT 1

Plant Science

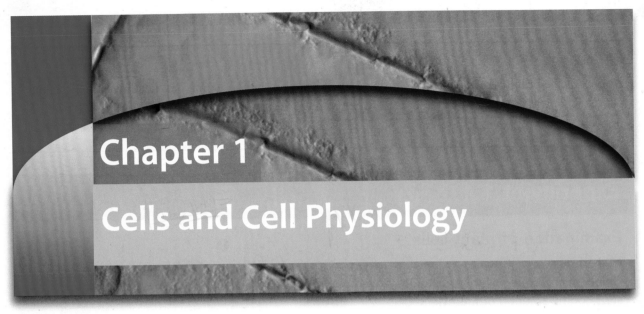

Chapter 1

Cells and Cell Physiology

≡ Cells

The basic unit of all living organisms is the cell. Organisms such as bacteria and some fungi are unicellular (these organisms are studied in Chapter 6), while the majority of organisms are multicellular. Most cells are not visible to the naked eye and have to be viewed under a microscope. Upon examination it is clear that both plant and animals cells have many features in common.

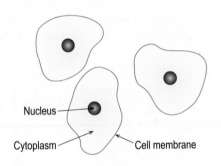

||||| Fig 1.1 Animal cheek cell

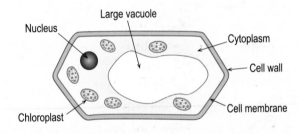

||||| Fig 1.3 Plant cell

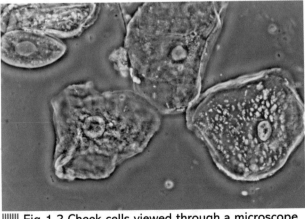

||||| Fig 1.2 Cheek cells viewed through a microscope

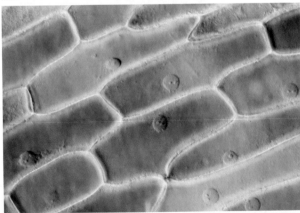

||||| Fig 1.4 Onion cells viewed through a microscope

Both animal and plant cells have a nucleus, a cell membrane, cytoplasm and several other organelles in common, some of which can only be seen with an electron microscope. In addition, plant cells have a cell wall, large vacuoles and chloroplasts.

Project link

As part of the practical examination, students must have carried out some practical investigations on plants. Chapters 1–4 have a range of experiments that are suitable for the completion of this part of the coursework.

Experiment 1.1

Examination of plant cells

Materials

Onion, microscope, microscope slides, cover slips, iodine solution or methylene blue, chopping board, sharp knife, mounted needle, forceps, filter paper, dropper, deionised water

Method

1 Cut the onion carefully with the sharp knife.

2 Separate two leaves of the onion and carefully remove the thin epidermal layer on the inside of the leaf. Cut the epidermis into small pieces.

3 Using the forceps, transfer the piece of epidermis onto the slide. Place a drop of water onto the piece of epidermis. This prevents the cells from drying out.

4 Place the cover slip at a right angle to the slide and use the mounted needle to lower the cover slip onto the epidermis, ensure that no air bubbles become trapped.

5 Add a drop of iodine to one side of the cover slip. Draw the iodine across the slide by placing a piece of filter paper at the opposite end of the cover slip.

6 Remove any excess stain or water from the slide before placing the slide on the microscope's stage.

7 Observe the slide under low power first and then under high power. Identify the cell wall, cell membrane, cytoplasm and nucleus in the plant cell.

8 Draw a labelled diagram of your observations.

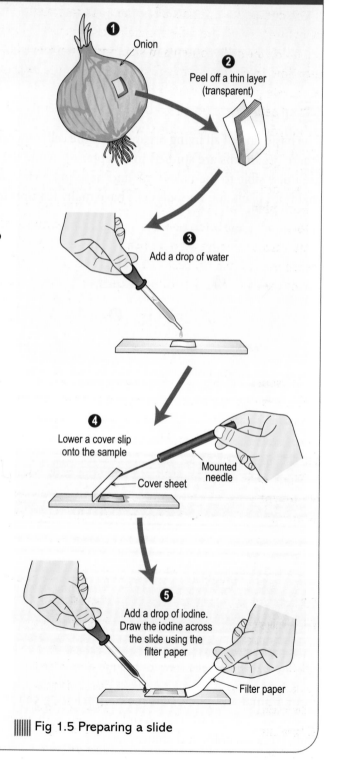

Fig 1.5 Preparing a slide

Cell structure

The nucleus is the control centre of the cell and is composed of a substance called chromatin. Chromatin is a mixture of DNA (deoxyribonucleic acid) and protein. During cell division, the chromatin condenses to form chromosomes. The chromosomes contain the genetic instructions that control the structure and functions of the cell.

A **eukaryotic cell** is a cell containing a membrane-bounded nucleus that holds genetic information and membrane-bounded organelles (e.g. mitochondria and chloroplasts).

The nucleus is separated from the contents of the cytoplasm by a nuclear membrane. Therefore, plant and animal cells are classified as eukaryotic cells.

The cytoplasm consists of a watery fluid called the cytosol and all the cell's organelles are suspended in it. Plant and animal cells each have a cell membrane that holds the cell's contents in shape and controls what enters and leaves the cell. The cell membrane does not allow free movement of all substances into and out of the cell, and for this reason it is known as a selectively permeable membrane.

Plant cells have a porous cell wall that surrounds the cell membrane. The cell wall is composed of a rigid carbohydrate called cellulose, which protects and strengthens the cell. The mineral element, calcium, is essential for the production of healthy cell walls. Plant cells also have large vacuoles, which are normally filled with a watery fluid that gives extra support to the plant cell and in some cases can be used for the storage of dissolved substances such as sugars and salt. Animal cells have much smaller vacuoles.

Both plant and animal cells contain mitochondria, which are not visible using a light microscope. The mitochondria are often referred to as the powerhouse of the cell, as they are involved in the release of energy from glucose during aerobic respiration. During this chemical reaction, glucose is broken down in the presence of oxygen to produce carbon dioxide, water and energy in the form of ATP, which is the energy source used by cells. The overall equation for the reaction is:

$$\text{Glucose} + \text{Oxygen} \longrightarrow \text{Carbon dioxide} + \text{Water} + \text{Energy}$$

$$C_6H_{12}O_6 + 6O_2 \longrightarrow 6CO_2 + 6H_2O + \text{Energy}$$

The first stage of respiration, known as glycolysis, occurs in the cytosol. Glucose is broken down into two molecules of pyruvic acid. If oxygen is available, the pyruvic acid passes into the mitochondria and goes through a series of chemical reactions, collectively known as the Krebs cycle and hydrogen carrier system. Here, pyruvic acid is completely broken down into carbon dioxide and water and in the process produces a large amount of ATP.

Plant cells contain chloroplasts that hold the green pigment chlorophyll, which is essential for photosynthesis. (Photosynthesis is covered in greater detail in Chapter 2.) Both chloroplasts and mitochondria contain their own DNA allowing them to reproduce themselves by division.

Table 1.1 The function of cell contents

Structure	Cell type	Function
Cell wall	Plant cell only	Strengthens and protects cell
Cell membrane	Plant and animal	Controls the passage of substances into and out of the cell
Cytoplasm	Plant and animal	Fluid contains cell organelles
Nucleus	Plant and animal	Controls centre of the cell, cell division; contains DNA
Mitochondria	Plant and animal	Respiration
Chloroplasts	Plant cell only	Photosynthesis, contains chlorophyll
Large vacuole	Plant cell only	Support and storage of dissolved substances

Experiment 1.2

To investigate if heat is released from germinating seeds

Materials
Two thermos flasks, seeds (peas), two thermometers, cotton wool, Milton or mild disinfectant

Method
1 Soak peas in a beaker of water overnight.

2 Wash and disinfect the thermos flasks before you begin. This kills any bacteria that might be present.

3 Divide the peas into two equal groups, A and B. Place one batch into a beaker with some water. Boil group A over a Bunsen burner for five minutes. This will kill the peas. Allow the peas to cool.

4 Sterilise both batches of peas by placing them in separate beakers of water containing a weak solution of Milton. Leave for 10 minutes.

5 Label the thermos flasks A and B. Place batch A peas into thermos A and batch B into thermos B.

6 Seal both flasks with some cotton wool and place a thermometer in each. Record the initial temperature of both flasks.

7 Over the next week, check and record the temperature of the flasks.

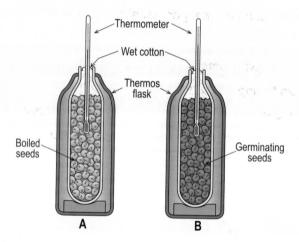

||||| Fig 1.6 Set up of experiment to measure heat released by germinating peas

Table 1.2 Heat released from germinating seeds							
Flask	Day 1	2	3	4	5	6	7
A							
B							

Result
The temperature of flask B, the live peas, should increase. This is due to the germinating peas respiring and as a result producing heat. There should be no change in the temperature of flask A, the dead peas, as dead peas do not respire.

Movement of substances across the cell membrane

As previously stated, cell membranes are selectively permeable and allow the free movement of gases O_2 and CO_2 across them, but restrict the movement of other molecules. The movement of substances across the cell membrane occurs by the following mechanisms: diffusion, osmosis and active transport.

Diffusion

The random movement of particles causes diffusion as they spread out to occupy all the space available to them. Diffusion is a passive process; therefore it does not require any energy. Oxygen and carbon dioxide diffuse across cell membranes along a concentrated gradient. For example, blood capillaries surrounding the body's cells contain a

> **Diffusion**: The movement of a substance from an area of high concentration to an area of low concentration along a concentration gradient.

high concentration of oxygen, while the cells have a low concentration of oxygen. As a result, oxygen moves from the blood cells into the cells. Diffusion can easily be demonstrated in the lab.

Experiment 1.3

To demonstrate diffusion in a liquid

Materials
Beaker, water, crystal of potassium permanganate, straw or glass tubing, forceps

Method
1 Fill a beaker two-thirds full with water.
2 Place the straw or glass tubing into the water.
3 Using the forceps drop a crystal of the potassium permanganate down the tube.
4 Place your finger over the end of the tube and remove it from the water.
5 Leave the beaker to stand for an hour, observing it regularly.

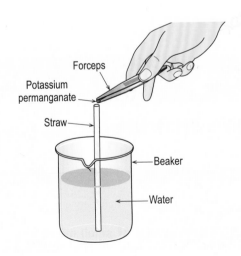

||| Fig 1.7 Addition of potassium permanganate to water

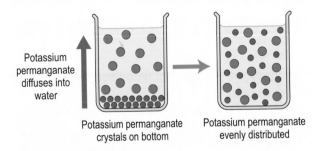

||| Fig 1.8 Diffusion of potassium permanganate in water

Experiment 1.3

Result

The purple colour of the potassium permanganate spreads out until it is evenly dispersed throughout the liquid. This is caused by the diffusion of the potassium permanganate particles.

||||| Fig 1.9 Potassium permanganate

Osmosis

Osmosis is a special type of diffusion as it directly refers to the movement of water across a semipermeable membrane. If the fluid inside the cell contains a lot of dissolved solutes and very little water, it is said to be concentrated. If the fluid

> **Osmosis**: The movement of water across a semipermeable membrane from an area of high water concentration to an area of low water concentration.

outside the cell contains a lot of water and very little dissolved solutes, it is dilute. Therefore, water will move into the cells across the semipermeable membrane by osmosis. Osmosis is passive, requiring no energy.

Experiment 1.4

To investigate osmosis across a semipermeable membrane

Materials
Visking or dialysis tubing, deionised water, sucrose solution, electronic balance, two beakers, paper towels

Note: Visking or dialysis tubing has tiny pores in it that allow the movement of small molecules like water across it, but prevent the movement of larger molecules like sucrose. Thus it behaves similarly to cell membranes found in living organisms.

Experiment 1.4

Method

1   Cut two pieces of dialysis tubing the same length, about 30 cm.

2   Under a stream of running water, soften the pieces of dialysis tubing until they separate. Tie a knot in one end.

3   Carefully half fill one dialysis tubing bag with the sucrose solution. Fill the other half with deionised water; this is the control. Squeeze as much of the air as possible out of each bag and tie a knot in the other end.

4   Dry both tubings with paper towels and record their mass in a table similar to the one below.

5   Half fill both the beakers with deionised water. Place the tube containing the sucrose solution in one beaker and the tube containing the deionised water in the other. Set up the apparatus as shown in Fig 1.10.

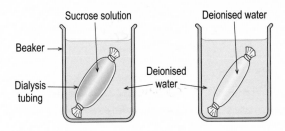

Fig 1.10 Movement of water by osmosis

6   Leave the apparatus to stand for at least one hour.

7   Remove the tubes containing the sucrose and the deionised water from the beakers. Dry with a paper towel and reweigh them. Observe any changes that have occurred to the sucrose tubing.

Result

Table 1.3 Osmosis across a semipermeable membrane			
Contents of tube	Start mass	Final mass	Change
Sucrose			
Deionised water			

From your results, the mass of the tube containing the sucrose will have increased and the contents of the tube will increase. Osmosis will have occurred, as the concentration of water inside the bag is low, while outside it is high. Water will move into the dialysis tubing across its membrane resulting in an increase in the mass of the tubing containing sucrose. Sucrose cannot move out of the dialysis tubing, as its particles are too large to pass through the pores in the dialysis tubing. No change will have occurred in the tubing containing deionised water.

Experiment 1.5

To demonstrate osmosis in living cells

Materials

Potato, two petri dishes, deionised water, salt, sharp knife, beaker, boiling water

Method

1 Cut the potato in half. At the rounded end of each half, remove some of the skin and make a small hollow.

2 Place one half of the potato into some boiling water and boil it for several minutes to kill it.

3 Fill two petri dishes with equal amounts of deionised water. Place the potatoes into the petri dish as shown in Fig 1.11.

4 Add equal amounts of salt to each hollow and leave to stand for at least one hour.

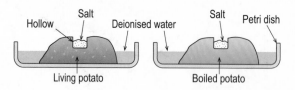

||||| Fig 1.11 Demonstration of osmosis in living cells

5 Record you observations.

Result

In the living potato, water will have moved into the hollow by osmosis. There will be no change to the dead potato as boiling has destroyed the cell membranes and therefore osmosis cannot occur.

Cytoplasm

The cytoplasm of plant cells contains many dissolved solutes. As a result, the concentration of cytoplasm is far greater than that of pure water. This causes water to move into plant cells by osmosis, causing the cytoplasm to swell and push against the rigid cell wall. This results in a pressure building up known as turgor pressure. This pressure provides mechanical support to plants and during hot weather or when there is a lack of water, plants will start to wilt due to a loss of turgor pressure. If plant cells are placed in a concentrated salt solution, then water moves out of the cell by osmosis. This causes the cytoplasm and cell membrane to shrink away from the cell wall. Such cells undergo plasmolysis.

Turgor pressure and plasmolysis

Turgor pressure

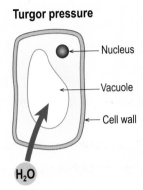

Nucleus

Vacuole

Cell wall

H₂O

Plasmolysis

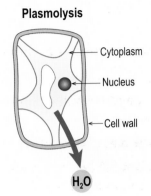

Cytoplasm

Nucleus

Cell wall

H₂O

▐▐▐ Fig 1.12 Cells exhibiting turgor pressure and plasmolysis

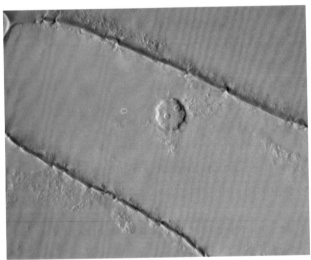

▐▐▐ Fig 1.13 Red onion cells showing turgor pressure

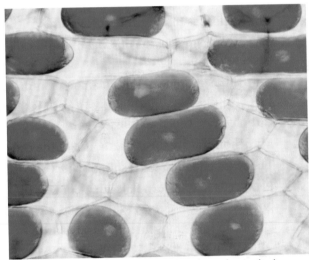

▐▐▐ Fig 1.14 Red onion cells showing plasmolysis

Plasmolysis is easily demonstrated in the lab with a piece of red onion epidermis.

1   Prepare a slide with the red onion epidermis as previously described in Experiment 1.1, page 4.

2   Observe the slide under a microscope. The red pigmentation of the red onion makes it easy to observe the cell wall, the cytoplasm and cell membrane.

3   Using a dropper add some concentrated salt solution to one side of the cover slip.

4   Draw this solution across the onion epidermis using some filter paper.

5   Leave the slide to stand for a few minutes.

6   Observe the slide under the microscope and this time notice that the cell membrane and the cytoplasm have decreased in size due to the movement of water out of the cell by osmosis.

7   These cells can be returned to normal by adding deionised water to the cells and leaving them for a few minutes.

Active transport

Plants get important nutrients such as nitrates and phosphates from the soil. These nutrients are dissolved in the soil water and are absorbed into the plant through the root hairs. Unlike water, which enters the root hairs by osmosis, these nutrients have to be actively imported across the cell membranes. This requires energy, supplied by ATP,

Active transport: The movement of a substance from an area of low concentration to an area of high concentration against a concentration gradient; this movement requires energy.

and this process is known as active transport. Here, the movement of nutrient ions is from a region of lower concentration (soil solution) to a region of high concentration (root hairs) against a concentration gradient.

Summary

- The cell is the basic unit of all living organisms.
- Plant and animal cells have a nucleus, cell membrane and cytoplasm in common. Only plant cells have a cell wall, chloroplast and large vacuoles.
- The nucleus is the control centre of the cell.
- The cytoplasm consists of a watery fluid called the cytosol and all the cell's organelles are suspended in it.
- The cell membrane of both plant and animal cells is selectively permeable.
- Plant cells have a cell wall that surrounds the cell membrane and it is composed of a rigid carbohydrate called cellulose.
- Mitochondria are the powerhouse of the cell and they have a role in aerobic respiration.
- The word equation for respiration is: Glucose + Oxygen → Carbon dioxide + Water + Energy
- Plant cells have chloroplasts that contain the green pigment chlorophyll, which is essential for photosynthesis.
- Diffusion is the movement of a substance from an area of high concentration to an area of low concentration along a concentration gradient without the use of energy.
- Osmosis is the movement of water across a semipermeable membrane from an area of high water concentration to an area of low water concentration.
- Osmosis is responsible for maintaining turgor pressure in plant cells.
- Active transport is the movement of a substance from an area of low concentration to an area of high concentration against a concentration gradient; this movement requires energy.
- Plant nutrients in soil water move into plant cells by active transport.

QUESTIONS

1 Draw a labelled diagram of a plant cell.
2 Explain the function of the following parts:
   (a) Cell wall
   (b) Cell membrane
   (c) Nucleus
   (d) Mitochondria
   (e) Chloroplast.

QUESTIONS

3   Where in the cell would you find the following substances?
   (a) DNA
   (b) Chlorophyll
   (c) Mitochondria
   (d) Cellulose.
4   Describe how you would prepare a slide of plant tissue.
5   Distinguish between each of the following:
   (a) Chromatin and chromosome
   (b) Cell membrane and cell wall
   (c) Osmosis and diffusion
   (d) Turgor pressure and plasmolysis
   (e) Chloroplast and mitochondria.
6   Apart from the nucleus, what other organelles in the cell contain DNA?
7   Distinguish between active transport and diffusion.
8   Cell membranes are described as being *selectively permeable*. Explain the meaning of this term.

EXAM QUESTIONS

1   Draw a diagram of a simple animal cell (e.g. cheek cell), as seen under a light microscope. Label any three parts. Where in the cell are chromosomes found? (LC, OL, 2003)
2   State two differences between plant and animal cells. (LC, HL, 2003)
3   Define osmosis. Describe, with the aid of a labelled diagram, a laboratory investigation to demonstrate osmosis. (LC, OL, 2006)
4   Explain why energy is expended in the uptake of mineral nutrients in ionic form by plant roots. (LC, HL, 2002)
5   Name (a) a polysaccharide and (b) a mineral element that form the main structural units of the cell wall of plants. (LC, HL, 2007)
6   Give a scientific explanation for:
   (a) The production of carbon dioxide in the body
   (b) The absorption of water by the root hairs of plants
   (c) Potted plants losing turgidity on a warm day. (LC, HL, 2003)
   (d) The production of carbon dioxide in the animal body. (LC, HL, 2004)

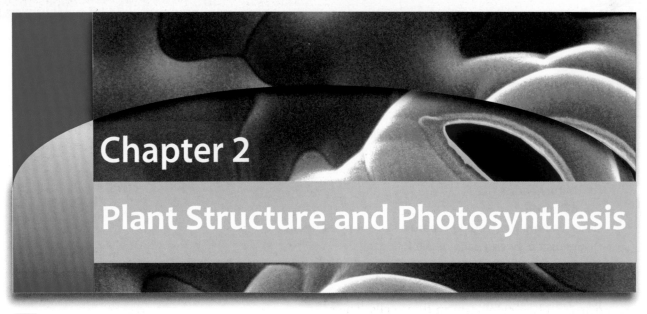

Chapter 2
Plant Structure and Photosynthesis

≡ Flowering Plants

Flowering plants are the most important group of plants in agriculture. Dandelions, daisies and buttercups with their bright petals and attractive scents are instantly recognisable as flowering plants; but you have to look closely at grasses and cereals to recognise the same basic flower structure, which is a little less obvious, to see that they too belong to this group called the angiosperms.

||||| Fig 2.1 Grass flower

||||| Fig 2.2 Dandelion flowers

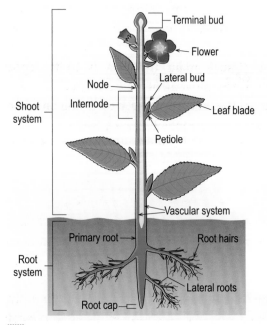

||||| Fig 2.3 The shoot system and the root system of a flowering plant

The flowering plant structure can be broken up into two parts: the shoot system and the root system.

The shoot system consists of the stem, leaves and flowers and its main functions are photosynthesis and the transport of water, minerals and food.

The functions of the root system are to anchor the plant into the ground, to absorb water and minerals and, in some cases, to store food.

☰ Plant Tissue

Plant tissues can be divided into dermal tissue, ground tissue and vascular tissue.

- **Dermal tissue** forms the outer layer of a plant and its function is protection.
- **Ground tissue** has many functions depending on its location in the plant. Some of these functions include photosynthesis, storing food and support.
- **Vascular tissue** is transport tissue and is composed of xylem and phloem. Xylem tissue transports water and minerals from the roots up to the leaves. Phloem transports the sugars produced by photosynthesis from the leaves usually to the roots or other parts of the plant for storage.

Xylem

The xylem is composed of two main types of cell: the xylem vessel and tracheids. Xylem cells are dead; there is no nucleus and no cytoplasm in these cells. Their cell walls are reinforced with lignin, a very strong and durable carbohydrate, which provides strength and support to the cells.

Xylem vessels are much larger than tracheids and lack end walls. The tracheids are elongated cells with tapered ends. Pits in the walls of the xylem vessels and tracheids allow for the lateral movement of water. Both xylem vessels and tracheids are arranged in plants so that there is a continuous route for water to travel from the roots to the leaves.

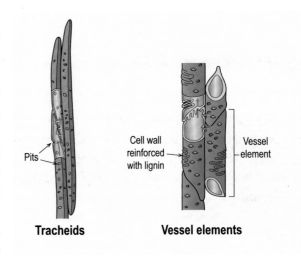

Fig 2.4 Xylem vessels and tracheids

Phloem

Phloem tissue is composed of a sieve tube with its companion cell. Unlike xylem tissue, phloem tissue is composed of living cells. Sieve tubes do not have nuclei; therefore, companion cells control and maintain the sieve tube. Sieve tubes are long cells with perforated end walls known as sieve plates.

Phloem tissue's main function is to transport sugars. However, movement of the sugars can occur up and down the phloem tissue, depending on where the food is required. In the stems and leaves of plants, xylem and phloem tissues are found together in vascular bundles.

Monocotyledons and dicotyledons

Flowering plants can be divided into two groups: monocots and dicots, depending on the number of cotyledons or seed leaves that the plant has. Monocots have only one cotyledon and dicots have two cotyledons.

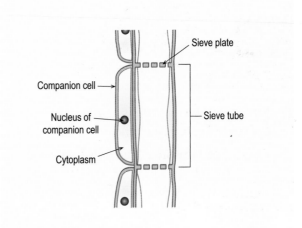

Fig 2.5 Phloem tissue showing sieve tubes and companion cells

The cotyledons provide energy for the germinating seed until the true leaves have formed and can start photosynthesising. Grasses and cereals are monocots while daisies, dandelions and most other plants are dicots. Monocots and dicots have several other structural differences as summarised in Table 2.1, page 16.

Table 2.1 Characteristics of monocots and dicots	
Monocot	**Dicot**
• One cotyledon in the seed • Fibrous root, no main root • Narrow leaf with parallel veins • Vascular bundles are scattered in the stem • The flower parts are arranged in threes or multiples of three	• Two cotyledons in the seed • One large root known as a tap root • Broad leaf with netted veins • Vascular bundles are arranged in a ring in the stem • The flower parts are arranged in multiples of four or five

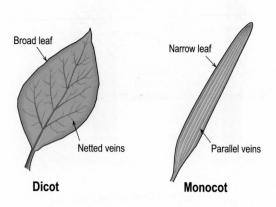

||||| Fig 2.6 A narrow leaf showing parallel veins and a broad leaf showing netted veins

||||| Fig 2.7 A fibrous root and a tap root

Dicot root

Figure 2.8 shows that the dicot root is broken up into several regions: root cap, zone of cell division, zone of elongation and zone of differentiation.

- **Root cap**: The root cap is a protective layer of cells over the meristematic tissue behind it.

- **Zone of cell division**: The cells in this region are meristematic cells, meaning that they are constantly dividing by mitosis to produce new cells for the root cap and for the zone of elongation.

- **Zone of elongation**: Here the new cells grow and become larger.

- **Zone of differentiation**: This zone is easily identified by the presence of root hairs. In this region, the cells become specialised, taking on specific roles. Some cells will become xylem tissue; others will become phloem tissue, ground tissue and dermal tissue.

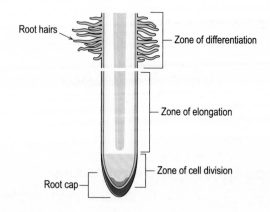

||||| Fig 2.8 A longitudinal section of a dicot root

If the dicot root is cut above the zone of differentiation and examined in transverse section it will look like Fig 2.9.

In the dicot root, the xylem tissue appears in the centre and is in the shape of a cross. The phloem tissue occurs between the arms of the xylem. Outside this is a layer of cells called the endodermis. These cells control the movement of substances from the cortex into the vascular tissue. The cortex, which is composed of ground tissue and is often used for food storage, is surrounded by a layer of dermal tissue.

Monocot and dicot stems

Examine Figures 2.10 and 2.11 of monocot and dicot stems. The most obvious difference between the two is the arrangement of the vascular bundles (xylem and phloem). In the monocot stem, the vascular bundles are scattered, while in the dicot stem, the vascular bundles are arranged in a circular manner. In addition, the vascular bundles of a dicot stem have a layer of cambium tissue between the phloem and the xylem. This tissue allows for secondary thickening in shrubs and trees. Note that in a dicot stem, the xylem tissue is on the inside and the phloem is on the outside of the vascular bundles.

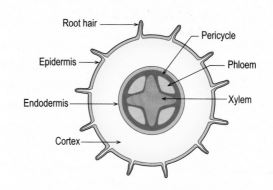

Fig 2.9 A transverse section of a dicot root

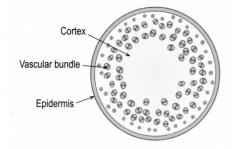

Fig 2.10 (a) A monocot stem

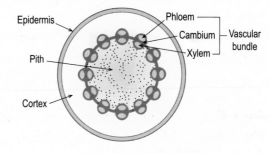

Fig 2.11 (a) A dicot stem

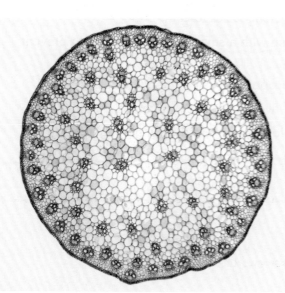

Fig 2.10 (b) A monocot stem

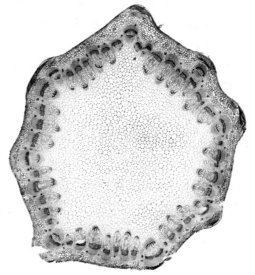

Fig 2.11 (b) A dicot stem

Experiment 2.1

To prepare a slide of a dicot stem and examine it under a light microscope

Materials

Herbaceous plant (busy lizzies or geraniums work well), elder pith, scalpel or a safety blade, microscope slides, cover slip, microscope, petri dish, small paintbrush, water

Method

1   Cut a section of the stem between two nodes as shown in Fig 2.12.

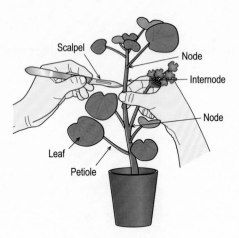
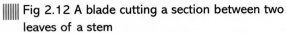

▓ Fig 2.12 A blade cutting a section between two leaves of a stem

▓ Fig 2.13 A blade cutting thin sections of the stem

2   Lay the stem flat on the bench and use a wet blade to cut very thin sections of the stem at right angles to the stem and away from your fingers. If this is proving difficult, the stem can be placed into some elder pith, which will make the stem easier to cut.

3   Place the cut sections of the stem into a petri dish with a small amount of water to prevent them drying out.

4   Transfer the thinnest section of stem to a microscope slide using the paintbrush.

5   Place the cover slip onto the stem at an angle to avoid trapping air bubbles.

6   View the slide under the microscope; first using low power and then under high power.

7   Draw and label a diagram of what you observed.

☰ The Leaf and Photosynthesis

The leaf is a highly specialised organ, whose main function is to produce food by photosynthesis. For this reason, plants are autotrophic. Here light energy from the sun is trapped by chlorophyll in the chloroplasts and this energy is used to combine hydrogen from water and carbon dioxide to make glucose and oxygen. The balanced chemical equation is:

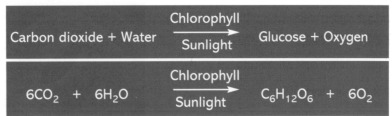

$$\text{Carbon dioxide} + \text{Water} \xrightarrow[\text{Sunlight}]{\text{Chlorophyll}} \text{Glucose} + \text{Oxygen}$$

$$6CO_2 + 6H_2O \xrightarrow[\text{Sunlight}]{\text{Chlorophyll}} C_6H_{12}O_6 + 6O_2$$

Even though oxygen is often seen as a waste product of photosynthesis, the plant does not excrete all the oxygen it produces. Plant cells also respire and oxygen is required for respiration. Only the excess oxygen is excreted through the stomata.

The leaf has many adaptations for photosynthesis. Firstly, the leaf is flat, which maximises the surface area for photosynthesis. Most plants have a waxy cuticle on the upper surface of the leaf. This prevents the leaf from losing water from the upper surface. Underneath the epidermis is a layer of tightly packed elongated cells, called the palisade cells. These cells contain large numbers of chloroplasts and they carry out the majority of photosynthesis in the leaf. The spongy mesophyll layer has many air spaces between the cells and this allows for the rapid diffusion of gases to and from the palisade layer.

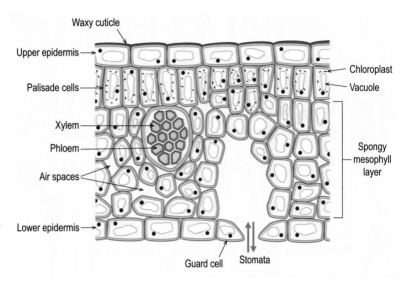

▥ Fig 2.14 A transverse section of a leaf

Vascular tissue present in the leaf facilitates transport. Xylem tissue supplies water to the cells. Phloem tissue removes the sugars produced by photosynthesis. On the lower leaf surface there are many openings called stomata. These stomata allow carbon dioxide to diffuse into the leaf from the air and oxygen, and water vapour to diffuse out. The opening and closing of these stomata are controlled by guard cells. Stomata are normally

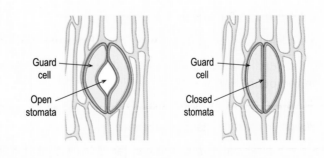

▥ Fig 2.15 An open and closed stomata

open during the day to facilitate photosynthesis. However, plants lose vast amounts of water vapour through the stomata. If water is not plentiful in the soil, the guard cells close the open stomata to prevent further water loss by the plant.

Table 2.2 Adaptations of leaf for photosynthesis

Structure	Adaptation
Leaf	Flat shape gives large surface area
Cuticle	Prevents water loss
Palisade layer	Contains a large number of chloroplasts. The cells are tightly packed together to maximise sunlight captured
Spongy mesophyll	Many air spaces to allow rapid diffusion of gases
Vascular tissue	Transport of water and food
Stomata	Gaseous exchange
Guard cells	Open and close stomata

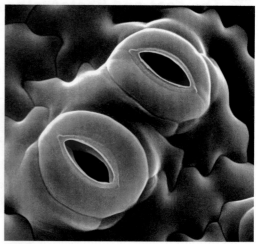

|||| Fig 2.16 Stomata viewed through a microscope

Experiment 2.2

To separate the pigments in chlorophyll using chromatography

Materials

Fresh grass or other plant material (spinach works well), sand, pestle and mortar, acetone, petroleum ether, gas jar and lid, filter paper, a capillary tube

Method

1 Place some fresh grass in a mortar with some sand and a small volume of acetone.

2 Grind up the mixture with the pestle. The sand helps to break up the cells and releases the chlorophyll.

3 Pour solvent (acetone or equal parts of petroleum ether and acetone) to the depth of 1 cm into the gas jar and cover with the lid.

4 Cut a piece of filter paper into long strips.

5 Use a pencil to draw a line about 2 cm from the end of the filter paper.

6 Use the capillary tube to transfer a drop of the chlorophyll extract to the filter paper and place it on the pencil line.

7 Allow the drop to dry and repeat the procedure several times until a concentrated spot of chlorophyll extract has been formed.

8 Place the filter paper into the gas jar. Ensure that the level of the solvent is below the pencil line.

9 The solvent will rise up through the filter paper and will separate out the pigment in the chlorophyll.

Experiment 2.2

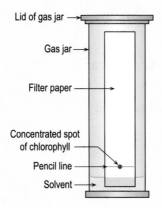

Lid of gas jar →
Gas jar →
Filter paper →
Concentrated spot of chlorophyll
Pencil line →
Solvent →

▦ Fig 2.17 A gas jar with solvent and filter paper

Result
The chlorophyll extract will separate into five pigments. The order in which they appear and their colour from the bottom of the filter paper is: chlorophyll b (green), chlorophyll a (blue-green), xanthophyll (yellow-brown), phaeophytin (yellow-grey) and carotene (yellow).

Experiment 2.3

To demonstrate that light is necessary for photosynthesis and to test a leaf for starch

Materials
Geranium plant (geraniums have no waxy cuticle, making it easier to remove the chlorophyll), aluminium foil, lamp, methylated spirits, test tube, hotplate, beaker, forceps, white tile, iodine solution

Method
1   Place the geranium plant in a cupboard for 48 hours to destarch it.
2   Wrap a piece of aluminium foil around a leaf. This is the control.
3   Leave the geranium plant in strong sunlight or overnight with a table lamp shining on it.
4   Half fill a beaker with water and heat it on a hotplate until it boils.
5   Remove the control leaf and another leaf from the plant and dip them into a beaker of boiling water to kill them. Turn off the hotplate.

Note: If you use a Bunsen burner to heat the water make sure that you keep the Bunsen away from the methylated spirits as it is flammable.

Experiment 2.3

6   Half fill two test tubes with methylated spirits. Place the leaves into the test tubes of alcohol and place the test tubes in the hot water for a few minutes. The warm alcohol will remove the chlorophyll from the leaf.

7   Remove the leaves from the methylated spirits and dip the leaves in the hot water to soften them.

8   Spread out the leaves onto a white tile and add iodine to the surface of the leaves.

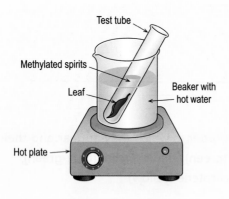

||||| Fig 2.18 Removal of chlorophyll from the leaf

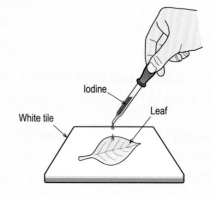

||||| Fig 2.19 Addition of iodine solution to the leaf

Result

The iodine solution will turn blue-black, indicating the presence of starch in the leaf that has been exposed to light. There will be no change to the colour of the iodine solution on the control leaf. As the control leaf was not exposed to light it could not photosynthesise; therefore no starch is present.

||||| Fig 2.20 On the left the control leaf has not changed colour, on the right the leaf exposed to light has turned blue-black, indicating the presence of starch

Experiment 2.4

To demonstrate the effect of light intensity on the rate of photosynthesis

Materials
Elodea (also known as pond weed), large beaker, funnel, strong light source (e.g. lamp), test tube, sodium hydrogen carbonate, a metre stick

Method
1. Three-quarters fill the large beaker with some pond water.

2. Add a small amount of sodium hydrogen carbonate to the pond water. This ensures that there is plenty of CO_2 in the pond water and this will not be a limiting factor in the experiment.

3. Cut a piece of Elodea and remove the leaves around the cut part of the stem.

4. Set up the apparatus as shown in Fig 2.21. Place the stem of the Elodea upwards. This is where the bubbles of oxygen will emerge.

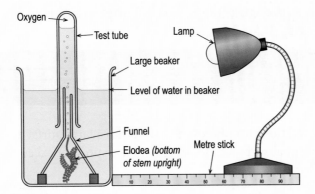

Fig 2.21 Effect of light intensity on photosynthesis

5. Set the Elodea 100 cm away from the light source and leave it for 5 minutes to adjust.

6. Count the number of oxygen bubbles that emerge from the cut end of the stem for one minute. Repeat this twice.

7. Move the Elodea to 80 cm away from the light source. Allow the elodea to adjust for 5 minutes and then repeat step 6.

8. Continue to move the Elodea closer to the light source (60 cm, 40 cm and 20 cm). Count the number of oxygen bubbles that emerge at each distance.

9. Calculate the average number of oxygen bubbles produced at each distance. Plot a graph of distance in cm (horizontal axis) with the average number of bubbles of oxygen per minute (vertical axis).

Result
As the Elodea is moved closer to the light source, the number of bubbles of oxygen produced by the Elodea will increase. However, a point will come where no further increase in the number of oxygen bubbles will occur. This point is known as saturation point and this happens when the plant is photosynthesising at its maximum rate.

The apparatus can be left for a few days in strong sunlight and the oxygen produced can be collected in the test tube, and tested to confirm that it is oxygen, by using a glowing splint.

Summary

▦ The flowering plant structure can be broken up into two parts: the shoot system and the root system.

▦ Plant tissues can be divided into dermal tissue, ground tissue and vascular tissue.

▦ Vascular tissue is divided into xylem and phloem. Xylem is responsible for the transport of water and minerals and phloem for the transport of sugars.

▦ Xylem is composed of two main types of cell: xylem vessel and tracheids. Xylem tissue is composed of dead cells and the cell wall of these cells is reinforced with lignin.

▦ Phloem tissue is made up of a sieve tube with its companion cell. Phloem tissue is composed of living cells.

▦ Flowering plants are divided into two groups: monocots and dicots.

▦ The dicot root is divided into four regions: root cap, zone of cell division, zone of elongation and zone of differentiation.

▦ The vascular bundles are scattered in a monocot stem and are arranged in a circle in a dicot stem.

▦ Plants are autotrophic as they make their own food by photosynthesis.

▦ The chemical equation for photosynthesis is:

$$6CO_2 \;+\; 6H_2O \;\xrightarrow[\text{Sunlight}]{\text{Chlorophyll}}\; C_6H_{12}O_6 \;+\; 6O_2$$

▦ The leaf has many adaptations for photosynthesis. It has a large surface area to maximise the amount of sunlight it can absorb; it has a waxy cuticle to prevent excess water loss and it has many stomata for gaseous exchange.

QUESTIONS

1 What is the function of each of the following: (a) root, (b) leaf, (c) xylem and (d) phloem?

2 Write a brief note on monocotyledons and dicotyledons.

3 Fig 2.22 shows a longitudinal section of a dicot root.
   (a) Identify A, B, C and D.
   (b) What is the function of A?
   (c) What type of cell division occurs at B?
   (d) Where in the longitudinal section of the root will you find xylem and phloem cells?
   (e) What is the function of the root hairs?

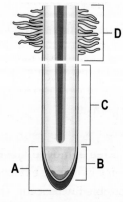

▦ Fig 2.22

QUESTIONS

4   Draw a labelled diagram of a transverse section of a monocot stem and a dicot stem. Identify **one** difference between a monocot stem and a dicot stem.

5   Distinguish between respiration and photosynthesis.

6   The following experiment (see Fig 2.23) was set up to investigate the effect of light intensity on the rate of photosynthesis.
  (a) Identify the plant labelled A used in this experiment.
  (b) Describe how you varied the light intensity in this experiment.
  (c) Describe how you measured the rate of photosynthesis in this experiment.
  (d) Name **three** other factors required for photosynthesis.
  (e) Describe a test you could carry out to prove that the gas produced by photosynthesis is oxygen.

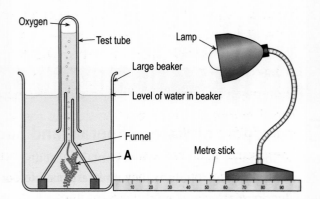

Fig 2.23

EXAM QUESTIONS

1   Plants use sunlight to make food during photosynthesis.
  (a) What is the main gas released in photosynthesis?
  (b) Name the major pigment needed by plants for photosynthesis.
  (c) Describe, with the aid of a labelled diagram, a laboratory investigation to show that light is needed for photosynthesis. (LC, OL, 2006)

2   The diagram shows a section through part of a leaf.
  (a) Name the cells labelled A, B, C and D.
  (b) Give two features of the leaf that are related to its role in photosynthesis.
  (c) Name two gases that may leave the leaf through the stoma.
  (d) Write a balanced chemical equation for the process of photosynthesis. (LC, HL, 2008)

3   Describe a laboratory method to extract the pigments in a sample of grass. (LC, HL, 2006)

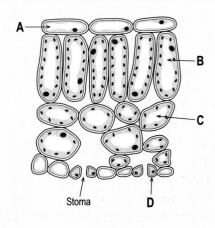

Fig 2.24

Chapter 3
Transport in Plants

☰ Transport of Water, Minerals and Sugar

As described in Chapter 2, plants contain vascular tissue, xylem and phloem. These tissues are responsible for the movement of materials around the plant in much the same way as the circulatory system transports substances around the human body. Xylem is responsible for the transport of water and minerals by a process called transpiration. Phloem is responsible for the movement of sugars by a process known as translocation.

Transpiration

Water is an essential ingredient in photosynthesis. It is vital that plant cells have a plentiful supply of water in the leaves for this process. The plant does not have a pump to bring this water up. However, a combination of four forces – root pressure, cohesion, adhesion and transpiration – ensures that water moves in a continuous column from the roots to the leaves.

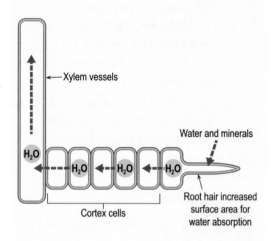

‖‖‖ Fig 3.1 Movement of water into a plant root system

Root pressure is caused by the continuous movement of water by osmosis, from the soil into the root hairs. This build up of pressure forces water and minerals upwards into the xylem vessels, as shown in Fig 3.1

Root pressure can be illustrated by cutting a herbaceous plant close to the bottom of the stem. A little bubble of water will form on the top of the cut stem. However, root pressure on its own will not push water all the way up the xylem vessels.

In the leaf, water is continuously lost through the stomata in the leaves by transpiration. Transpiration is the loss of water by evaporation from the leaves. Water is drawn out of the xylem vessels to replace that lost through evaporation. This pulls water up the xylem vessels.

> **Transpiration:** The loss of water by evaporation from the leaves.

Finally, water is polar in nature, which means that the water molecule has a slight positive charge on one side of the molecule and a slight negative charge on the other side, which causes the water molecules to be attracted to one another. As a result, water molecules stick to each other, causing a force known as cohesion. This causes the water molecules to form a continuous column. Water molecules are also attracted to the cellulose cell walls of the xylem vessel and this draws water along the xylem vessels by a force called adhesion.

Thus, this combination of cohesion, adhesion, root pressure and transpiration is responsible for the continuous upward movement of water and minerals in the xylem vessels from the roots to the leaves.

The rate of transpiration is not constant. It is influenced by a number of external factors. Temperature, wind, soil, water and light can increase or decrease the rate of transpiration.

On hot days, the rate of transpiration increases as water evaporation from the leaves helps to cool the leaves.

On calm days, water vapour builds up around the stomata,

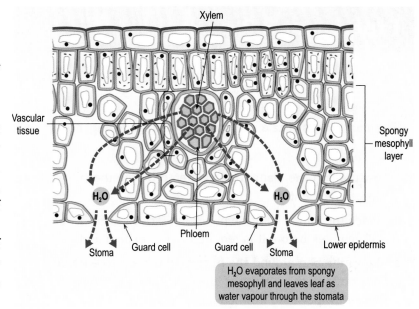

Fig 3.2 Water is lost through transpiration from the leaves

increasing the humidity. This slows down the evaporation of water from the cells in the leaf, as the surrounding air is saturated with water vapour.

In contrast, on windy days the rate of transpiration increases as air movement across the stomata prevents the build up of this humid air.

Plants require a continuous supply of water to their leaves to replace that lost by transpiration. If plants experience a water shortage, as in the case of droughts, the stomata in the leaf close, reducing the rate of transpiration in an effort to conserve water. Finally, light stimulates the opening of the stomata, increasing the rate of transpiration.

Experiment 3.1

To demonstrate transpiration

Materials
White carnations or celery stalks with leaves, beaker, food colouring (red or blue works best), water

Method
1   Half fill a beaker with water and add a few drops of food colouring.

2   Place the celery stalks or carnation into a beaker.

3   Leave the beaker for a few days in a sunny spot and observe.

4   If using celery, cut the stalk and observe the location of the dye in the stem.

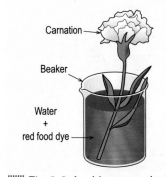

Fig 3.3 A white carnation is dyed pink as a result of transpiration

Result
As the plant transpires it will draw the coloured water up through the stem to the leaves and flowers. The white carnation will change colour. It is possible to see the pathway of the dye in the xylem tissue in the leaves of the plant. Observe the location of the xylem tissue in the cut stem of celery that is dyed with the food colouring.

Experiment 3.2

To demonstrate the production of water vapour during transpiration

Materials
Geranium or busy lizzie in a pot, bell jar, plastic bag, cobalt chloride paper

Method
1 Ensure that the plant is well watered before the start of the experiment.

2 Place the cobalt chloride paper in an oven at 50°C for 30 minutes before it is required in the experiment.

3 Wrap the bag around the base of the plant to enclose the pot and the surface of the soil. This is to prevent water evaporating from the soil.

4 Place the plant under the bell jar.

5 Leave in a sunny location for a few days.

6 Condensation will build up on the inside of the bell jar.

7 Test for the presence of water using cobalt chloride paper.

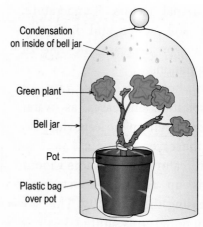

Fig 3.4 Water vapour is produced during transpiration

Result
Condensation builds up on the inside of the bell jar. When tested with cobalt chloride paper, the paper turns from blue to pink to indicate the presence of water. The build up of water on the inside of the bell jar is due to water evaporating from the leaves of the plant.

Translocation

Translocation refers to the movement of sugars produced in the leaves to other regions of the plant. Phloem tissue is responsible for the movement of sugars from their **sources** (sites of photosynthesis) to regions where sugars are required or are stored; these regions are known as **sinks**. The movement of phloem sap, a mixture of water and sugars, can occur up and down the phloem tissue. Important sinks for the storage of sugars as starch include: roots, flowers, fruits and stems.

The mechanism by which phloem sap moves is best described by the **pressure–flow hypothesis**.

In photosynthesising leaves (sources), sugars are moved into phloem tissue by active transport. This increases the concentration of sugars inside the phloem cells. As a result, water moves into the phloem cells by osmosis. As the walls of the phloem cells are rigid a pressure builds up.

> **Translocation:** The movement of sugars produced in the leaves to other regions of the plant.

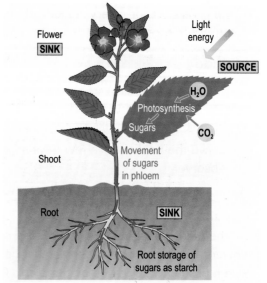

Fig 3.5 Translocation in the flowering plant

In non-photosynthetic regions (sinks) sugars are constantly being removed for storage or for use. As a result, water also exits phloem tissue by osmosis causing a decrease in pressure. This produces a pressure gradient between the source and the sink, which causes the phloem sap to flow from source to sink.

Summary

- Phloem is responsible for the movement of sugars by the process of translocation.
- Xylem is responsible for the transport of water and minerals by the process of transpiration.
- A combination of four forces – root pressure, cohesion, adhesion and transpiration – causes water to move in a continuous column from the roots to the leaves in a process called the transpiration stream.
- Root pressure is caused by the continuous movement of water by osmosis from the soil into the root hairs.
- Water is continuously lost through the stomata in the leaves by transpiration. Water is drawn out of the xylem vessels to replace that lost through evaporation.
- Water molecules stick to each other, causing a force called cohesion.
- Water molecules are attracted to the cellulose cell walls of the xylem vessel and this draws water along the xylem vessels by a force called adhesion.
- The rate of transpiration is not constant. It is influenced by a number of external factors. Temperature, wind, soil, water and light can increase or decrease the rate of transpiration.
- Movement of phloem sap, a mixture of water and sugars, can occur up and down the phloem tissue.
- The mechanism by which phloem sap moves is by the pressure–flow hypothesis.

QUESTIONS

1   Identify the tissue responsible for the transport of:
  (a) Water
  (b) Sugars
  (c) Minerals.
2   Explain the difference between transpiration and translocation.
3   Outline the role played by each of the following in the movement of water from the roots to the leaves:
  (a) Root pressure
  (b) Adhesion and cohesion
  (c) Transpiration.
4   Describe a laboratory method used to show the transport of water in plants.
5   Explain how each of the following factors affects the rate of transpiration: light, wind, soil and water.
6   Translocation in plants is often described as the movement of sugars from **source** to **sink**. Explain what is meant by the highlighted terms.
7   Briefly describe the theory of pressure flow mechanisms of transporting sugars in plants.

Chapter 4

Plant Reproduction

The Life Cycle of Flowering Plants

Flowering plants have two main stages in their life cycle; these stages may alternate. The first stage is known as the **sporophyte**. The plant has a full set of chromosomes and is referred to as being diploid (see Chapters 17 and 18). The plant produces a flower that has both male and female parts. The male part (stamen) produces the male gamete and the female part (carpel) contains the ovaries that produce the female gametes.

A type of cell division known as meiosis produces gametes. This type of cell division reduces the number of chromosomes in the gamete to half that of the parent plant. Gametes are referred to as being haploid. This is the second stage of the plant's life cycle and is known as the **gametophyte**.

At fertilisation, the male gamete fuses with the female gamete producing a diploid zygote and restoring the chromosome number to that of the adult plant. The zygote grows and develops into a seed. Once the seed germinates it will grow into a plant. The flowering plant only spends a brief amount of time as a gametophyte and the remainder of its life is spent as the sporophyte.

The Structure and Function of the Flower

The reproductive organs of flowering plants are contained in the flower. Normally both male and female reproductive parts occur together. The male part, the stamen, consists of the anther and the filament. The anther produces pollen grains and the male gametes develop inside the pollen grains. The female part, the carpel, consists of the stigma, style and ovary. Pollen lands on the stigma during pollination; the male gametes travel down the style to the ovary, which contains the eggs.

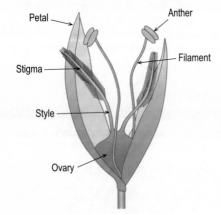

||||| Fig 4.1 A wind-pollinated flower

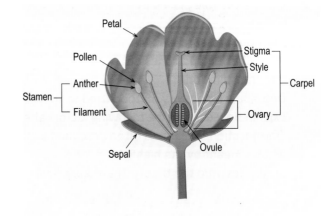

||||| Fig 4.2 An insect-pollinated flower

Flowers generally have petals and sepals. In insect-pollinated plants, the petals are large and brightly coloured to attract insects for pollination. The sepals protect the flower when it is a bud.

Grass and cereal flowers rely on wind for pollination and, as a result, the petals are greatly reduced and lack colour.

> **Pollination**: The transfer of pollen from the anther of one flower to the stigma of another flower of the same species.

There are two types of pollination: insect and wind.

Insect-pollinated plants

Plants such as dandelions, daisies and buttercups are all insect-pollinated plants. These flowers have a number of adaptations for this function. The flowers often have a scent or produce nectar, a sugary liquid, to attract the insects. The nectarines are located at the bottom of the flower to encourage the insect to go down into the flower so that they rub against the anthers to gather the pollen on their journey.

Fig 4.3 An insect carrying pollen on its body

Insect-pollinated plants produce small amounts of pollen. The pollen is sticky or has little spines on it to attach to the insect's body so that it can be transported.

The stigmas of insect-pollinated flowers are also sticky in order to trap the pollen from the bodies of visiting insects. Both male and female parts are contained inside the flower.

Wind-pollinated plants

Grasses and cereal flowers have many adaptations for wind pollination. As these flowers do not need to attract insects, their petals are smaller and are not brightly coloured. Wind-pollinated flowers have no scent and no nectarines. Unlike insect-pollinated flowers, the stamens

Fig 4.4 A grass flower releasing large amounts of pollen

and stigmas hang outside the flower. The stamens produce large amounts of light pollen, which can be picked up by air currents. The stigmas are large and feathery to trap any pollen in the air. Inflorescence is the term used to describe the arrangement of the flowers on the stem of the grass.

Table 4.1 Adaptations of wind-pollinated flowers and insect-pollinated flowers		
Structure	**Wind-pollinated**	**Insect-pollinated**
Petals	Small, green, no scent, no nectarines	Large and brightly coloured, scented and nectarines
Stamens	Hang outside the plant	Lie inside the plant
Stigma	Large and feathery, hang outside the plant	Small, sticky and inside the plant
Pollen	Large amounts and very light	Small amounts, sticky or with spines

Experiment 4.1

To examine the structure of a flower

Materials

Lily, tulip or another large flower, scalpel, dissecting board, magnifying glass, microscope, slides

Method

1 Identify the sepals if present. Remove some of the petals surrounding the carpel and stamens. Draw a labelled diagram of the internal structure of the flower.

2 Remove a stamen and if the anther is mature it will have pollen on it. Using a small paintbrush dust some of the pollen onto a microscopic slide. View the slide under low power on the microscope. Observe the surface of the pollen.

3 Identify the three sections of the carpel, the stigma, style and ovary. Touch the top of the stigma with your finger.

4 Using the scalpel, separate the base of the carpel from the flower. Cut this in half and identify the ovaries inside. With care, these can be removed from the flower and viewed using a magnifying glass.

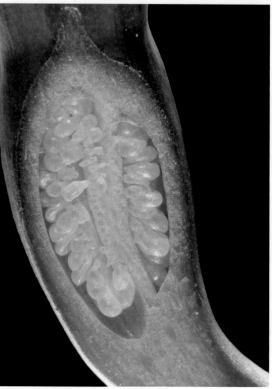

Fig 4.5 A plant ovary

Fertilisation and Seed Formation

The pollen grain contains two male gametes and a tube nucleus. Once the pollen has landed on the stigma, the tube nucleus forms a pollen tube from the top of the stigma down to the ovary and into the embryo sac. Once it reaches the opening in the embryo sac, it disintegrates.

One of the male gametes fuses with the egg to form the zygote, while the other male gamete fuses with a pair of cells to form the endosperm. The endosperm is sometimes used as a food reserve, as the zygote grows into an embryo. The fate of the endosperm depends on the plant. In monocots, the endosperm remains present and on germination the cotyledon

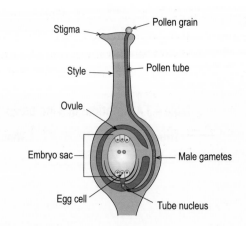

Fig 4.6 A pollen tube containing male gametes on route to the embryo sac

makes the energy in the endosperm available to the embryo. In most dicots the cotyledons grow and absorb the endosperm completely.

The embryo consists of the radicle, the plumule and the cotyledons (seed leaves). If two cotyledons are present then the seed is a dicot and if only one cotyledon is present it is a monocot. The radicle is the future root and the plumule is the future shoot of the new plant. A seed coat forms around the embryo, known as the testa. The ovary of many flowers develops into a fruit.

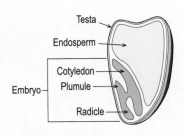

Fig 4.7 A monocot seed (sunflower seed)

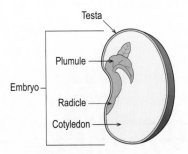

Fig 4.8 A dicot seed (broad bean)

Seed dispersal

Seed dispersal is vital in order to avoid competition with the parent plant for light, water, minerals and space. It also offers an opportunity for plants to colonise new areas. Seed dispersal occurs by the following mechanisms: wind, animals, self-dispersal and water.

Wind

Dandelion and ragwort seeds are examples of seeds dispersed by wind. They are extremely light and are attached to a parachute (see Fig 4.9). This allows them to be picked up by light breezes. Sycamore trees have wings attached to their fruits.

Animals

Seeds dispersed by animals can be of two types: edible fruits or dry fruits with hooks.

Strawberries and blackberries are edible fruits that are eaten by animals (see Fig 4.10). The seeds pass through the animal unharmed and when they eventually pass out of the animal with the faeces, they have been carried a long distance from the parent plant.

Animals also disperse cleavers and burdock (see Fig 4.11). These plants produce a fruit with hooks on it, which attaches itself to the fur of animals.

Fig 4.9 A dandelion seed

Fig 4.10 Blackberries on a blackberry bush

Self-dispersal

Gorse bushes disperse their seed by self-dispersal. The seeds of the gorse are contained within a pod. The pods dry out and split open, firing the seeds out of them.

Water

Only a few species of plants use water as a mechanism for dispersal. Water lilies produce a spongy layer that makes them buoyant and allows them to float (see Fig 4.12).

 Fig 4.11 Burdock seeds with their hooks

Fig 4.12 A water lily floating in water

Germination

Germination is the growth of a new seed. For seeds to germinate they require three conditions: water, oxygen and a suitable temperature. Water is a solvent and it is needed for many enzyme reactions. The rate of enzyme reactions is determined by temperature. If the temperature is less than 5°C, enzyme activity is very slow, but as the temperature increases so does the rate of the enzyme activity. Finally, oxygen is required by the germinating seeds to produce energy by aerobic respiration.

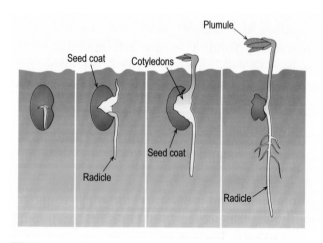

Fig 4.13 Hypogeal germination of a broad bean

Germination is classified as either hypogeal or epigeal depending on whether or not the cotyledons come above the ground and photosynthesise.

Hypogeal germination

The broad bean is an example of hypogeal germination. The radicle first emerges and grows downwards, followed by the plumule. The cotyledons remain below the ground and supply energy for the growing plumule and radicle. As they become used up they start to shrivel. Once above the ground, the plumule opens up its first leaves and starts photosynthesising.

Hypogeal: The cotyledons (seed leaves) of the germinating seed remain below the ground.
Epigeal: The cotyledons (seed leaves) of the germinating seed emerge above the surface of the ground.

Epigeal germination

In epigeal germination, the radicle emerges from the seed and grows downwards. The region between the radicle and the cotyledons, known as the hypocotyl, starts to grow. This pushes the cotyledons above the ground. The old seed coat falls off; the cotyledons emerge and start to photosynthesise. Sunflower seeds are an example of epigeal germination.

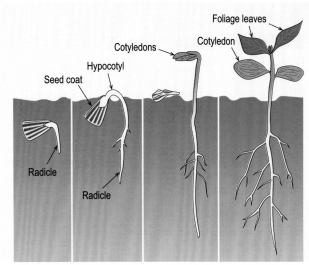

Fig 4.14 Epigeal germination

Experiment 4.2

To investigate the factors required for germination

Materials

Test-tube rack, four test tubes, cotton wool, boiled water that has cooled, oil, cress seeds, access to a fridge

Method

1 Place the four test tubes in a test-tube rack and add a small amount of cotton wool to each.

2 Add some water to the first test tube to moisten the cotton wool and place a few cress seeds on top. This is the control.

3 Add cress seeds to the second test tube and two-thirds fill the test tube with cooled, boiled water. The water has been boiled to remove the oxygen from it. A layer of oil is poured onto the water. This prevents any oxygen entering the water.

4 Add some cress seeds to the third test tube. The cotton wool in this test tube is left dry.

5 Moisten the cotton wool in the fourth test tube and add some seeds. Place this test tube in the fridge. Place all the other test tubes in a warm location.

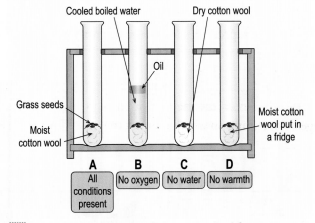

Fig 4.15 Investigating factors required for germination

Experiment 4.2

6   Leave the apparatus for a few days and record your observations in a table similar to the one below.

Result

Test tube	Factor absent	Observation
1	None	
2	Oxygen	
3	Water	
4	Warmth or suitable temperature	

Table 4.2 Results

Only the seeds in test tube 1 will germinate, as these seeds have oxygen, water and a suitable temperature.

☰ Modified Organs and Vegetative Reproduction

Many plants have modifications to organs for food storage, while others use their modifications as a means of asexual reproduction. Asexual reproduction only requires one parent, while sexual reproduction requires a male and female gamete or two parents. Strawberry plants, creeping buttercup and scutch grass have modifications that allow them to produce identical copies of themselves.

Strawberries and creeping buttercup reproduce asexually by producing runners. At the end of the runner a small plant develops. When the end of the runner comes into contact with the ground, roots grow and anchor the plant to the ground. After some time, the new plant can become independent of the parent plant.

Scutch grass reproduces asexually by rhizomes. These underground stems make this weed notoriously difficult to get rid of.

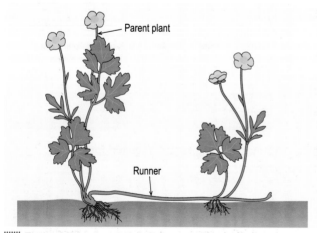

Fig 4.16 A creeping buttercup plant with a runner

Fig 4.17 Scutch grass

The majority of modifications in plants are for food storage and are associated with the lifespan of the plant.

Annuals complete their life cycle in one year. Annual meadow grass, groundsel and charlock are common weeds that all grow, flower and produce seeds in one growing season.

Biennials complete their life cycle in two years. Carrots and sugar beet are biennials. They store the food that they produced in the first season in a tap root and use the food to produce flowers and seeds in the second year. After this the plant dies.

Perennials regrow every year from the root, producing flowers and seeds. Perennial ryegrass and clover are important perennials in grassland.

Modified roots

The carrot, parsnip and sugar beet are all examples of a modified root called a tap root. The tap root is a main, central root, with some smaller lateral roots branching out from the tap root (see Fig 4.18).

Tap roots are found in dicot plants and grow deep into the soil. This root can be modified to store food in the form of starch or sugars. If lateral roots are modified for food storage they are called tuberous roots or root tubers. Dahlias are plants with tuberous roots.

Modified stems

Stems are normally associated with the aerial part of the plant. However, some plants have a modified stem that grows underground. Potato tubers are an example of a modified underground stem. The potato plant produces tubers that swell for the storage of food in the form of starch. Tubers have lateral buds known as 'eyes'. New shoots can grow from these lateral buds (see Fig 4.19).

Rhizomes are modified underground stems. Here the stem grows horizontally under the ground, sending up aerial shoots. Adventitious roots grow from the nodes on the stem. If rhizomes are broken into pieces, each piece can produce a new plant.

Corms are modified stems that grow vertically. In some plant species the corm is replaced every year with the growth of a new corm. The crocus is an example of a plant with a corm (see Fig 4.20).

Fig 4.18 A carrot is an example of a tap root

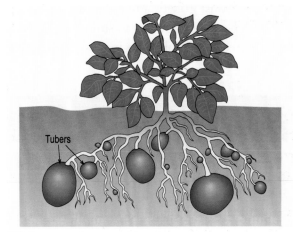
Fig 4.19 Potato with tubers

Fig 4.20 A corm is an example of a modified stem

Modified leaves

A bulb is an example of modified leaves used for food storage. Onions and tulips are examples of bulbs (see Fig 4.21). Plants that have bulbs are monocots. The leaves in an onion surround the stem in the centre of the bulb. At the base of this stem adventitious roots are produced.

≡ Plant Tropism

Tropism is a plant's growth response to an external stimulus. Phototropism is a plant's growth response to light. If you have a plant growing on a windowsill at home, you may notice that the plant bends slightly and its leaves turn to face outwards. The advantage of growing towards the light is that it enables plants to capture more sunlight and increases photosynthesis.

Plants also respond to gravity. This is called geotropism. When a seed germinates its root will grow downwards with gravity, demonstrating a positive response to the stimulus, while the shoot will grow up against gravity, a negative response to the stimulus. Growth responses to stimuli in plants are under the control of plant hormones called auxins.

Fig 4.21 An onion bulb is an example of modified leaves

Tropism: A plant's growth response to an external stimulus.
Phototropism: A plant's growth response to light.
Geotropism: A plant's growth response to gravity.

Experiment 4.3

To investigate phototropism in plants

Materials
Shoebox, petri dishes, cotton wool, cress seeds

Method
1 Divide the shoebox in half. On one half cut a window in the side of the box. On the other side cut a window in the lid of the box.

2 Place some cotton wool in two petri dishes. Moisten the cotton wool with water.

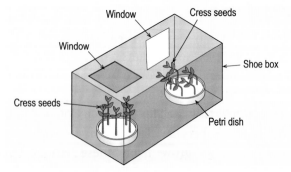

Fig 4.22 Phototropism in plants

3 Add equal numbers of cress seeds to both petri dishes.

4 Place the petri dishes in the shoebox and leave them for over a week, watering occasionally.

5 Record your observations.

Result
The cress seeds have germinated and started to grow. The cress seeds with the window on the lid of the shoebox have grown straight up, while the cress seeds with the window on the side are bending towards the window. All the cress seeds are growing towards the light.

Experiment 4.4

To investigate geotropism

Materials

Large beaker, cotton wool or soil, sheet of paper, broad bean seeds, water

Method

1   Soak the broad bean seeds overnight in water. This softens the testa (seed coat) and breaks the seeds' dormancy.

2   Place the sheet of paper around the inside of the beaker.

3   Fill the inside of the paper with soil or with cotton wool.

4   Place the seeds between the sheet of paper and the glass, orientating the seeds in different positions. Moisten the soil or cotton wool with water.

5   Leave the seeds in a sunny spot and water occasionally.

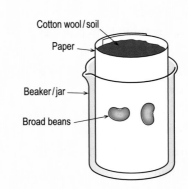

Fig 4.23 To demonstrate geotropism

Result

All the seeds should germinate, and, regardless of the position of the seed, the roots of all the broad beans grow downwards with gravity and the shoots grow upwards against gravity.

Summary

- The reproductive organs of flowering plants are contained in the flower.
- The male part of the flower is called the stamen and it consists of the anther and the filament.
- The anther produces pollen grains and the male gametes develop inside the pollen grains.
- The carpel is the female part and consists of the stigma, style and ovary.
- The ovary contains the egg cell.
- Insect-pollinated plants have large, brightly coloured petals to attract insects for pollination.
- Grass and cereal flowers are wind-pollinated and, as a result, the petals are greatly reduced and lack colour.
- Pollination is the transfer of pollen from the anther of one flower to the stigma of another flower of the same species.
- Both insect- and wind-pollinated plants have many adaptations for pollination.
- At fertilisation, one of the male gametes fuses with the egg to form the zygote while the other male gamete fuses with a pair of cells to form the endosperm.

Summary

- Seed dispersal helps to avoid competition with the parent plant for light, water, minerals and space. Seeds can be dispersed by animals, wind, water or self-dispersal.
- Seeds require three conditions for germination: water, oxygen and a suitable temperature.
- Germination is classified as either hypogeal or epigeal. In hypogeal germination, the cotyledons remain below the ground. In epigeal germination the cotyledons come above the ground.
- Asexual reproduction only requires one parent, while sexual reproduction requires a male and female gamete or two parents.
- Strawberries and creeping buttercup reproduce asexually by producing runners. Scutch grass reproduces asexually by rhizomes.
- Annuals complete their life cycle in one year. Biennials complete their life cycle in two years. Perennials regrow every year from the root, producing flowers and seed.
- Many plants have modified organs for food storage. Carrots have a modified tap root to store food in the form of starch or sugars.
- Potato tubers are an example of a modified underground stem.
- Corms are modified stems that grow vertically.
- Onions are bulbs and are examples of where modified leaves are used for food storage.
- A tropism is a plant's growth response to an external stimulus. Phototropism is a plant's growth response to light. Geotropism is a plant's growth response to gravity.

QUESTIONS

1 State three ways in which wind-pollinated flowers differ from insect-pollinated flowers.
2 Draw a labelled diagram of a wind-pollinated flower.
3 Explain the term *pollination*. Identify two methods by which pollination occurs.
4 Describe two methods of seed dispersal and give examples of each.
5 Describe an experiment to investigate the three factors required for germination.
6 Explain the meaning of the term *germination*.
7 What is the function of each of the following parts in the seed: plumule, testa, radicle and cotyledons?
8 Distinguish between epigeal and hypogeal germination and give an example of each type of germination.
9 (a) Explain each of the following terms: *annual*, *biennial* and *perennial*.
  (b) Give an example of an agricultural crop that is (i) a biennial and (ii) a perennial.
10 Plants have the ability to respond to stimuli in their environment. These responses are called tropisms.
  (a) Name one tropism that you have studied.
  (b) Describe an experiment to demonstrate a plant's response to the tropism named in part (a).
  (c) What controls plant responses to these stimuli?

EXAM QUESTIONS

1   (a) Identify the parts labelled A, B, C and D in the diagram of a flower.
    (b) Explain how this flower is pollinated. Give one reason for your answer.
    (c) Where is the pollen produced in the flower?
    (d) Which part of the flower will become the fruit? (LC, OL, 2004)

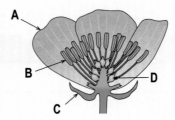

||||| Fig 4.24

2   The diagram shows four modified food storage organs in plants.

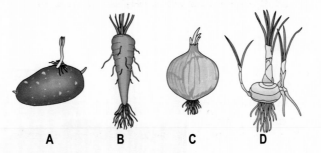

||||| Fig 4.25

    (a) Name these four types of food storage organs.
    (b) Give an example, in each case, of plants that use these organs.
    (c) Name a food substance that is found in any one of these.
    (d) Describe a test for this food substance. (LC, OL, 2005)

Chapter 5

Plant Identification and Ecology

Project link

In the practical examination for Agricultural Science, students are expected to identify five plants and their plant families. The plants on offer during the examination usually cover a wide range and many are plants of agricultural importance, e.g. perennial ryegrass and clover; agricultural products, such as potatoes and cereals and agricultural weeds, some of which are noxious and poisonous to livestock. This chapter will look at some common plant families and provides a short habitat study.

≡ Identifying Plant Families

Family Gramineae

Gramineae is the most important plant family in agriculture. It is a very large one and has an estimated 10 000 species. This family contains productive perennial ryegrass varieties (*Lolium perenne*) used for grazing, hay and silage, and cereals such as wheat (*Triticum aestivum*), barley (*Hordeum vulgare*) and maize (*Zea mays*), which are mainly used as animal feeds.

All the members of this family are monocots, having one cotyledon in the seed. The part of the grass plant commonly referred to as the flower is composed of many florets (small flowers, see Fig 5.2) contained in a structure called the spikelet. The florets contain the stamens and the carpel. The members of this family can be distinguished from each other on the basis of their inflorescence.

||||| Fig 5.1 A field of clover

Inflorescence: The fixed arrangement of spikelets on the stem.

The inflorescence of some common grass species is shown in the following pictures.

||||| Fig 5.2 An individual floret

||||| Fig 5.3 A spike: perennial ryegrass's inflorescence

The inflorescence of perennial ryegrass is called a **spike**. This is an unbranched inflorescence with the spikelets attached directly to the main stem.

Wild oats are troublesome weeds in tillage crops as they are highly competitive, produce a large number of seeds and are a host for a number of cereal diseases. They have an open branched inflorescence known as a panicle, with spikelets held out on the branches.

Annual meadow grass is an annual or short-lived perennial. It is often in flower even at short heights and tends to form small tussocks. Its inflorescence is branched and has a spreading panicle

||||| Fig 5.4 Wild oats

||||| Fig 5.5 Annual meadow grass

with small spikelets. This grass is usually found on acid soils.

Cocksfoot is a common perennial grass found in permanent grassland. Its inflorescence is a triangular-shaped panicle with green or purple tinged spikelets.

Family Compositae

Compositae is the largest plant family containing many grassland weeds such as daisy, dandelion, thistle and ragwort, and commercial crops such as sunflowers. The flower heads of these plants are composed of many individual flowers that all share the same receptacle. The individual flowers are so densely arranged that they resemble a single flower. Members of the Compositae family use wind to disperse their seeds.

||||| Fig 5.6 Cocksfoot is a common perennial grass

Ragwort is a noxious weed that is poisonous to cattle and horses. Sheep can tolerate some ragwort. Livestock do not usually graze ragwort. However, care must be taken to ensure that this weed is not incorporated into silage, as livestock selectivity is reduced and animals will eat it.

Ragwort is a biennial plant. In its first year it can be identified as a rosette; a cluster of leaves in a circular form. In its second year, it produces yellow flowers in late spring, which can produce thousands of seeds that are mainly dispersed by wind.

Dandelions are a common perennial plant of permanent grassland. They produce yellow flowers from early summer until October. A single flower head produces an average of 180 seeds. Dandelions can be difficult to remove as they have long tap roots that have the ability to regenerate if they are broken. The dandelion plant over-winters as a rosette.

 Fig 5.7 Ragwort flowers ||||| Fig 5.8 A ragwort rosette

Family Cruciferae

The Cruciferae family is commonly called the cabbage family. This family's name is due to the similarity of its four-petalled flowers to a cross.

||||| Fig 5.9 A dandelion plant ||||| Fig 5.10 A dandelion rosette

This is a large plant family that includes many important agricultural crops, e.g. turnips, oilseed rape, kale and cabbage.

Charlock is a common annual weed found in arable land. It flowers between May and July and has a bright yellow flower. Its seeds can remain dormant for many years and can appear on land that has been permanent grassland after it has been ploughed for the first time.

Family Leguminosae

Family Leguminosae is also known as Fabaceae or the pea family. White clover (*Trifolium repens*) and red clover (*Trifolium pratense*) are two important agricultural plants. Both contain the bacteria Rhizobium, which lives in the root nodules of these plants. Rhizobium has the ability

||||| Fig 5.11 Charlock

to fix nitrogen into nitrates for plant use. The leaves of clover are trifoliate (each leaf is composed of three leaflets) and the flowers are normally white or red.

Peas and beans are also members of this family.

||||| Fig 5.12 Red clover ||||| Fig 5.13 White clover

Family Polygonaceae

Docks are members of the Polygonaceae family. There are two main species of dock: the curled dock and the broadleaf dock. Both species can affect the productivity of a grassland sward. Docks thrive in an open sward and, as a result, are a problem in pasture used for silage and in grassland that has been overgrazed or poached.

||||| Fig 5.14 Curled dock

||||| Fig 5.15 Broadleaf dock

Docks are perennial and they have large tap roots and leaves. They produce big clusters of green flowers that turn red when mature.

Family Ranunculaceae

Creeping buttercup, meadow buttercup and the lesser celandine are all members of the family Ranunculaceae, commonly called the buttercup family. Both creeping buttercup and meadow buttercup can reduce the productivity of a grassland sward as they are unpalatable to stock.

||||| Fig 5.16 Creeping buttercup

||||| Fig 5.17 Meadow buttercup

Creeping buttercup can be identified by its bright yellow flower with five petals (flowers between May and July), hairy leaves and stem. It can reproduce both by seed and asexually by producing runners, which can rapidly colonise an area of land.

Meadow buttercup is a serious weed of older permanent grassland. It has a more upright growth habit in comparison to the creeping buttercup and it too has the ability to reproduce by seed and asexually from an underground rhizome. Meadow buttercup flowers from May to July.

Family Umbelliferae

The Umbelliferae family contains many important food crops including carrots, parsley and parsnips. Cow parsley is a common weed found in hedgerows and at field edges. Its inflorescence is called an umbel, which consists of a number of short stalks with small, white flowers that all originate from the same point.

||||| Fig 5.18 Cow parsley

Family Urticaceae

The common nettle is a member of the Urticaceae family and it is frequently found in hedgerows. The nettle is not a hermaphrodite and plants bear either male or female flowers. They are wind-pollinated. Livestock normally avoid eating the growing weed but will eat it in hay.

||||| Fig 5.19 Common nettle

☰ Habitat Study

Project link

Ecology is another area examined in the practical examination. Your local school environment can be used in a habitat study especially if you have access to a hedgerow on the school grounds.

The plants and animals that live in a particular habitat are influenced by the abiotic, edaphic and biotic factors of that habitat.

Habitat: The place where a plant or animal lives.

Abiotic are the non-living factors in a habitat.
Edaphic are factors relating to the soil, soil pH, soil temperature, drainage.
Biotic are the living factors in a habitat.

Experiment 5.1

Abiotic factors and edaphic factors

Aspect
Use a compass to find the direction that a hedgerow faces. South-facing hedgerows will get more sun than north-facing hedgerows. How does aspect affect the types of plants that grow in a north-facing hedgerow compared to a south-facing hedgerow?

Soil temperature
Soil temperature is important for plant growth and the germination of seeds. Plant growth in Ireland usually ceases if soil temperature drops below 6°C.

Materials
Soil site, soil thermometer, screwdriver

Method
1 To measure soil temperature, use a normal thermometer that has the bulb covered in a layer of wax, or use a soil thermometer (see Fig 5.20).

2 Select a site that is representative of the habitat. Shade the thermometer from bright sunlight.

3 Make a hole in the ground for the thermometer, using a screwdriver.

4 Insert the thermometer into the hole to a depth of 12 cm. Allow time for the thermometer to adjust to the soil temperature.

5 Record the temperature.

||||| Fig 5.20 A soil thermometer

Experiment 5.1

Soil pH

Soil pH affects the types of plants growing in a habitat. The pH scale is a range from 0 to 14 and is determined by calculating the concentration of H^+ ions in the soil. A pH between 0 and 6 is acidic, a pH of 7 is neutral and a pH between 8 and 14 is alkaline. Some plants, e.g. sorrel, nettles, dandelion and buttercup, thrive in acidic soils, while cow parsley and chickweed prefer neutral or slightly alkaline soils.

Materials

Test tube, soil sample, universal indicator, barium sulfate, pH scale colour card or a soil testing kit

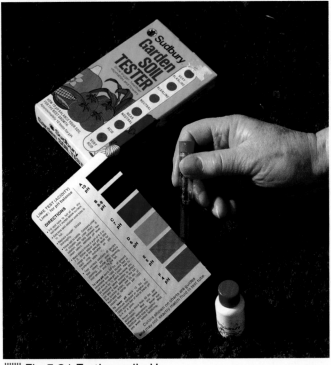

▌▌▌▌ Fig 5.21 Testing soil pH

Method

1　Place a small amount of soil in the bottom of a test tube (approximately 1 cm³).

2　Add a pinch of barium sulfate.
　　Note: Barium sulfate is a flocculating agent and it causes small, suspended particles to clump together and settle out of the solution, making it easy to read the colour change of the universal indicator.

3　Add 2 cm³ of universal indicator solution to the test tube.

4　Stopper the test tube and shake.

5　Allow the contents to settle.

6　Compare the colour of the solution to the pH colour chart.

7　Record the pH of the soil.

Biotic factors

Biotic factors in the habitat include the types of plants and animals in the habitat and how these affect other living organisms in the habitat. Animals compete with other animals for food, shelter and mates. Some animals will prey on others for food. Plants compete for sunlight, space, water and minerals. In this section we will investigate some techniques used to collect and identify organisms that live in a habitat.

Experiment 5.2

Animal collection for a habitat study

Materials

Beating tray, pooter

Method

1 Place the beating tray under a brush or a tree.

2 Shake or hit the plant.

3 Small insects will fall onto the beating tray.

4 Collect the insects with the pooter.

5 Use a key to identify the organisms.

Fig 5.22 Using a pooter to collect insects

Result

Insects collected using this technique may include: aphids, ladybirds, spiders, snails and lacewings.

Tullgren funnel

The Tullgren funnel is used to extract small invertebrates from soil and leaf litter. The technique works by driving the invertebrate animals away from the heat source. They fall down through the sieve and into the beaker where they are preserved.

Materials

Sample of soil or leaf litter, beaker, funnel, sieve, lamp with low wattage bulb, beaker and some ethanol or methylated spirits, small pipette, microscopic slides, magnifying glass, microscope

Method

1 Place the sample of soil on the sieve.

2 Leave overnight under the lamp.

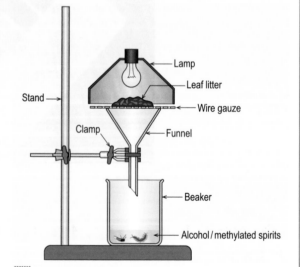

Fig 5.23 A Tullgren funnel

3 Without disturbing the alcohol, remove any small, floating insects. Place them on a microscopic slide and examine them under a microscope. (Insects floating on the surface of the alcohol are normally springtails, an insect commonly found in leaf litter.)

4 Remove any other small invertebrates from the alcohol and examine with a magnifying glass, if large enough, or a microscope.

5 Use a key to identify all the animals extracted.

Results

Springtails, mites, earthworms, beetles and insect larvae are found using a Tullgren funnel.

Experiment 5.3

Quantitative survey of permanent grassland and a temporary ley

Note: A school football pitch is a great example of a temporary ley if it is reseeded regularly.

Materials

Access to permanent pasture, quadrat, pen, result table

||||| Fig 5.24 Students using a quadrat

Method

1   In the pasture throw a pen randomly over your shoulder.

2   Place the quadrat where the pen lands.

3   On the result sheet tick the plants that occur in the quadrat.

4   Repeat ten times.

5   Calculate the percentage frequency by counting how many times a plant is present in a quadrat. For example, if dandelions occurred in six out of the ten quadrats then the percentage frequency is calculated as: $\frac{6}{10} \times \frac{100}{1} = 60\%$

Table 5.1 Permanent grassland

Plant name	1	2	3	4	5	6	7	8	9	10	Total	% Frequency
Grass												
Daisy												
Dandelion												
Plantain												
Ragwort												
Clover												
Dock												
Buttercup												

Table 5.2 Temporary ley

Plant name	1	2	3	4	5	6	7	8	9	10	Total	% Frequency
Grass												
Daisy												
Dandelion												
Plantain												
Ragwort												
Clover												
Dock												
Buttercup												

Result

Note: There is a greater variety of weeds in permanent grassland than in a temporary ley. The reason for this is that a temporary ley is reseeded on a regular basis and, as a result, weeds do not have a chance to become established.

Experiment 5.4

To examine the change in vegetation from a hedgerow into a field

This is investigated using a line transect which is placed at the hedgerow and then extended out into the field.

Materials

String or rope with intervals of 1 m marked on it, pen, result sheet

Method

1 Select an area that is representative of the habitat.

2 Stretch the rope from the hedgerow out to the field.

3 Record the plants that touch the line at each interval.

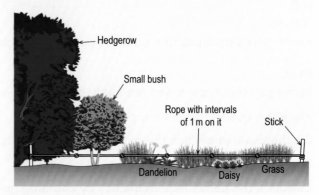

Fig 5.25 A line transect

Results

The vegetation changes as you move from the hedgerow to the openness of the field. There are more shade-loving plants close to the hedgerow.

Summary

- Gramineae is the most important plant family in agriculture. This family contains productive perennial ryegrass varieties and cereals: wheat, barley, oats and maize that are used as animal feeds.

- The members of the grass family can be identified based on their inflorescence.

- Inflorescence is the fixed arrangement of spikelets on the stem.

- Family Compositae is the largest plant family containing many grassland weeds, e.g. daisy, dandelion and ragwort and commercial crops, e.g. sunflowers.

- The Cruciferae family is commonly called the cabbage family and has many important agricultural crops, e.g. turnips, oilseed rape, kale and cabbage.

- Members of family Leguminosae include white clover and red clover. Both contain the bacteria Rhizobium, which lives in root nodules of these plants.

- Rhizobium fixes nitrogen into nitrates for plant use.

- Docks are a member of the family Polygonaceae. Docks are a problem in pasture used for silage and in grassland that has been overgrazed or poached.

- The buttercup family is Ranunculaceae. Creeping buttercup and meadow buttercup can reduce the productivity of a grassland sward as they are unpalatable to stock.

- The Umbelliferae family contains many important food crops including carrots, parsley and parsnips.

- Habitat is the place where a plant or animal lives.

- Abiotic are the non-living factors in a habitat.

- Edaphic are factors relating to the soil, soil pH, soil temperature and drainage.

Summary

- Biotic are the living factors in a habitat.
- The types of animal life in a habitat can be collected using a pooter, beating tray and Tullgren funnel. These animals can then be identified using a key.
- The plant life in a habitat can be sampled using a quadrat and a line transect.

QUESTIONS

1   Identify each of the following plants and give its plant family.

(a)

(b)

(c)

(d)

2   To which plant family does clover belong?

3   To which family do wild oats belong? Give three reasons why wild oats are troublesome weeds in tillage crops.

4   Distinguish between perennial ryegrass and cocksfoot based on their inflorescence.

5   Explain each of the following terms: (a) habitat, (b) abiotic factor, (c) edaphic factor and (d) biotic factor.

6   Outline how you would measure an abiotic and edaphic factor of a named habitat.

7   Describe how you could collect and identify animals in (a) a hedgerow and (b) a leaf litter. List two types of animals you might find in (a) and (b).

EXAM QUESTIONS

1 State one characteristic that would distinguish members of the family Compositae from members of the family Cruciferae and name a plant from each family. (LC, HL, 2008)

2 Identify the plant in Fig 5.26.
   (a) State the family to which the plant belongs.
   (b) Describe the growth habit of this plant as shown in the picture. (LC, HL, 2004)

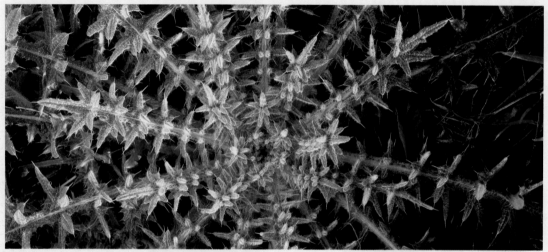

|||||| Fig 5.26

3 Recently your school received a gift of ten hectares of very old and neglected pasture. Describe a method that could be used to determine the botanical composition of this pasture. List four plants commonly found in this type of pasture. (LC, HL, 2004)

UNIT 2

Microbiology

Chapter 6

Microbiology

Microbiology is the study of micro-organisms. Bacteria, fungi and viruses are micro-organisms. Bacteria and fungi are classified as living organisms, while viruses are not because they lack a cellular structure and they can only reproduce inside another living cell, i.e. a plant or an animal cell.

Micro-organisms are extremely small and are only visible with the aid of a microscope.

In agriculture, micro-organisms can have many benefits, but perhaps are best known for the number of diseases that they cause in farm animals.

☰ Bacteria

Bacteria belong to the kingdom Monera. They usually range in size from 0.1 to 15 micrometres. A micrometre is one millionth of a metre (some countries refer to a micrometre as a micron). They are probably the most diverse of all the micro-organisms in their mode of nutrition. Some bacteria are autotrophic and can photosynthesise, but the majority of them are heterotrophic. The ones that are most important in agriculture fall into three categories.

Pathogen: A micro-organism that causes a disease.

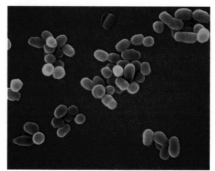

|||| Fig 6.1 *Brucella abortus* is a bacterial pathogen that causes brucellosis in cattle

Autrophic: An organism that makes its own food.

Heterotrophic: An organism that cannot make its own food and relies on food made by other organisms.

1 **Decomposers**: Soil bacteria break down dead and decaying organic matter and help to recycle important plant nutrients in both the carbon and nitrogen cycles. Souring in milk is caused by the decomposition of sugar and protein by bacteria.

2 **Symbiotic bacteria**: Rhizobium lives in the root nodules of red and white clover. This bacterium fixes atmospheric nitrogen into soluble nitrates that clover uses to produce protein. In return, the bacterium gets sugars from the plant and a place to live. This increases the protein content of the herbage in grassland. Bacteria that live in the rumen (see page 84) of cattle and sheep help to break down cellulose. This is another example of a beneficial, symbiotic relationship (see page 58).

3 **Pathogenic bacteria**: Cause disease in plant crops and animals. Diseases such as bovine tuberculosis (TB), brucellosis and scour are all caused by bacteria and can result in significant financial loss for a farm, e.g. through loss of productivity or death of farm animals.

The structure of bacteria

Bacteria are prokaryote, i.e. their genetic material (DNA or RNA) is not bound within a membrane. Therefore, unlike animals, there is no nucleus in bacteria cells. They also lack other membrane organelles such as mitochondria. In some bacteria, other separate pieces of genetic information can be found in the form of circular pieces of DNA called plasmids. Scientists have shown that these plasmids can contain information such as antibiotic resistances in some bacteria. The plasmids and the bacteria's DNA are suspended in the cytoplasm.

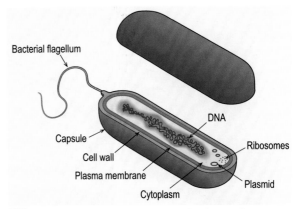

Fig 6.2 The basic structure of a bacterium

Ribosomes used to synthesise proteins are found also in the cytoplasm. A cell wall surrounds the cell membrane. Some species of bacteria have a capsule that surrounds the cell wall and this offers additional protection against drying out. The presence of a capsule can often delay detection of the bacteria by an animal's immune system. Some bacteria have flagella that help them to move.

Bacteria are classified according to shape. There are three basic shapes of bacteria: cocci or spherical-shaped bacteria, rod-shaped bacteria and spiral-shaped bacteria.

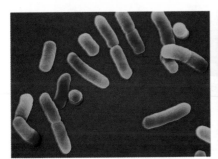

Fig 6.3 Rod-shaped bacteria

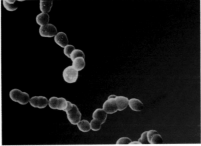

Fig 6.4 Spherical-shaped (cocci) bacteria

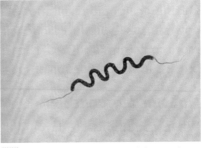

Fig 6.5 Spiral-shaped bacteria

Most bacteria are either rod-shaped or spherical. Table 6.1 shows some of the common diseases found in cattle and sheep and lists the type of organism responsible for the disease.

Table 6.1 Diseases found in cattle and sheep		
Disease	**Type of bacteria**	**Name of bacteria**
Bacterial scour	Rod-shaped	*Escherichia coli* (E. coli) (see Fig 6.6)
Bovine tuberculosis	Rod-shaped	*Mycobacterium bovis* (see Fig 6.7)
Mastitis	Spherical	*Staphylococcus aureus* and *Streptococcus uberis* (see Fig 6.8)
Blackleg	Rod-shaped	*Clostridium chauvoei*

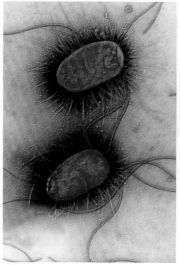

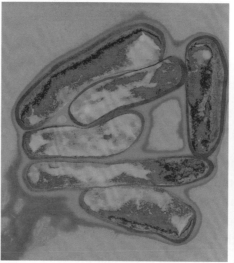

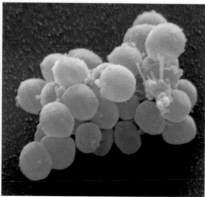

|||||| Fig 6.6 E. coli |||||| Fig 6.7 *Mycobacterium bovis* |||||| Fig 6.8 *Staphylococcus aureus*

Mode of respiration

Aerobic bacteria have the ability to release energy from sugars in the presence of oxygen and carry out aerobic respiration. *Mycobacterium bovis*, the bacteria responsible for tuberculosis, is an example of an aerobic bacteria.

Other bacteria, like lactobacillus, can release energy in the absence of oxygen and are known as anaerobic bacteria. During anaerobic respiration, lactobacillus bacteria break down sugars to produce lactic acid. This type of respiration is more commonly known as fermentation and is an important process in the production of silage (see Chapter 30).

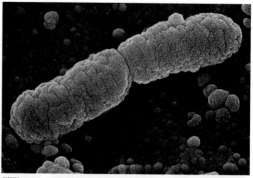

|||||| Fig 6.9 Bacteria undergoing binary fission

Mode of reproduction

When conditions are favourable, bacteria can reproduce rapidly asexually by binary fission. Here, the bacteria cell replicates its genetic information and then divides in two. Several generations can be produced in just a few hours. If conditions become unfavourable, some bacteria have the ability to survive by producing an endospore.

Endospores are highly resistant structures that allow the bacteria to survive in harsh conditions, e.g. heat, freezing, drying and even chemicals. Once conditions become favourable again, the spore will germinate and a new bacteria cell is formed, which will then divide by binary fission.

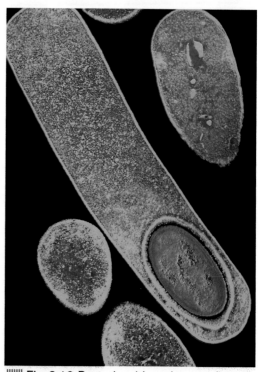

|||||| Fig 6.10 Bacteria with endospore (in red)

Case Study

Bovine tuberculosis

Causes of bovine tuberculosis

Mycobacterium bovis causes bovine tuberculosis. It is highly contagious and can spread quickly through a herd. It is a zoonose.

> **Zoonose**: A disease that can pass from animals to humans.

Bovine tuberculosis is transmitted to humans via infected milk. However, pasteurisation of milk kills this bacterium. Bovine tuberculosis spreads within a herd from cow to cow by inhalation especially in winter housing and through water supplies, urine and faeces. It can survive for up to 18 days in drinking water. It can be spread from cow to calf through milk and colostrum.

Symptoms of bovine tuberculosis

Mycobacterium bovis replicates very slowly and it can take years for the disease to develop. Signs of infection include: swollen lymph nodes in the animal's head; failure to thrive; the animal becomes weak and lethargic, loses a lot of body weight (emaciated) and a soft chronic cough develops. Due to the slow progression of the disease, the latter symptoms are rarely seen in animals as they would be identified by TB testing.

Prevention of bovine tuberculosis

Good farm management helps to prevent the entrance of this disease onto the farm. For example, the use of strong fences to prevent cattle having contact with cattle on neighbouring farms; the farm breeding all its replacement stock; quarantining or isolating bought-in cattle; using fresh water supplies.

Treatment of bovine tuberculosis

There is no treatment for bovine tuberculosis. An eradication programme by the Department of Agriculture commenced in Ireland in 1950 and became compulsory in 1962. Cattle herds are regularly tested under this programme. A veterinary surgeon does a skin test on the cattle. Three days later, the cattle are tested for a reaction. If an animal is infected with TB, the animal's immune system will react to the skin test and cause a swelling where the test was done. Such animals are called reactors.

Reactors are immediately slaughtered and restrictions are placed so that animals cannot be moved onto or off the affected farm. Farmers are compensated for slaughtered animals under this programme. A herd must have two clear tests 60 days apart before restrictions are lifted.

Fig 6.11 Testing for bovine TB

Case Study

Rhizobium and clover

Rhizobium is a unique rod-shaped bacterium, which has a symbiotic relationship with the roots of leguminous plants such as clover.

The bacteria are found in the root nodules of these plants where they fix atmospheric nitrogen into nitrates. The plant uses nitrates to produce protein. The Rhizobium obtains sugars from the clover plant.

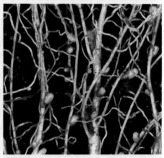

Fig 6.12 Nodules on the roots of a clover plant

A **symbiotic relationship** occurs when two different species have a close relationship that benefits both organisms.

Project link

For the practical examination, students must show evidence of a practical investigation carried out in microbiology.

Experiment 6.1

To isolate and grow rhizobium bacteria from the root nodules of clover

Materials

Disinfectant (Milton), 70 per cent alcohol solution, sterile petri dish, sterile water, sterile glass rod, sterile scalpel, yeast mannitol agar, clover plant, inoculating loop, incubator

Method

1 Wash the roots of a clover plant under running water.

2 Use a scalpel to remove a portion of the root that has a large pinkish nodule.

3 Sterilise the surface of the nodule and the root with some Milton and then wash with some alcohol.

4 Rinse the root with sterile water to remove the alcohol and the disinfectant.

5 Crush the root nodule with the sterile glass rod in a clean, sterile petri dish.

6 Sterilise the inoculating loop in a Bunsen burner flame until it glows red hot. Allow the loop to cool for 20 seconds.

7 Transfer some of the contents of the root nodule onto the yeast mannitol agar.

8 Incubate upside down at a temperature of 25°C for one week.

Result

Small colonies grow on the agar plates.

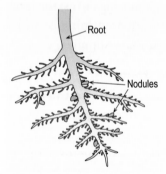

Fig 6.13 Pink nodules on a clover root

Fig 6.14 Sterilising the inoculating loop in a Bunsen burner

☰ Fungi

Fungi belong to the kingdom Fungi. They lack chlorophyll, so they are unable to photosynthesise. As a result, fungi have two modes of nutrition. Some fungi are free-living saprophytic decomposers. They have an important role in agriculture, breaking down organic matter and recycling nutrients in the soil, particularly in carbon and nitrogen cycling.

There are a number of parasitic fungi, causing diseases in both plants and animals. For example, ringworm is a common fungal infection that affects animals. A range of fungal diseases such as blight, mildew and rust affects plants.

|||| Fig 6.15 Ringworm on the eye of a cow

> **Saprophyte**: An organism that breaks down dead and decaying organic matter.

Basic structure of fungi

Rhizopus, commonly known as bread mould, is shown in Fig 6.16. Fungi consist of filaments called hyphae. The entire mass of hyphae is called mycelium. The rhizoids anchor the fungus into the substrate that it is growing on and absorb nutrients from it.

A stolon is a horizontally growing hyphae. These hyphae allow the fungus to spread over the substrate. Hyphae that grow upwards are called sporangiophores and they have a sporangium on top that produces thousands of spores.

|||| Fig 6.16 Rhizopus

Mode of reproduction

Fungi can reproduce both sexually and asexually. Fungi reproduce sexually to produce a zygospore. This later germinates to produce new fungal hyphae. Fungi also reproduce asexually by producing spores in the sporangium.

Case Study

Potato blight

An airborne fungus called *Phytophthora infestans* causes potato blight. It is a parasitic fungus. The blight zoospores germinate to produce hyphae, which invade the cells of the potato leaves.

> **Zoospore**: A mobile spore. Each spore has two flagella that help the spore to move.

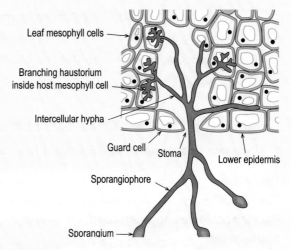

|||| Fig 6.17 Potato blight on a potato leaf

Case Study

The ends of the hyphae produce specialist structures called haustoria, which remove the nutrients from the cells of the leaves. Hyphae branches exit through the stomata where they develop into sporangia. Once mature, the sporangia are shed and are dispersed by the wind.

Warm, humid weather favours the development of zoospores inside the sporangia. The zoospores have flagella that enable them to swim in water. The zoospores then infect other leaves and stems in plants and if washed into the soil they will infect the tubers.

Symptoms of potato blight
Brown spots appear on the leaves and stems of the potato plant. Eventually the whole plant turns black and dies. Infected tubers have black patches on them.

Prevention of potato blight
To prevent potato blight, spray plants with a fungicide when the Meteorological Service issues blight warnings. Grow blight-resistant varieties. Remove all tubers when harvesting to prevent any tubers harbouring blight.

Experiment 6.2

To demonstrate the presence of micro-organisms in soil and air

Materials
Sterile nutrient agar plates, soil, inoculating loop, Bunsen burner

Method
1. Label three nutrient agar plates A, B and C. A is the control and remains unopened, B is air and C is soil.

2. Open agar plate B and expose it to the air for 15 minutes.

3. Shake up 1 g of soil in 5 cm³ of sterile, distilled water.

4. Heat an inoculating loop in a Bunsen burner until it glows red. Allow it to cool for 20 seconds.

5. Dip the inoculating loop into the soil solution.

6. Streak the agar plate labelled C with the soil solution.

7. Close agar plate B and C. Seal all the plates.

8. Incubate upside down at 25°C for a few days.

Fig 6.18 Streaking an agar plate with soil solution

Result
Fungal and bacterial growths occur on agar plates B and C. No growths occur on agar plate A. Bacterial colonies appear raised, shiny and circular, while fungal growths often have a furry appearance.

Viruses

Viruses are extremely small, ranging from 0.01 to 0.03 micrometres and can only be seen with an electron microscope. Viruses can only reproduce inside other living organisms; as a result, all viruses are parasites. Fig 6.19 shows the simple structure of a virus. Viruses are composed of some nucleic material in the form of DNA or RNA. A protein coat surrounds the nucleic material.

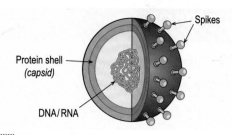

Fig 6.19 Basic structure of a virus

As viruses lack a cellular structure, antibiotics are ineffective at treating viral diseases. Some viral diseases can be vaccinated against.

Case Study

Bovine viral diarrhoea (BVD)

A virus causes bovine viral diarrhoea (BVD) in cattle. Symptoms include diarrhoea, respiratory infections, infertility, abortion and weak or ill-thriving calves. The virus is also an immunosuppressive agent, increasing the risk of infections, especially respiratory infections in calves. The virus is spread through saliva, semen, urine, milk, nasal discharges and faeces.

Calves can be born with the virus if the cow is exposed to BVD during the first four months of gestation. These calves are known as persistently infected (PI) animals and over the course of their lifetime shed huge quantities of the virus. There is no treatment for animals with BVD and infected animals should be culled. Vaccinations are available to prevent the disease. Breeding cattle should be vaccinated before breeding commences.

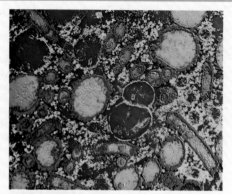

Fig 6.20 BVD viral particles seen as small, round, red particles in cell organelles through an electron microscope

Farmers can prevent BVD by ensuring that their cattle have no contact with the cattle on neighbouring farms. Bought-in cattle should be tested for BVD or quarantine on arrival. Ensure newborn calves get colostrum. BVD is not a zoonose, so humans cannot contract BVD from infected animals.

BVD can cause significant financial losses to affected farms.

Table 6.2 Summary of the advantages and disadvantages of bacteria and fungi	
Advantages	**Disadvantages**
• Bacteria are used in the production of yoghurt • Fungi are used to produce cheese; some fungi are edible • Bacteria and fungi are used to produce antibiotics • Bacteria and fungi break down organic matter • Rhizobium fixes nitrogen to nitrates in clover • Lactobacillus bacteria ferment grass into silage • They help digest cellulose in the rumen of cattle and sheep	• Bacteria cause souring of milk • Fungi cause spoilage of food • Bacteria and fungi cause many diseases • In waterlogged soils, denitrifying bacteria convert nitrates into atmospheric nitrogen

Summary

- Microbiology is the study of micro-organisms including bacteria, fungi and viruses.
- Micro-organisms are extremely small and are only visible with the aid of a microscope.
- A pathogen is an organism that causes a disease.
- Many bacteria cause both plant and animal diseases.
- Soil bacteria are called decomposers. They help break down organic matter and recycle important plant nutrients in both the carbon and nitrogen cycles.
- Rhizobium is a symbiotic bacterium that lives in the root nodules of red and white clover and fixes nitrogen into nitrates.
- Bacteria are classified according to shape.
- Bacteria can reproduce rapidly asexually by binary fission.
- Fungi belong to the kingdom Fungi. They lack chlorophyll and are unable to photosynthesise.
- Potato blight is caused by the fungus *Phytophthora infestans*.
- Blight can be prevented by spraying the crop with a fungicide during warm, humid weather.
- Viruses can only reproduce inside other living organisms.
- Viruses lack a cellular structure.
- Antibiotics are ineffective at treating viral diseases. Some viral diseases can be vaccinated against.
- Bovine viral diarrhoea is caused by a virus.

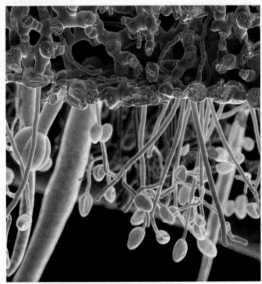

Fig 6.21 Sporangium of potato blight under an electron microscope

QUESTIONS

1. Draw a diagram of the basic structure of a bacterium. Label the following parts: cell wall, capsule, genetic material, plasmid and flagella. Outline the function of three of these parts.
2. Describe an investigation to demonstrate the presence of micro-organisms in the soil.
3. Define the term *pathogen*.
4. Describe an experiment to demonstrate the presence of bacteria in the root nodules of clover.
5. Explain the term *symbiosis* and give an example of a symbiotic relationship.
6. Give three beneficial effects of bacteria in agriculture.
7. Give two examples of infectious diseases that occur in farm animals. In the case of any one disease, state the cause, main symptoms and a method of prevention.
8. Give a scientific explanation for the issuing of blight warnings by the Irish Meteorological Service.

EXAM QUESTIONS

1. Describe the life cycle of a named parasitic fungus that causes a disease in a crop, under the following headings:
   (a) Mode of reproduction
   (b) Mode of nutrition
   (c) Environmental conditions that favour the spread of the disease. (LC, HL, 2006)
2. The following equipment was used in an investigation to show the presence of bacteria in a sample of milk.

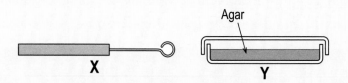

|||| Fig 6.22

   (a) Name the two pieces of equipment X and Y used in the experiment.
   (b) What are the functions of X and Y in the investigation?
   (c) What result would you expect if bacteria was present in the milk?
   (d) How is X sterilised during the investigation? (LC, OL, 2002)

●●● UNIT 3

Animal Physiology

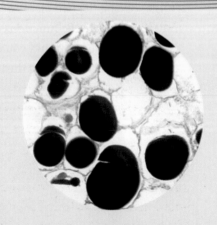

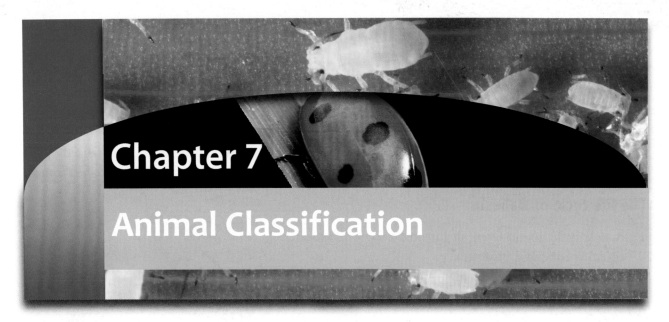

Chapter 7

Animal Classification

Animal Classification introduces animals that are of importance to agriculture. Some of the animals are bred for their meat, milk or wool, while others provide indirect benefits. Some animals carry diseases affecting both plant and animal life.

Project link

As part of the practical assessment, candidates are required to identify ten different animals. Three of these animals must be food-producing animals (e.g. cattle, sheep and pigs) and the candidate should be able to identify the breed and their bodily characteristics.

Candidates must also be able to identify seven other animals that are of importance to agriculture. Along with identifying them, they should be able to state the importance of that animal to agriculture. Non-food-producing animals will be focused on in this chapter, while food-producing animals will be studied in detail in the Animal Husbandry section.

≡ Classification of Animals

In biological terms, living organisms are classified into one of five kingdoms. Each kingdom is further split into smaller groups called **phyla** (singular: phylum). Within a phylum smaller divisions are created for organisms with common traits called **classes**. Further divisions of classes are called **orders** and within these orders an organism has a generic name called a **genus**. A genus is given by its Latin name; it is written with a capital letter and it is italicised. Members classed together under a genus that can interbreed are known as species and they, also, have a Latin name that is written after the genus in lower case.

Horse: *Equus caballus* **Donkey**: *Equus asinus*	Both horse and donkey belong to the same breed and can interbreed but are different species

≡ Phylum Protozoa

The members of phylum Protozoa are microscopic in size. They are unicellular (single-celled) animals and are classified by their locomotion.

Motility in protozoans

Protozoans have three main methods of movement. These methods include whip-like tails called flagella, foot-like structures called pseudopods (false feet) and hair-like structures called cilia. Other protozoans do not move at all. Spores are an important part of their life cycle.

The most important protozoans in agricultural terms are those that produce spores, as they are responsible for causing a number of diseases in both animals and humans. All of the spore-producing protozoans are parasites of humans or animals.

Common diseases in humans include malaria caused by the spore-producing protozoan *Plasmodium falciparum* and cryptosporidiosis (crypto) caused by the parasite Cryptosporidium.

One of the most common diseases found in livestock is redwater fever (babesiosis). It is caused by the protozoan Babesia, which is transmitted to the animal through a bite from the sheep tick (*Ixodes ricinus*).

The life cycle of Babesia

1   A tick sucks blood from an infected cow. The blood contains Babesia sporozoites.

2   They form gametes that form a zygote (sexual reproduction).

3   Many spores are then formed in the tick by asexual reproduction.

4   When the tick next bites the cow to suck blood, it transmits the spores into the cow's bloodstream.

5   The spores form sporozoites that enter red blood cells of the cow and break them down. The haemoglobin that is released from the red blood cells is passed in the urine of the cow, giving the name redwater fever.

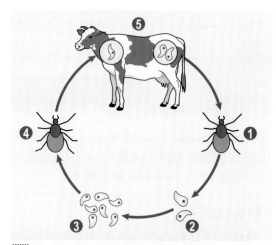

Fig 7.1 The life cycle of Babesia

Symptoms of babesiosis (redwater fever)

Symptoms of redwater fever appear in an animal 10–20 days after infection. Physical symptoms include:

- Red urine due to the presence of haemoglobin produced by the rupture of the red blood cells.

- An increased pulse rate.

- Diarrhoea followed by constipation.

Fig 7.2 Liver fluke

≡ Phylum Platyhelminthes

The animals of the phylum Platyhelminthes are flatworms. Two of the groups of animals – class Cestoda (tapeworms) and class Trematoda (flukes) – are endoparasitic animals.

All flatworms exhibit some common physical characteristics.

- Flatworms are bilaterally symmetrical, possessing a distinct front and rear end.
- They do not possess an internal body cavity (aceolomate structure).
- They possess three cell layers, i.e. triploblastic.
- They are flattened dorsoventrally.
- They are hermaphrodites.

Endoparasite: A parasitic organism that lives in the internal organs of an animal.

Hermaphrodites: Organisms that contain both male and female reproductive organs.

Class Cestoda: tapeworms

Tapeworms (*Taenia*) have flat, elongated bodies. They live in the intestine of the animals that they infect. They attach themselves to the intestinal wall via a scolex – a series of hooks in the head of the tapeworm. As the tapeworm has no digestive system, it simply absorbs nutrients from the host's gut. Tapeworms are not a major problem in Irish agriculture and are controlled by the regular dosing of animals with anti-helminths.

Class Trematoda: flukes

The liver fluke (*Fasciola hepatica*) is the most important trematode in Irish agriculture. Flukes are parasites of cattle and sheep. They have flat, leaf-shaped bodies, with an oral sucker and a ventral sucker, which allow them to attach themselves to their host. They are found in the liver and bile ducts of cattle, sheep, pigs and goats.

Liver flukes are hermaphrodites and their reproductive organs occupy a large part of their body. Flukes normally cross-fertilise but can self-fertilise if necessary.

The life cycle of the liver fluke (Fig 7.3) includes two hosts: a primary host where it matures (cow, sheep, etc.) and a secondary host, the mud snail (*Lymnaea truncatula*, phylum Mollusca) in which the larvae develop.

Life cycle of the liver fluke

1 The adult fluke lays its eggs in the bile duct of the primary host and the eggs make their way to the intestines, where they are excreted.

2 If conditions are suitable (temperature greater than 10°C), the eggs hatch larvae known as a miracidium. The miracidium must then find a mud snail within 24 hours to act as a host.

3 The miracidium burrows into the mud snail and undergoes a number of larval stages.

4 The miracidia produce a larval stage called a redia, which can produce even more rediae asexually.

5 The rediae develop into cercaria, which are tadpole-like in their physical structure.

6 At this point, the cercaria leave the mud snail and form cysts on vegetation.

7 If the cyst is eaten by an animal, it releases the young fluke which burrows its way to the bile ducts and matures. A mature fluke can produce approximately 20 000 eggs per day.

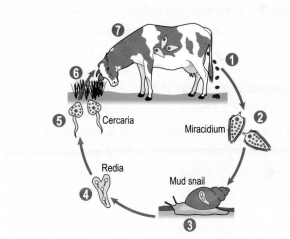

||||| Fig 7.3 The life cycle of the liver fluke

Symptoms of fluke in animals

▨ Weight loss.

▨ Reduced milk yields in dairy cattle.

▨ Lowered weight gains.

▨ Loss of condition.

Prevention and treatment of liver fluke

Animals can be dosed with an anti-helminth solution to control liver flukes in the host. However, prevention is a far more effective method of control. Fluke numbers can be controlled in a number of ways:

- Molluscides can be used to remove snails, which removes one of the hosts of the fluke, breaking the life cycle.
- Fence off waterlogged, swampy pastures and prevent livestock from grazing land where flukes are most likely to thrive.
- Drainage of land should be considered in areas where there is a high chance of fluke infestation.
- The introduction of ducks and geese to waterlogged land can control snail populations, as ducks and geese are a predator of the snail.

Phylum Nematoda

Nematodes are a diverse group of animals and are found in almost every habitat, including freshwater, marine and terrestrial habitats. All of the nematodes studied in this course are parasites of animals or plants.

Physical characteristics of nematodes

- Rounded in cross-section.
- Separate sexes: the male is usually smaller than the female and has a coiled tail with a spicule to attach himself to the female during copulation.
- A body cavity known as a pseudocoelome.
- The body is covered in a cuticle.

Plant parasites: eelworms

Eelworms are free-living or plant parasitic nematodes. Sizes range from microscopic to a couple of millimetres in length. They attack the stems and roots of crops such as potatoes, onions and strawberries. The most important eelworm in Irish agriculture is the potato eelworm (*Heterodera*). The eelworm feeds on the roots of the potato plant, which causes stunted growth and small tubers. Crop rotation helps to prevent the build up of eelworms in the soil.

Animal parasites: roundworms

There is a variety of roundworms including hookworms, lungworms and hairworms. A number of these worms cause infection in cattle.

Table 7.1 Worms that cause infections in cattle		
Name of worm	**Found in**	**Symptoms**
Cooperia	Small intestine	Diarrhoea and poor weight gain
Ostertagia	Abomasum	Scouring and weight loss
Nematodirus	Small intestine	Ill-thrift, diarrhoea and dehydration
Dictyocaulus (hoose)	Bronchial tubes	Husky cough, difficulty in breathing in severe cases

Life cycle of roundworms

Although some details vary, the life cycle of all the gastro-intestinal roundworms of cattle follows a similar pattern (see Fig 7.4):

1   Female roundworms lay eggs that pass in the faeces of cattle.

2   Free-living larvae develop and hatch from the egg.

3   The larvae undergo two more stages of development. At this point, they can infect cattle.

4   The larvae attach themselves to grasses that are ingested by the cow. They mature in the intestines of the cow and reproduce. Females can produce eggs two to four weeks after ingestion.

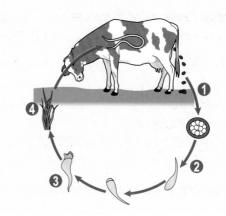

Fig 7.4 The life cycle of roundworms

☰ Phylum Annelida

The main animal of importance in this phylum is the earthworm *Lumbriscus terrestris*. The phylum consists of a large group of segmented worms.

Physical characteristics of the earthworm

- Segmented body.
- Rounded in cross-section.
- Has a clitellum (saddle).
- Body cavity known as a coelome.
- Bristles known as setae or chaetae.

Fig 7.5 Earthworm

Earthworms are hermaphrodites. They cross-fertilise each other, each secreting sperm and eggs into the mucus produced by the clitellum of each worm.

The clitellum plays an important role in the reproductive system of the earthworm. It is a thick, ring-shaped saddle, which is lighter in colour than the rest of the body. It secretes a fluid, allowing the formation of a cocoon for the earthworm's eggs.

Locomotion in earthworms

- Earthworms move by peristalsis, where the body contracts and expands, shortening and lengthening as it moves.
- The chaetae allow the earthworm to anchor its body as it moves along.

Benefits of earthworms

The benefits of earthworms are numerous.

- They convert organic matter (e.g. leaf litter) into humus, which improves soil fertility.
- They improve soil structure through burrowing by creating channels that improve and aid aeration and drainage.
- They mix layers of soil by bringing organic matter to deeper levels through burrowing.
- Worm casts created by excretion are high in nitrogen, phosphates and potash due to the breakdown of organic and mineral matter by the earthworm's digestive system. This leads to higher nutrient levels in the soil.

Vermiculture

A particular species of worm, the tiger worm (*Eisenia foetida*), is especially adapted to breaking down organic matter on a small scale. Organic waste can be fed to these worms, which are kept in a wormery, producing a form of compost.

≡ Phylum Mollusca

Phylum Mollusca is one of the most diverse groups of species and includes a large variety of saltwater species, e.g. clams, squid and octopus. About 80 per cent of all known molluscs belong to a subgroup known as class Gastropoda. This group of gastropods includes slugs and snails.

Characteristics common to the gastropods

- A muscular foot, which secretes a mucus to aid movement.
- A rasping tongue known as a radula.
- Dorsal concentration of internal organs.

The main difference between a slug and a snail is that a snail has a shell and a slug does not.

Slugs are pests in agricultural and horticultural environments. They favour leafy foliage and will eat leaves, flowers and ripened fruit and vegetables. This can speed up rot in ripened crops and lead to crops that cannot be sold.

||||| Fig 7.6 Garden slug

||||| Fig 7.7 Garden snail

The snail *Lymnaea truncatula,* which is found in freshwater habitats, plays an important role in the life cycle of the liver fluke *Fasciola hepatica.* It acts as a secondary host for the fluke. Snails can be removed from a habitat by using a molluscide or by the introduction of ducks and geese, which will predate on the snails.

≡ Phylum Arthropoda

Over one million species belong to phylum Arthropoda, which includes insects, arachnids and crustaceans. Arthropods, like the members of the other phyla so far discussed, are invertebrates (do not possess a backbone). They have segmented bodies and jointed limbs. They possess an exoskeleton made of chitin, which protects their bodies. They shed this exoskeleton regularly as they mature, to allow them to grow and produce another exoskeleton. This shedding or moulting is known as ecdysis.

There are numerous classes of arthropods, but the two classes that are most important in Irish agriculture are class Arachnida (spiders) and class Insecta (insects).

Class Arachnida

The arachnids have several physical characteristics that differentiate them from insects. They have eight legs in four pairs, and two main body segments called the cephalothorax and abdomen. They do not possess antennae or wings.

Arachnids in agriculture are parasitic by nature. They are ectoparasites of both plants and animals. Examples include spiders, ticks and mites.

Ectoparasite: An external parasitic organism that lives on the skin or exterior of the body.

Red spider mite

The red spider mite is a plant parasite that sucks the sap of many fruit and vegetable plants including cucumbers, strawberries, apples and potatoes. Mites cause the stunting and yellowing of leaves. They can be controlled by the use of a pesticide or by the introduction of a predator mite.

Mange mite

Mange or scabies is caused by the mange mite and spreads by close contact with infected animals. The female burrows into the skin to lay eggs, which leads to further burrowing when the larvae hatch. The burrowing action of the mite causes itching in the animal and if left untreated can lead to open wounds and other infections.

Ticks

Ticks live on the skin of sheep and cattle, sucking their blood. The most important tick in Ireland is the sheep tick (*Ixodes ricinus*), a carrier of Babesia, which causes redwater fever in animals.

Class Insecta

Insects, like all other arthropods, have segmented bodies. Their bodies are divided into three parts: head, thorax and abdomen. They have six legs, in three pairs, two antennae and compound eyes. They normally have two pairs of wings attached to the thorax.

All insects undergo a process of development called metamorphosis. There are two types of metamorphosis: incomplete metamorphosis and complete metamorphosis.

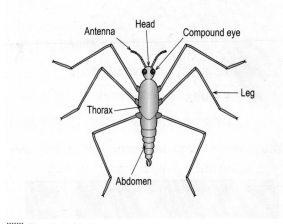

||||| Fig 7.8 An insect

Incomplete metamorphosis

During incomplete metamorphosis, the immature insect undergoes a series of moults, shedding its exoskeleton at each stage to allow for growth and development. Immature insects undergoing this process of development are known as nymphs. They are similar in appearance to their adult counterparts, only smaller. Wings do not appear on these insects until they reach adulthood.

Aphids, dragonflies and damselflies are examples of insects that experience incomplete metamorphosis. The life cycle of an insect that undergoes incomplete metamorphosis is:

Egg ➔ Nymph ➔ Adult

Aphids or greenfly cause a lot of damage to plants. They suck sap from the plant, leading to stunted growth and curled, yellowing leaves. They also transmit viruses as they move from plant to plant. Cereals, potatoes and sugar beet are all examples of crops that can suffer from viruses transmitted by aphids.

Aphids can be controlled by the use of aphidicides and by ladybirds, which are a natural predator of the aphid. Cool, wet, windy weather does not provide favourable conditions for the development of aphids.

Complete metamorphosis

During complete metamorphosis, each stage of the life cycle is physically different to the previous stage.

The larval stage is worm-like in appearance and is the feeding stage in the life cycle. The larva develops into a pupa, which is often protected by a cocoon: this is a resting stage and very little movement occurs during this time.

The insect undergoes much change in the pupal stage and emerges as an adult insect.

Butterflies are the most well-known insects that undergo complete metamorphosis.

The life cycle of an insect that undergoes complete metamorphosis is:

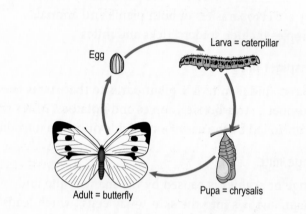

Egg

Larva = caterpillar

Adult = butterfly

Pupa = chrysalis

|||||| Fig 7.9 Butterfly life cycle

Egg → Larva → Pupa → Adult

A number of insects are pests in both their larval and adult forms. Examples of these are listed in Table 7.2.

Table 7.2 Insect pests that undergo a complete metamorphosis		
Insect	**Larval form**	**Importance in agriculture**
Crane fly	Leatherjacket	Leatherjackets eat the roots of grasses, cereals, vegetables and strawberries
Click beetle	Wireworm	Feed on the roots of grasses. Damage potato tubers sown after grass

|||||| Fig 7.10 Wireworm

|||||| Fig 7.11 Leatherjacket

☰ Phylum Chordata

The previous six phyla contained species, all of which were classed as invertebrates. The members of phylum Chordata are vertebrates: they all possess a vertebrate structure at some point in their lives.

Two classes of chordates are important to agriculture: class Aves (birds) and class Mammalia (mammals).

> **Vertebrate**: An animal that has a backbone or spinal column.

Class Aves

Birds are winged, have feathers, have a beak with no teeth, are bipedal, lay eggs and are warm-blooded (endothermic) animals. They do not possess a bladder and so, faeces and uric acid are combined and excreted together as a semi-solid waste.

In agricultural terms, birds such as chickens, ducks, geese and turkeys (pictured below) are reared for meat and eggs. Other produce includes down feathers for clothing and bedding.

| Fig 7.12 Chicken | Fig 7.13 Ducks | Fig 7.14 Geese | Fig 7.15 Turkey |

Class Mammalia

There is a wide variety of mammals classified into subgroups. However, all mammals possess the following common characteristics:

- Hair (which may be modified in some species).
- Mammary glands (in the female to produce milk).
- Sweat glands.

> **Herbivore**: An animal that feeds on plant material.
> **Carnivore**: An animal that feeds on the flesh of other animals.
> **Omnivore**: An animal that feeds on both plants and animal material.

Most mammals have a placenta and give birth to live young. Most of the animals of importance in agriculture belong to a mammalian group called order Ungulata, the ungulates or hoofed animals. These include cattle, sheep, pigs, horses, donkeys and goats. These animals can be further subdivided into even-toed ungulates and odd-toed ungulates:

- Even-toed ungulates include cattle, sheep, pigs and goats.
- Odd-toed ungulates include horses and donkeys.

Most of the hoofed animals are herbivores and only eat plants, fruit and vegetable material. Pigs are omnivores, eating both plant and animal material.

Most of the animals of importance in agriculture are food-producing animals. They primarily produce meat, milk and wool. Cattle (both dairy and beef breeds), sheep and pigs are three of the most important food-producing animals in agriculture in Ireland.

Summary

- Animal classification involves putting living organisms in groups based on their characteristics. Each group is called a phylum.

- Phylum Protozoa are single-celled organisms classified by their locomotion.

- Babesia is a common protozoan that causes redwater fever in cattle.

- Phylum Platyhelminthes contains flatworms. Liver flukes belong to this phylum and cause damage to cattle and sheep. They are hermaphrodites, flattened dorsoventrally and bilaterally symmetrical.

- Endoparasites are parasites that live inside an animal and cause it damage.

- Ectoparasites live on the outside of an animal and cause it damage.

- Phylum Nematoda contains a wide range of parasitic worms including eelworms and lungworms. These worms are rounded in cross-section and have separate sexes.

- The most important member of phylum Annelida is the earthworm. It has a segmented body and is rounded in cross-section. It is particularly important to agriculture as it improves soil structure.

- Snails and slugs are found in phylum Mollusca. Molluscs typically have a shell. They are pests as they eat foliage and vegetation. The mud snail is also a host to the liver fluke.

- Phylum Arthropoda contains two classes of importance: class Insecta and class Arachnida.

- Class Insecta contains species with six legs and three body segments. Common insects include aphids, ticks and fleas. Many insects undergo incomplete metamorphosis in their life cycle. This is where each stage of the cycle is distinctly different in appearance to the previous stage.

- Class Arachnida contains species with eight legs and two body segments. All spiders belong to this class.

- Phylum Chordata contains organisms that have a backbone. They are known as vertebrates. Two classes of importance are Aves (birds) and Mammalia.

- Aves have a beak, feathers and two legs. Most of the birds of importance in agriculture are bred in the poultry sector such as chickens, ducks and turkeys.

- Mammals have hair, mammary glands and give birth to live young. They are often classified as carnivores, herbivores or omnivores depending on their diet. Cattle, sheep and pigs are all mammals.

QUESTIONS

1. State one characteristic of organisms from the phylum Protozoa.
2. Which organism causes redwater fever in cattle?
3. What are the symptoms of redwater fever in cattle?
4. State two characteristics of organisms from the phylum Platyhelminthes.
5. What is *Fasciola hepatica* better known as?
6. Describe the life cycle of the liver fluke.
7. State two characteristics from the phylum Nematoda.
8. State two characteristics of an organism from phylum Annelida.
9. What does the term *hermaphrodite* mean?

QUESTIONS

10 State two characteristics of an organism from phylum Mollusca.

11 Why is the mud snail of importance to agriculture?

12 Name two characteristics of insects and two characteristics of arachnids.

13 To which family do insects and arachnids belong?

14 Give one example of an insect and one example of an arachnid that are important in agriculture.

15 What is the difference between complete and incomplete metamorphosis?

16 What is a parasite?

17 Name one ectoparasite and one endoparasite.

18 Name two characteristics of an organism from class Aves.

19 List two characteristics of mammals.

20 What is the difference between a herbivore, a carnivore and an omnivore?

21 Identify the phylum to which each of the following organisms belong:

Organism	Phylum
Aphid	
Babesia	
Bluebottle	
Duck	
Earthworm	
Friesian	
Goose	
Ladybird	
Leatherjacket	
Fasciola hepatica	
Lungworm	
Lymnaea truncatula	
Mange mite	
Red spider mite	
Potato eelworm	
Slug	
Tapeworm	
Texel	
Wireworm	

QUESTIONS

22 Identify each of the following organisms and state its importance in agriculture:

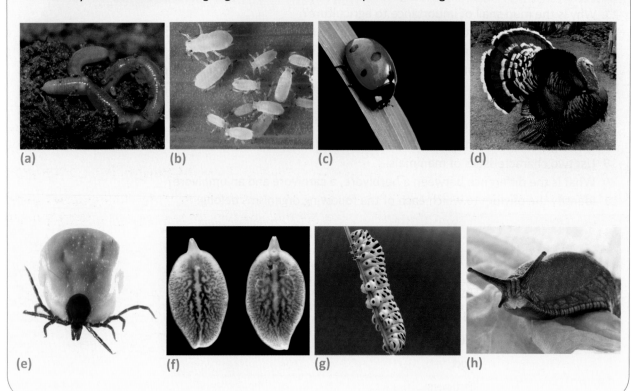

(a)   (b)   (c)   (d)

(e)   (f)   (g)   (h)

EXAM QUESTIONS

1   (a) Name an insect pest of a cereal crop.
    (b) How does the pest you have named damage the crop? (LC, OL, 2009)
2   (a) Name two farm animals in which liver fluke can be found.
    (b) State two symptoms an animal would have if infected with liver fluke
    (c) How can the farm animal be treated immediately for the liver fluke infection? (LC, OL, 2009)
3   (a) To which phylum do insects belong?
    (b) Describe a role insects can play in crop production.
    (c) Suggest two reasons why the number of some insect species is declining in farmland.
    (d) Name the stages in the life cycle of an insect that undergoes complete metamorphosis.
    (e) Explain what is meant by incomplete metamorphosis of insects. (LC, HL, 2009)

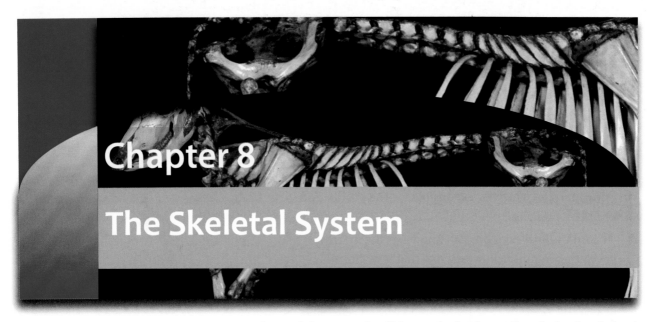

Chapter 8

The Skeletal System

Over the next seven chapters, the physiology of the animal will be studied. This will include the skeletal system, the digestive system, excretion, circulation, transport and storage in the animal, respiration, the nervous system, the endocrine system and reproduction.

> **Project link**
>
> As part of the Leaving Certificate Practical Assessment, students are required to carry out at least one experiment in relation to animal physiology. Investigations involving a number of organs have been included in the following chapters that may be suitable for their investigations.

☰ Function of the Skeleton

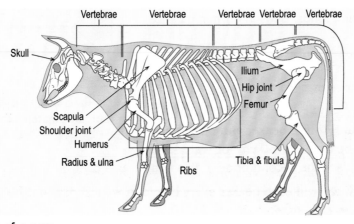

|||| Fig 8.1 Skeleton of a cow

The skeleton is the framework that gives the body its shape. It has a number of important functions including:

1   **Support**: It gives the body shape, supporting the soft tissues of the body, some of which are attached to the skeleton, e.g. muscle, tendons.
2   **Protection**: Some skeletal bones provide protection to the internal organs by enclosing them and protecting them from injury, e.g. the ribcage protects the heart and lungs, the skull protects the brain and the vertebrae protect the spinal cord.
3   **Movement**: Muscles are attached to bones, so when they contract they cause bones to move.
4   **Mineral storage**: Calcium (Ca) and phosphorus (P) are stored in bone. They can be released into the bloodstream when needed.
5   **Production of blood cells**: Red blood cells are produced in bone marrow.

The Structure of Bone

- A **joint** is the place where two or more bones meet.

- **Cartilage** is a layer of tissue that is found on bones in between joints. It is softer than bone and reduces friction where bones meet as joints.

- **Spongy bone** occurs in long bones and contains red bone marrow, which is responsible for the production of red blood cells.

- The **medullary cavity** is also known as the marrow cavity. It contains yellow marrow that is responsible for the production of white blood cells.

- **Compact bone** is the outer layer of bone. It is white in appearance and it is hard.

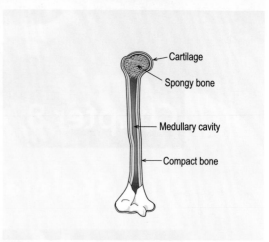

Fig 8.2 The main bones found in the mammalian body

The composition of bone is both organic and inorganic. One of the main organic components of bone is collagen, a form of protein that is mainly found in connective tissues such as tendons, ligaments and cartilage in addition to bone. It is not found in plants. The inorganic component of bone consists of bone minerals.

Experiment 8.1

To demonstrate the organic and inorganic components of bone

Materials
Fresh chicken bones with the flesh removed, dilute hydrochloric acid, beakers, tongs, Bunsen burner, balance

Method

Part A

1 Take two chicken bones of similar size and weigh each bone.

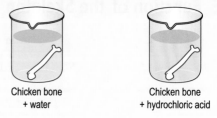

Fig 8.3 Testing for the presence of inorganic material in bone

2 Add 50 cm³ of dilute HCl to a beaker and place one of the bones in the beaker. Add 50 cm³ of water to a second beaker and place the second bone in this beaker as a control.

3 Change the acid and water in each beaker every day for a week, ensuring the same volume of water and acid is used each time.

4 Using tongs, remove the bone from the acid and rinse with water. Repeat for the control.

5 Reweigh both bones.

6 Test each bone for flexibility by bending it.

7 Record your results in the table below.

Result

Table 8.1 Results				
Bones	Initial mass	Final mass	Difference in mass	Flexibility test
Bone A (Acid)				
Bone B (Water)				

Experiment 8.1

Conclusion

The bone that was placed in acid should be soft and flexible, as the minerals in the bone have been removed by the acid. The bone placed in acid should exhibit a loss of approximately two-thirds of its mass. The bone placed in water should not bend. The bone placed in water should also exhibit no change in mass.

Part B

1 Weigh a fresh, clean chicken bone.

2 Use tongs to hold the chicken bone in the flame of a Bunsen burner.

3 Reweigh the bone every five minutes, and record its mass.

4 When the mass of the bone does not change, remove the bone from the flame.

5 Weigh the bone again and record its final mass.

6 Use the initial mass and the final mass to calculate the mass of organic matter that was removed from the bone by burning.

7 When the bone has sufficiently cooled, test it for flexibility.

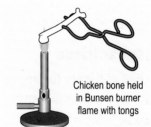

Chicken bone held in Bunsen burner flame with tongs

Fig 8.4 Testing for the presence of organic material in bone

Result

Table 8.2 Results				
Bones	Initial mass	Final mass	Difference in mass	Flexibility test

Conclusion

The bone should be inflexible, and when pressure is applied it should break. The organic matter, which gave it its flexibility, was removed. It should also have lost approximately one-third of its overall mass.

☰ Connective Tissue

Connective tissue in the animal body has a number of functions. It provides support and protection, stores fat, forms blood cells and binds structures (e.g. skeletal structures) together. There are several types of connective tissue in the mammalian body.

Loose connective tissue surrounding organs can allow the organs to expand when needed, but also protects the organs.

Fibrous connective tissue contains collagen and has a more specific role in the body.

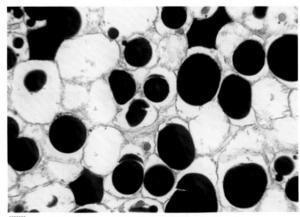

Fig 8.5 Connective tissue in an animal, e.g. adipose

Adipose tissue

Adipose tissue is a loose type of connective tissue. Its main function is to store fat. It is also used for insulation. It is found beneath the skin and around internal organs such as the kidneys.

Tendons

Tendons connect muscle to bone. They are inelastic fibres consisting of collagen. As muscles are attached to bones via tendons, when muscles contract the bones move with them.

Ligaments

Ligaments are another connective tissue, consisting of fibres of collagen. Ligaments connect two bones together at a joint. They are slightly elastic, allowing the joints to move, while at the same time controlling the range of movement of the joints.

Muscular tissue

Muscle accounts for approximately 40 per cent of the body's total weight. When muscles contract (or shorten) they cause movement in the body.

☰ Muscle Types

There are three types of muscle in the body: skeletal muscle, smooth muscle and cardiac muscle. Each has its own characteristic composition, location and function.

Skeletal muscle

Skeletal muscle is voluntary muscle that is attached to the bones of the skeleton. It is also found in the diaphragm and between the ribs.

Voluntary muscle is under conscious control, i.e. it does not move of its own accord. One of its main functions is for movement and breathing. In the mammalian body, skeletal muscle assists the movement of the legs.

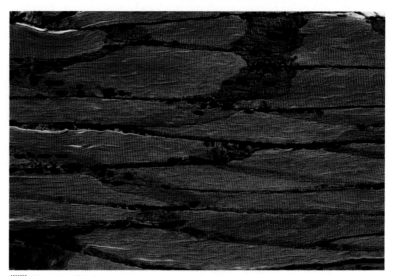

|||||| Fig 8.6 Skeletal tissue in an animal

Smooth muscle

Smooth muscle is involuntary muscle found in the internal organs such as the digestive system, the blood vessels and the reproductive system.

Involuntary muscle moves independently. Some of its main functions include the movement of food through the alimentary canal (oesophagus), which is known as peristalsis, and the dilation of the cervix during birth.

Cardiac muscle

Cardiac muscle is only found in the heart. It is involuntary muscle that does not fatigue, and it is responsible for pumping blood around the body in the circulatory system.

Summary

- The skeleton gives the body its shape. Its functions include support, protection, movement, mineral storage and production of blood cells.
- A joint is a place where two or more bones meet. Cartilage is found between joints. It is a soft tissue that reduces friction.
- Adipose tissue stores fat and provides insulation. It is found around internal organs such as the kidney.
- Tendons connect muscle to bone. When a muscle contracts the bone moves because of their connection by the tendon.
- Ligaments connect two bones that meet at a joint. They allow for movement of joints and are made of collagen.
- There are three types of muscle in the body: skeletal muscle, smooth muscle and cardiac muscle.
- Skeletal muscle is attached to bones and is needed for movement. It is voluntary muscle under conscious control.
- Smooth muscle is involuntary muscle and is found in the internal organs. Movement of food through the oesophagus is brought about by smooth muscle in a process called peristalsis.
- Cardiac muscle is found in the heart. It is involuntary muscle and does not fatigue.

QUESTIONS

1 Which bone protects the brain?
2 What is the purpose of the rib cage?
3 State the location of the following bones: (a) radius, (b) tibia and (c) sternum.
4 What is a joint?
5 What is the function of a tendon?
6 Name two minerals stored in bone.
7 What is the function of bone marrow?
8 What is the difference between cartilage and bone?
9 What is the function of adipose tissue?
10 State a location in the animal body where you would find (a) cardiac muscle, (b) skeletal muscle and (c) smooth muscle.

EXAM QUESTION

Mention the location in the animal body of the radius. (LC, HL, 1998)

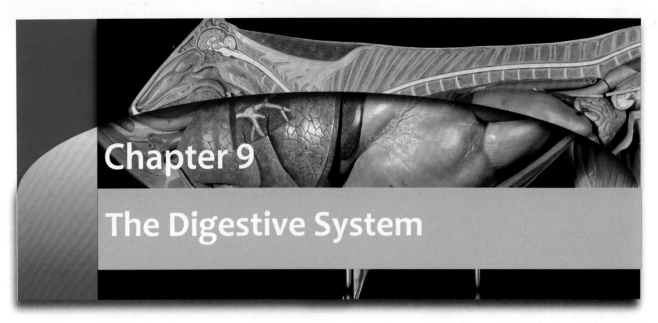

Chapter 9

The Digestive System

The intake of food in order to acquire nutrients is necessary for an animal's survival. The breakdown of food into components, which can be used within the body, is called digestion.

Digestion occurs in two ways: mechanical and chemical. Mechanical digestion is the physical breakdown of food into smaller pieces. Chemical digestion is the chemical breakdown of food by substances known as enzymes.

Food is taken into the body through the mouth, where both mechanical digestion and chemical digestion first occur.

☰ The Digestive Process

The first stage of the digestive process is known as ingestion. Ingestion is the intake of food into the mouth where it is chewed and swallowed. The initial stages of digestion take place in the mouth with the aid of the teeth, tongue and salivary glands. Both mechanical and chemical digestion take place at this stage. Mechanical digestion begins with the teeth.

The teeth

Teeth are used in the first stages of digestion to break up food into smaller pieces by tearing, crushing and grinding it. The tooth is a specialised structure for these tasks, with a hard outer coating of enamel.

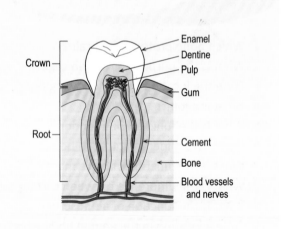

Fig 9.1 A longitudinal section of a tooth

There are four types of teeth: incisors, canines, premolars and molars. Each has a different shape and function.

The number and type of teeth present in an animal's mouth is related to the diet of the animal.

Herbivores eat plant material, so they use their premolars and molars for crushing and grinding material such as grass. Sheep, cattle and horses are all herbivores.

Carnivores eat meat, so they use their canine teeth for tearing flesh.

Incisors: Chisel-like teeth used for cutting and biting.
Canines: Pointed and sharp teeth used for tearing food.
Premolars: Relatively flat teeth used for grinding.
Molars: Flat teeth used for crushing food.

Omnivores, such as humans, who eat both plant material and meat, do not have a specialised dentition but use all the types of teeth listed to aid the digestion of a variety of foods.

Dental Formulas of Animals

Dental formulas are written to represent the dentition in the upper and lower jaw of the mouth of an animal. The formulas given below show the number of incisors, canines, premolars and molars present on one side of the mouth only, as the other side of the mouth is identical.

> Dental formula of a pig
>
> I: $\dfrac{3}{3}$ C: $\dfrac{1}{1}$ P: $\dfrac{4}{4}$ M: $\dfrac{3}{3}$

The dentition above shows that the pig has 3 incisors, 1 canine, 4 premolars and 3 molars in the upper jaw and the same in the lower jaw: a total of 22 teeth. As this dental formula represents only one half of the mouth, the same number of teeth is present in the other half, giving the pig 44 teeth.

> Dental formula of a herbivore (cow, sheep, goat)
>
> I: $\dfrac{0}{3}$ C: $\dfrac{0}{1}$ P: $\dfrac{3}{3}$ M: $\dfrac{3}{3}$

The dentition of a herbivore is quite different to that of a pig. As can be seen from the formula, the herbivore has no incisors or canines in the upper jaw. The front upper jaw instead consists of a horny pad that meets the lower incisors and canines to allow them to crop grass. The gap between the front teeth and the premolars and molars is called the diastema. It can store ingested material while the animal is chewing.

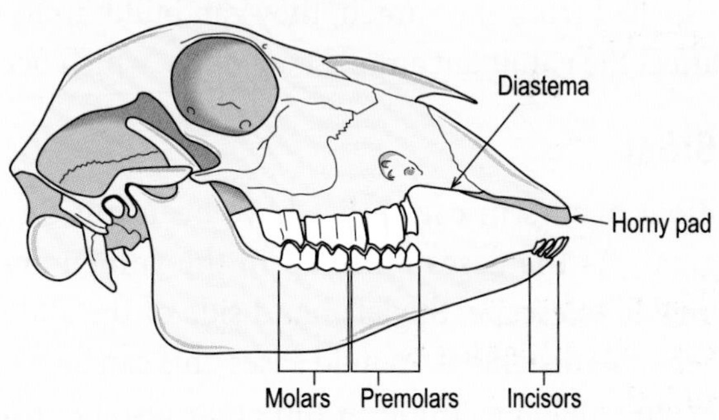

Fig 9.2 Sheep dentition

Chemical Digestion in the Mouth

The mouth has three pairs of salivary glands. The glands secrete an enzyme called amylase. The amylase breaks down starch to maltose. The more food that is chewed by the teeth, the more of it can be broken down chemically by amylase.

Saliva has a secondary function as a lubricant, which wets the food and makes it easier to chew

> Peristalsis: Food entering the oesophagus is moved along to the stomach by muscular contractions that have a rhythmic, wave-like motion.

and swallow. When food is swallowed it is passed to the oesophagus. It is prevented from entering the trachea by the epiglottis. Food is then moved to the stomach along the oesophagus by peristalsis.

Digestion in the Ruminant Animal

> A **ruminant animal** has a stomach that is modified and adapted for the digestion of cellulose. The stomach has four separate chambers, each with a specialised function. The animal breaks down the plant material in its mouth, passes it to the first chamber where partial digestion takes place. The material, now known as 'cud', is then regurgitated from the second chamber and chewed a second time before being swallowed and continuing through the remaining two chambers where it is fully digested.

Cattle and sheep are ruminant herbivores. They have a ruminant stomach with four chambers: the rumen, reticulum, omasum and abomasum. This allows them to digest cellulose, which is found in grass, the main constituent of their diet.

The rumen

Food that is swallowed by the ruminant animal is passed down the oesophagus to the rumen. The rumen contains micro-organisms such as bacteria and protozoans, which allow the ruminant animal to consume and digest fibrous plant material such as grass, hay and silage.

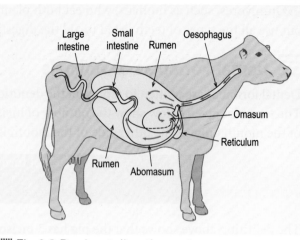

||||| Fig 9.3 Ruminant digestive system

The rumen is an anaerobic environment, i.e. there is no oxygen present. It has a pH in the range of 6.5 to 7.0. The microbes break down the cellulose into smaller molecules such as glucose to provide energy for the animal. Other products resulting from the breakdown of cellulose include carbon dioxide and methane gas. The rumen contracts to force these gases out of the rumen. However, if the gases are not expelled from the rumen, they can build up to cause a condition called bloat. Another condition that can affect the ruminant animal is acidosis, which occurs when the pH of the rumen drops below its normal level.

Bloat

Bloat occurs in cattle that have been put on early grass. As the gases build up in the rumen and are unable to escape, the left-hand side of the abdomen becomes distended. In mild cases, this can be relieved by an antacid solution. A tube may also be inserted through the mouth into the rumen to release the gas.

In more severe cases, the use of a trocar and cannula is necessary to relieve the bloat. An incision is made in the abdomen of the animal. The trocar and cannula are inserted through the abdomen into the rumen. The trocar is then removed, leaving the cannula (a thin metal tube) in the abdomen, which allows the gases to escape. The incision in the rumen and abdomen is then closed by a vet.

||||| Fig 9.4 Trocar and cannula

Acidosis

Acidosis is a disorder that occurs in ruminant animals when the pH of the rumen falls below 5.5. As a result, the rumen stops moving, which leads to a loss of appetite in the animal. Also the increased acidity changes the environment of the rumen, allowing acid-loving bacteria and microbes to flourish and take over. They produce even more acid, which makes the problem worse. The acid can be absorbed through the walls of the rumen, causing metabolic acidosis, which in severe cases can lead to death.

Acidosis is brought on by feeding a diet of high concentrates, or rapidly digestible carbohydrates, or a low fibre diet, where an excess of lactic acid is produced that cannot be used up quickly enough.

Signs of acidosis include a reduced milk yield, weight loss, loss of condition and a reduced appetite.

Symbiosis

The relationship between ruminant animals and the microbes that live in the rumen is an example of symbiosis. Both species benefit from the relationship. The microbes are provided with a suitable living environment and a ready supply of nutrients. At the same time, they provide the enzymes that break down the cellulose for the animal. They themselves are also digested by the animal, providing it with a supply of protein. The microbes are sources of vitamins E and K for the animal.

The reticulum

The reticulum is the second chamber of the ruminant stomach. It resembles a honeycomb in its appearance. It is responsible for regurgitating partially digested material from the rumen back to the mouth for further chewing. This is known as 'chewing the cud'.

The omasum

The omasum is the third chamber of the ruminant stomach. Food that has been regurgitated for further chewing is passed to the omasum when it is swallowed. The omasum has many layers of tissue and it is responsible for squeezing the food and reabsorbing water and liquid from it.

The abomasum

The abomasum is the fourth chamber in the ruminant stomach. It acts much like the stomach of a monogastric animal (human or pig). Gastric juices in the form of enzymes are secreted here to break down proteins and aid the final stage of digestion. Because of the similarity between the abomasum and the monogastric stomach, it is often called the 'true stomach'.

Digestion in the young ruminant

When calves or lambs are born, they do not have a fully functioning ruminant digestive system. Instead, ingested material (milk and milk replacer) is brought straight to the abomasum for digestion. As they begin to feed, cultures of micro-organisms develop in the rumen. It takes about six weeks for the rumen and reticulum to fully develop in the young ruminant.

The small intestine

The first section of the small intestine is called the duodenum. Bile and pancreatic juices are secreted into the small intestine to aid the breakdown of food and absorption of nutrients through the thin intestinal wall. Bile is secreted by the liver and stored in the gall bladder. Its role is to emulsify fats and lipids in the duodenum. It also helps to neutralise food that has come from the acidic stomach environment.

Pancreatic juice contains a number of enzymes including lipase, trypsin and pancreatic amylase, which aid in the digestion of food.

As the digested food makes its way through the duodenum, it passes through the jejunum and ileum, where about 90 per cent of the nutrients released in digestion are absorbed. Like the oesophagus, food is moved through the small intestine by peristalsis.

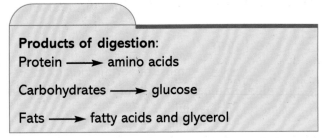

Products of digestion:
Protein ⟶ amino acids

Carbohydrates ⟶ glucose

Fats ⟶ fatty acids and glycerol

The large intestine

The large intestine consists of the caecum and the colon. Its main function is to absorb water and to pass waste to the rectum for excretion through the anus. Bacteria in the colon manufacture vitamin K, which is also absorbed by the body.

The Monogastric Animal

Pigs and humans have a monogastric digestive system. This means that they have only one stomach. They do not possess a rumen and cannot digest cellulose. The digestive system of a monogastric animal works in exactly the same way as that of a ruminant except for the absence of a rumen, reticulum and omasum. Food is passed from the oesophagus directly to the stomach for digestion. The human or pig stomach is the equivalent of the abomasum in a ruminant animal.

Assimilation and absorption of nutrients in the small and large intestines are carried out in the same way as in the ruminant. Fig 9.5 shows the digestive system of a pig.

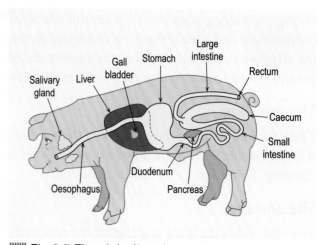

Fig 9.5 The pig's digestive system

The Digestive System of a Chicken

Digestion in poultry is different to that in ruminant and monogastric animals. Starting at the mouth, birds do not have teeth. Instead, they have a beak, which is adapted for different types of feeding, depending on the species. Chickens have a short, sharp beak, which aids them in eating grains.

Food is passed down the oesophagus to the stomach. Birds, unlike other animals, possess a crop that allows them to store food for later consumption. Food can be passed from the crop to the stomach when it is needed.

The stomach of a bird consists of two parts: the proventriculus and the gizzard. The proventriculus secretes enzymes and digestive juices much like the monogastric stomach to aid chemical digestion.

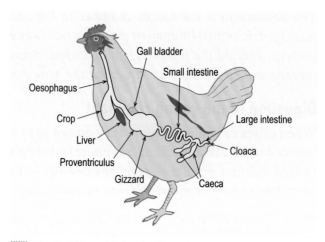

Fig 9.6 The chicken's digestive system

Birds swallow grit, which accumulates in the gizzard. When food enters the gizzard, the grit grinds down the food mechanically. Digested food is then passed to the intestines for assimilation. As birds do not have a separate digestive and urinary tract, urine and faeces are excreted together.

The Liver

The liver is one of the most important organs in an animal's body. It has a number of functions. Not only is it involved in the production of bile to aid digestion, but also one of its many other functions is to store the products of digestion.

Functions of the liver

- **Production**: The liver secretes bile, which emulsifies fats and lipids in the duodenum. Bile produced by the liver is stored in the gall bladder.

- **Storage**: Glucose in the form of glycogen is stored in the liver, along with minerals such as copper and iron, and fat-soluble vitamins A, D, E and K. Stored glycogen can be broken down into glucose for use in the body when blood glucose levels are low.

- **Breakdown of toxic substances**: Ammonia is converted to urea in the liver. Ammonia is one of the substances produced when excess amino acids are broken down. The breakdown of amino acids is called deamination. Other toxins such as hydrogen peroxide are also broken down here.

- **Breakdown of red blood cells**: Red blood cells are broken down in the liver and are used as pigments in the production of bile.

- **Temperature regulation**: Heat is produced by the liver and warms the blood as it passes through the organ. This helps to regulate the temperature of the body.

Experiment 9.1

To demonstrate the action of the enzyme liver catalase

Note: Hydrogen peroxide is one of the substances that the liver breaks down. It does this with the aid of the enzyme catalase. The hydrogen peroxide breaks down to form water and oxygen, which are both harmless to the body.

Materials

Fresh liver (sliced raw potato or radish can be substituted if liver is not available as both contain catalase), dilute hydrogen peroxide, test tubes and rack, knife, chopping board, pestle and mortar, hot plate, beaker, water, forceps

Method

1   Cut three equal-sized cubes of liver.

2   Place one cube of liver into the bottom of a test tube and fill the test tube to one-third full with hydrogen peroxide. Observe the reaction and note the bubbles given off.

3   Grind down the second piece of liver, using the pestle and mortar. Add it to the second test tube and fill it to the same depth with hydrogen peroxide. Observe and note the reaction.

4   Place some water in a beaker and heat it to boiling point on the hot plate. (This can be set up at the start of the experiment.) Add the third piece of liver to the boiling water to cook it.

5   Remove the cooked liver from the boiling water with the forceps and allow the liver to cool. Add it to a third test tube and add hydrogen peroxide, as in the previous two test tubes. Observe any reaction.

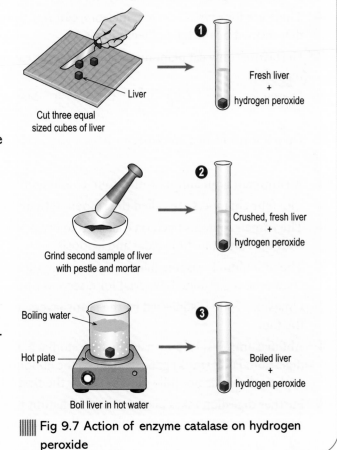

Fig 9.7 Action of enzyme catalase on hydrogen peroxide

Experiment 9.1

Result

Table 9.1 Enzyme activity			
Observations	Liver sample 1 (unchanged)	Liver sample 2 (crushed)	Liver sample 3 (cooked)
Bubbles observed			
Volume of bubbles/Strength of reaction			

Conclusion

Both the first and second liver samples reacted with the catalase, as bubbles were observed. There was no reaction in the third test tube where the liver was cooked. This is because enzymes are denatured (killed) at certain temperatures and cooking the liver destroyed the enzyme.

There was a faster reaction in test tube two, because the liver was crushed so that the hydrogen peroxide came into contact with a greater surface area, and therefore more of the catalase enzyme, so the reaction proceeded faster.

Summary

- There are two forms of digestion: mechanical and chemical. Mechanical digestion is the physical breakdown of food. Chemical digestion is the breakdown of food by enzymes.
- Digestion begins in the mouth by the teeth (mechanical) and saliva (chemical).
- There are four types of teeth: incisors, canines, premolars and molars. The diet of an animal is determined by the type of teeth it has.
- Herbivores only eat plant material, carnivores eat meat and omnivores eat both plant and animal material.
- Dental formula of a pig – I:$\frac{3}{3}$ C:$\frac{1}{1}$ P:$\frac{4}{4}$ M:$\frac{3}{3}$
- Dental formula of a cow/sheep – I:$\frac{0}{3}$ C:$\frac{0}{1}$ P:$\frac{3}{3}$ M:$\frac{3}{3}$
- A ruminant is an animal with a four-chambered stomach that can break down cellulose.
- The four chambers are called the rumen, reticulum, omasum and abomasum.
- The rumen contains bacteria that help to break down cellulose. Digestive disorders associated with the rumen include bloat and acidosis.
- The reticulum is responsible for the regurgitation of partially digested material. The animal chews the regurgitated material for a second time.
- Omasum: Food is squeezed by the many layers of tissue in the omasum. It reabsorbs water from the food.
- Abomasum: This is known as the true stomach. Gastric juices are secreted for the final stage of digestion. Food (milk) goes straight to the abomasum in newborn calves and lambs for digestion, as their rumen is not fully developed for the first six weeks.
- Further digestion takes place in the duodenum where bile and pancreatic juices are secreted. Absorption of nutrients takes place in the small intestine. Water is absorbed in the large intestine.

Summary

▦ Pigs have a monogastric stomach, which works like the human stomach.

▦ Digestion in poultry involves the proventriculus, which secretes enzymes, and the gizzard, which contains grit to grind down food.

▦ The liver stores glycogen, vitamins A, D, E and K, breaks down red blood cells and ammonia, secretes bile and regulates temperature.

QUESTIONS

1 Give the dental formula of a sheep.
2 Why is the dental formula of a sheep different to that of a human?
3 What is the first stage of digestion called?
4 Name the four types of teeth and give the function for each.
5 What does the term *monogastric stomach* mean?
6 What is the term given to an animal with a four-chambered stomach?
7 What are the names of the four chambers?
8 List the function of each chamber.
9 What is bloat and how can a cow with bloat be treated?
10 What causes acidosis in cattle?
11 List three functions of the liver.
12 Describe an experiment to demonstrate the action of the enzyme liver catalase.

EXAM QUESTIONS

1 Draw a labelled diagram of a longitudinal section through a mammalian tooth. (LC, HL, 2010)
2 Explain the functions of the following parts of the digestive system of poultry:
   (a) The crop
   (b) The gizzard. (LC, HL, 2009)
3 (a) Describe the dental formula of a ruminant.
   (b) Describe the process of digestion in the stomach compartments of a ruminant animal.
      (LC, HL, 2009)

EXAM QUESTIONS

4 (a) Sheep are ruminant animals. The diagram below represents the ruminant stomach. Name the parts labelled A, C and D.

   (b) Part A holds a large number of micro-organisms.

       (i)   What is the main function of these micro-organisms?

       (ii) What is the function of part C in the diagram?

       (LC, OL, 2009)

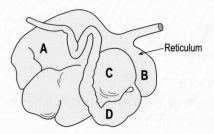

▐▐▌ Fig 9.8

5 Write notes on glycogen in the body of a mammal under the following headings:

   (a) Its site of production

   (b) Its function. (LC, HL, 2008)

6 (a) Digestion is the process during which food is broken down and absorbed.

       (i)   Name one enzyme that helps in digestion and name the food that it breaks down.

   (b) Bile is a liquid that helps to break down fats.

       (i)   Where is bile stored?

       (ii) Explain how this liquid affects fat molecules.

       (iii) State what substances fats are broken down into.

   (c) Give **three** functions of the liver.

   (d) In what part of the digestive system does absorption of food into the bloodstream take place?

   (e) State two differences between the digestive system of a pig and a sheep. (LC, OL, 2008)

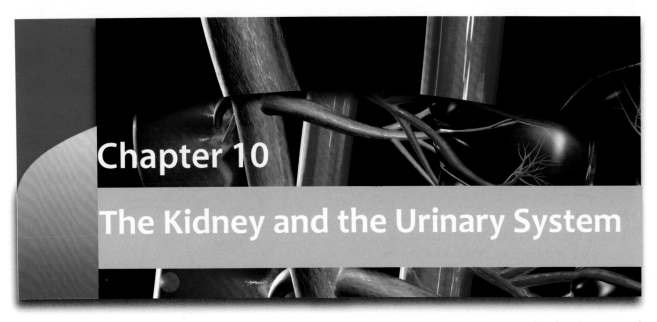

Chapter 10
The Kidney and the Urinary System

The main function of the kidney in the body is the production of urine. It is also responsible for the removal of wastes from the blood such as excess water, salt and urea.

Kidneys occur in pairs and are located in the abdominal cavity just below the diaphragm. The left kidney sits higher than the right kidney due to the presence of the liver on the right-hand side of the abdomen. They are bean-shaped and surrounded by two layers of fat for protection. The kidneys form an important part of the urinary system.

☰ The Urinary System

- **Kidney**: Site where urine is produced.
- **Ureter**: A duct that connects the kidney to the bladder, carrying urine to the bladder for storage.
- **Bladder**: Urine is stored here until it is passed from the body.
- **Urethra**: A duct through which urine is expelled from the body.
- **Renal artery**: Supplies oxygenated blood to the kidney from the dorsal aorta. This blood also carries wastes to be filtered from the blood.
- **Renal vein**: Carries blood away from the kidney, after it has been filtered.

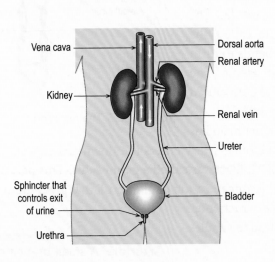

|||||| Fig 10.1 Urinary system

Experiment 10.1

Dissection of a kidney

Materials
Kidney from a sheep, cow or pig, dissecting board, forceps, scalpel

Method

1 Lay the kidney flat on the dissecting board and note its shape. Identify the ureter, renal artery and renal vein if present. There may also be some remnants of adipose tissue clinging to the surface of the kidney.

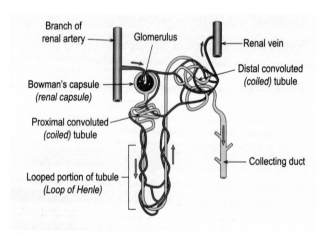

Fig 10.2 Longitudinal section of a kidney

2 Remove the renal capsule from the surface of the kidney with the forceps. The capsule resembles a layer of skin surrounding the kidney. Note the layer underneath the renal capsule, which is reddish-brown in colour. This is called the cortex.

3 Lay the kidney flat on the dissecting board, cut a longitudinal section through the kidney, and open it out on the board.

4 Identify the renal cortex and the renal medulla/pyramids. Observe the contrast in colour between the cortex and the medulla.

Structure of the kidney

The kidney consists of approximately one million tubules called nephrons. The function of the nephron is to produce urine. Nephrons are located in the cortex, but extend into the medulla. Each nephron consists of several parts (see Fig 10.3).

The C-shaped structure on the upper end of the nephron is called the Bowman's capsule. The nephron extends to form a tubule called the proximal convoluted tubule, which bends to form a U-shaped tube, called the loop of Henle. The loop of Henle ascends into the distal convoluted tubule, which leads into a collecting duct.

As can be seen from Fig 10.3, each nephron has its own blood supply. A branch of the renal artery enters the Bowman's capsule, which divides to form a number of capillaries. This cluster of capillaries is called a glomerulus. This part of the nephron is located in the cortex of the kidney and it is the concentration of glomeruli that gives the cortex its dark-red colour.

The capillaries drain into an arteriole, which loops around the nephron. The capillaries lead to venules, which in turn lead to the renal vein.

Fig 10.3 The nephron

Arteriole: A small branch of an artery.
Venule: A small branch of a vein.

Production of urine

Blood enters the glomerulus and is filtered under high pressure. Blood cells are too big to be filtered, but glucose, salts and waste filter from the glomerulus through the walls of the Bowman's capsule. The filtered blood leaves the glomerulus

> **Selective reabsorption**: The process by which the body reabsorbs certain molecules for use in the body by active transport.

through the arteriole. However, if glucose, salts and water were to be continually removed from the blood through filtration the body would soon become dehydrated and starved of nutrients. Selective reabsorption of nutrients prevents this from happening.

The filtrate moves from the Bowman's capsule to the proximal convoluted tubule for reabsorption. Nutrients and water can diffuse passively back into the capillaries surrounding the tubule. Also, Na^+ and Cl^- ions are reabsorbed. Other toxins accumulated by the body are added to the waste fluid as it passes through the distal convoluted tubule.

Excretion

As salt has already been reabsorbed, water is also reabsorbed from the collecting duct by osmosis. The amount of water that is reabsorbed is controlled by a hormone called the anti-diuretic hormone (ADH), which is produced in the pituitary gland. ADH increases the permeability of the collecting duct, allowing water to be absorbed. The more water that is reabsorbed, the smaller the volume of urine that is produced. If water is in excess, ADH is not produced by the pituitary gland. The collecting duct ceases to be permeable and water is not reabsorbed. A greater volume of urine is produced.

Summary

- The function of the kidney is to produce urine. It also removes excess waste such as water, salt and urea.
- The kidney contains nephrons that produce urine.
- The upper end of the nephron is called the Bowman's capsule. It contains a number of capillaries. This part of the nephron is located in the cortex of the kidney.
- Glucose, salts and waste are filtered through the capillaries (glomerulus) into the Bowman's capsule. The filtered blood leaves through an arteriole, which is a small artery.
- Selective reabsorption prevents too many salts and too much water being removed from the body.
- Absorption of water is controlled by a hormone called ADH (anti-diuretic hormone). Water is absorbed by osmosis.

QUESTIONS

1 What are the main functions of the kidney?
2 Where are the kidneys located?
3 Draw a labelled diagram of a kidney showing the cortex, medulla, renal artery, renal vein and ureter.
4 What is the function of the nephron?
5 What happens in the Bowman's capsule?
6 What is selective reabsorption?
7 Where does reabsorption take place?
8 What substances are reabsorbed by the kidney?
9 What does ADH stand for and where is it produced in the body?
10 What is the function of ADH?

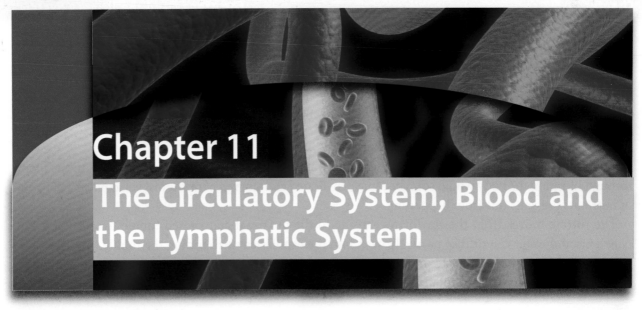

Chapter 11
The Circulatory System, Blood and the Lymphatic System

The Circulatory System

The circulatory system in mammals is essential to the smooth functioning of every cell in the body. Cells need a supply of oxygen and nutrients, and also a method of getting rid of waste generated within the cell. The circulatory system within the animal body provides the means by which to carry out all of these essential tasks.

The circulatory system in vertebrates is a closed system and is known as the cardiovascular system. The heart is central to this system and acts as a pump to keep blood moving around the body. Blood is transported around the body in three types of blood vessels: arteries, veins and capillaries.

Arteries

- Arteries transport blood away from the heart.
- Have thick walls.
- Walls are elastic and contain smooth muscle to allow for expansion.
- Do not contain valves.
- Blood flow is fast and has a pulse.

Veins

- Veins transport blood to the heart.
- Have thin walls.
- Have valves to prevent the backflow of blood. This ensures that the movement of blood is in one direction only.
- Blood flow is slow and there is no pulse.

Fig 11.1 A cross-section of an artery, a vein and a capillary

Capillaries

- Capillaries connect arteries to veins; blood flows from smaller arteries (arterioles) to smaller veins (venules).
- Walls of capillaries are only one cell thick.
- Do not contain valves.
- Blood flow is slow and there is no pulse.
- Capillary walls are semipermeable, allowing the exchange of gases, nutrients and waste materials. Exchange occurs by diffusion.

The circulation of blood

1 Deoxygenated blood (low in O_2, high in CO_2) is carried to the heart through the vena cava and enters the right atrium (auricle).

2 Blood then passes from the right atrium, through the tricuspid valve into the right ventricle.

3 It then leaves the right ventricle through the pulmonary artery, which brings the deoxygenated blood to the lungs, where gaseous exchange takes place (see Chapter 12, The Respiratory System).

4 Oxygenated blood leaves the lungs through the pulmonary vein and is brought back to the heart where it enters the left atrium.

5 It passes through the bicuspid valve into the left ventricle. It exits the left ventricle through the aorta to be pumped around the body.

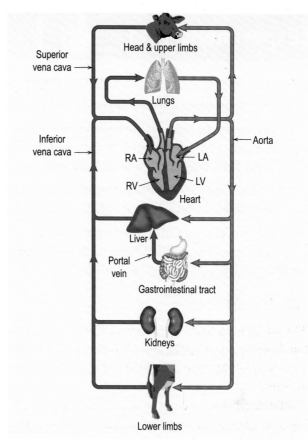

||||| Fig 11.2 Blood circulation

Experiment 11.1

Dissection of a heart (sheep or ox)

Materials

Heart, dissecting board, scalpel

Method

1 Rinse the heart in cold water to remove any blood from its surface and internally and place it on a dissecting board.

2 Identify the ventral surface (front) of the heart. It will be more rounded than the dorsal surface. The arteries to the front also have thicker walls.

3 Identify the pulmonary artery, pulmonary vein, aorta and vena cava. Identify the coronary blood vessels on the heart's surface. These arteries and veins transport the heart's own blood supply.

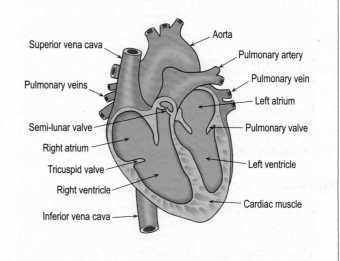

||||| Fig 11.3 The heart

Experiment 11.1

4   Identify the left and right atria and the left and right ventricles.

5   Use the scalpel to make two incisions down either side of the heart.

6   Cut away the wall of the right ventricle and identify the tricuspid valve. Cut away a section of the wall of the left ventricle. Compare the difference in thickness between the left wall and the right wall. Why is there such a difference in thickness?

7   Locate and identify the bicuspid valve. Compare the walls of the atria with the walls of the ventricles. Locate and identify the septum dividing the left- and right-hand side of the heart.

8   Draw a diagram of the external structure of the heart and another labelled diagram of the dissected heart, identifying each of the parts.

☰ Blood

Blood has a number of important functions in the animal body including transport, providing immunity and temperature regulation. Blood consists of a liquid called plasma. Three types of cell are suspended in the plasma. The cells are called red blood cells, white blood cells and platelets.

Plasma

Plasma contains many types of molecules including nutrients such as glucose, proteins, minerals, vitamins and salts. It also contains wastes. The salts and proteins help to maintain osmotic pressure in the blood, which ensures water enters the capillaries.

Red blood cells (red blood corpuscles or erythrocytes)

Red blood cells are small biconcave disks that have no nuclei. They contain the pigment haemoglobin. Haemoglobin contains iron, which has the ability to bind to oxygen molecules. Oxygen is transported around the body in the bloodstream through this bond with the haemoglobin. If there are not enough red blood cells in the bloodstream, or if they lack haemoglobin (low iron levels), this causes a deficiency disease called anaemia. Symptoms of anaemia include feeling run down and lethargic.

Anaemia is a common disease in pigs, but can be prevented by giving newborn bonhams (piglets) an injection of soluble iron. Red blood cells are produced in bone marrow.

White blood cells (leukocytes)

White blood cells lack the haemoglobin present in red blood cells but do possess a nucleus. They are far less numerous than red blood cells and are larger in size. Their main function is in immune response, where white blood cells move to the site of an infection by micro-organisms to destroy the invading pathogen. Lymphocytes (see The Lymphatic System, page 97) also play a role in immune response.

Platelets

Platelets are fragments of cells produced in bone marrow. Their main function is blood clotting.

Blood clotting

▨ Two proteins, fibrinogen and prothrombin, are produced in the liver and deposited in blood plasma.

▨ When a blood vessel is damaged, platelets form a cluster at the site to partially seal the wound.

▨ The damaged tissue and the platelets release an enzyme called thromboplastin.

- This converts the protein prothrombin into a substance called thrombin. Calcium ions need to be present for this reaction to take place.

- Thrombin then converts fibrinogen from its soluble form in the blood plasma into an insoluble form. The insoluble fibrinogen is simply known as fibrin.

- Fibrin forms threads that trap red blood cells, allowing a blood clot to form. This seals the wound, preventing further blood loss and preventing microbes from entering the wound.

The functions of blood

- **Transport**: Nutrients are transported around the body in blood plasma; these include glucose, vitamins, minerals and amino acids. Oxygen is transported by red blood cells. Wastes such as carbon dioxide and urea are also carried in the blood. Hormones are carried in the blood to the site of action.

- **Immunity**: Defence against disease-causing pathogens through the production of antibodies. Blood clotting by platelets prevents pathogens entering an open wound.

- **Temperature regulation**: Heat produced in the liver, as a result of metabolism, is carried around the body in the bloodstream. The regulation of body temperature is very important in animals and can have a huge effect on animal production levels.

Regulation of body temperature

- **Normal body temperature**: The animal body works at a constant temperature and only fluctuates within a very small range. If the temperature rises or falls outside of this range, it can prevent the various systems in the body from working properly. Cattle, sheep and pigs have normal body temperatures in the range of 38–39°C, which is slightly higher than that of a human. There can be a slight variation in these temperatures depending on the animal.

Animals can control their body temperature in a number of ways:

- **Keeping the body warm**: Movement (walking, running, shivering), wool, hair, burning energy through respiration.

- **Keeping the body cool**: Lying in a shaded area, sweating, rolling in mud (pigs).

≡ Environmental Considerations and Critical Temperature

The environment an animal is kept in, plays an important role in thermoregulation. This is particularly the case in pig production. If housing is too cold, the pig must use energy to keep warm and if it is using energy for warmth it is not using it to gain weight. The same can be said if housing is too warm and an animal needs to cool down. The point at which pigs must use energy to increase heat production within the body to keep warm is called the lower critical temperature. The point at which they need to cool down is called the upper critical temperature. Pigs should be kept within the upper and lower range for optimum production.

The factors that affect the critical temperature of an animal include: age, weight, feed intake, feed type, building type, building insulation and floor type. A typical pig production unit will have good insulation and flooring and low roofs to keep temperatures at an optimum. If temperature can be controlled in this way, farmers will have less feeding costs as animals will not need to use the energy gained from food to keep warm, and instead will use it to gain weight.

≡ The Lymphatic System

The lymphatic system transports fluid called lymph around the body. It consists of a network of capillaries, ducts and nodes, separate to the circulatory system, while at the same time being closely linked to it.

Functions of the lymphatic system

The lymphatic system has three main functions:

1 To collect excess tissue fluid and return it to the bloodstream.
2 To absorb fats from the intestine and transport them to the bloodstream.
3 To defend the body against disease.

The lymphatic system extends to every part of the body. Larger lymphatic vessels branch into smaller capillaries. The bigger vessels have valves similar to those found in veins. When lymph moves past a valve, the valve closes, preventing the backflow of lymph and ensuring that movement is one way. One of the biggest differences in the movement of lymph and the movement of blood is that the movement of lymph is dependent on muscle contractions. When muscle contracts, lymph is moved forward in a vessel towards the heart.

Absorption of excess tissue fluid

Fluid that has diffused from blood capillaries is absorbed by lymph capillaries. Once it enters these capillaries, it is called lymph. It is transported to larger lymph vessels and ducts and eventually empties into the subclavian vein, which brings it to the heart.

Lymphoid organs

A number of organs and tissues in the body play an important role in the lymphatic system. They include bone marrow, lymph nodes, the spleen and the thymus. Bone marrow produces lymphocytes. The thymus also produces lymphocytes. Both are types of white blood cell that are important for immunity within the body. Lymph nodes occur at points along the lymphatic vessels. They contain lymphocytes and remove infectious organisms such as bacteria from lymph. Essentially they act as a filter in the lymphatic system. The spleen, which is located below the diaphragm, acts in much the same way as the lymph nodes. However, its role is slightly different as it filters blood rather than lymph.

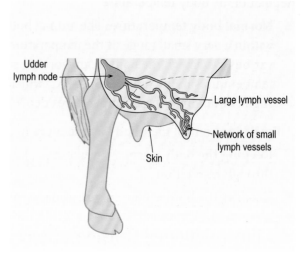

Fig 11.4 Lymph vessel in cow's udder

Fig 11.4 shows the lymphatic vessels within a cow's udder. The vessels remove waste fluids from the udder, destroy infectious organisms and provide immunity through the production of lymphocytes. Sometimes, first-time, calvers suffer from a condition called oedema, which is a swelling of the lymph glands due to a build up of lymph fluid. This is caused by the presence of milk in the udder, which puts pressure on the lymphatic system.

☰ The Immune System

There are two types of immunity: active immunity and passive immunity.

Immunity: The ability of an organism to resist disease through the production of antibodies and white blood cells in response to exposure to the disease; through inoculation against the disease, or the transfer of antibodies from a mother to her young.

Active immunity

Active immunity is acquired when the body is infected by bacteria or a virus. The body produces antibodies to fight the infection. These antibodies persist to provide protection against the disease in the future.

Active immunity can also be acquired artificially by means of a vaccine. Vaccines are viruses and bacteria that have been treated so they no longer cause disease. When a vaccine is administered to an animal, its body produces antibodies in response. If the animal is exposed to the disease, those antibodies are ready to attack the bacteria or virus and protect the body.

A common vaccine given to sheep is the clostridial vaccine, which protects against disease caused by strains of the bacteria *Clostridium*. Tetanus, blackleg, lamb dysentery and pulpy kidney are just some of the sheep and lamb diseases that can be caused by these bacteria and subsequently prevented by administering the appropriate vaccine.

Passive immunity

Passive immunity is a short-term immunity because the animal does not produce the antibodies itself, but acquires them either through the mother's milk in the days following birth, or when antibodies were passed across the placenta from mother to foetus. The young animal acquires the same antibodies present in the mother's body.

It is important for young animals to consume the first milk produced by the mother for this reason. The milk known as colostrum (beastings) contains high levels of antibodies, offering the newborn calf or lamb immunity to disease.

Absorption of these antibodies by the young animal is at its highest level in the first 24 hours after birth, after which the ability to absorb antibodies declines, so the intake of colostrum cannot be underestimated.

Summary

- The circulatory system allows oxygen and nutrients to be supplied to cells, while at the same time removing waste from cells.
- The circulatory system consists of the heart, which acts as a pump, and blood vessels for the transport of blood. There are three types of blood vessel: arteries, veins and capillaries.
- Arteries take blood away from the heart; veins bring blood to the heart. Capillaries connect arteries to veins and allow the exchange of gases, nutrients and waste by diffusion.
- Deoxygenated blood is brought into the heart by the vena cava. It leaves the heart through the pulmonary artery. It goes to the lungs where a gaseous exchange takes place.
- Oxygenated blood is brought from the lungs to the heart by the pulmonary vein. It leaves the heart through the aorta.
- Blood consists of plasma, red blood cells, white blood cells and platelets.
- Plasma is a liquid medium that transports nutrients and wastes. Haemoglobin in red blood cells transports oxygen around the body. A lack of haemoglobin to carry out this function can lead to anaemia.
- The main role of white blood cells is to provide immunity. Platelets are needed for blood clotting.
- The main functions of blood are: transport, immunity and temperature regulation.
- The point at which an animal must use energy to keep warm is known as the lower critical temperature. The upper critical temperature is the point at which the animal uses energy to cool down.
- The main function of the lymphatic system is to collect excess tissue fluid, absorb fat, and transport them to the bloodstream. It also defends the body against disease.
- Immunity is the ability of an organism to resist disease through: the production of antibodies and white blood cells in response to exposure to the disease, inoculation against the disease, or the transfer of antibodies from a mother to her young.

Summary

▪ Activity immunity is acquired by exposure to a disease or by means of a vaccine.

▪ Passive immunity is acquired from antibodies in the mother's milk in the first few days after birth.

QUESTIONS

1 Describe the path that the blood takes when travelling around the body, starting with the left ventricle.
2 Why is the wall of the left ventricle thicker than the wall of the right ventricle?
3 Name the four components of blood.
4 What is the function of red blood cells?
5 What is the function of white blood cells?
6 What substances are carried in plasma?
7 Explain how blood clotting is carried out.
8 What is the normal body temperature range for cattle, sheep and pigs?
9 State two ways in which animals can keep warm and two ways in which they can keep cool.
10 What is meant by the term *critical temperature*?
11 List three factors that affect critical temperature.
12 Why is it important to have warm housing for animals?
13 State two functions of the lymphatic system.
14 How is lymph moved in the lymphatic system?
15 Describe the role of lymphocytes in the body.
16 Oedema is the swelling of the lymph glands. Give one reason why this may happen in a first-time calver.
17 What is the difference between active and passive immunity?
18 State one way in which a calf may acquire passive immunity.
19 What is a vaccine?

EXAM QUESTION

(a) List three types of blood cell.
(b) Give the function of each type of blood cell.
(c) Newborn bonhams often suffer from a blood-related illness called anaemia. What is the cause of anaemia?
(d) Describe how anaemia in bonhams can be prevented. (LC, OL, 2010)

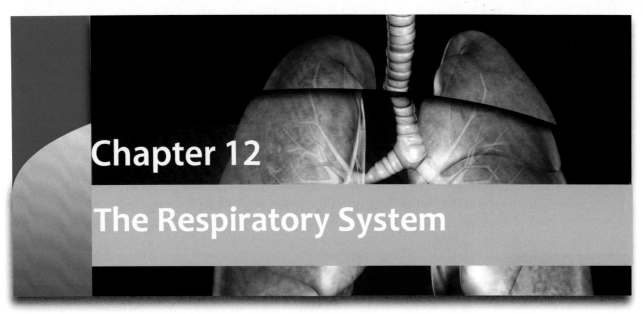

Chapter 12

The Respiratory System

Respiration

The mammalian body cannot store oxygen gas. It also needs an efficient method of removing waste gases such as carbon dioxide from the body. The respiratory system allows the intake of oxygen to the body and the removal of carbon dioxide from the body, via the lungs. The intake of oxygen and expulsion of carbon dioxide is known as a gaseous exchange.

Air is inhaled through the nose and mouth. It passes into the pharynx (throat) and through the glottis, which is an opening into the larynx. A piece of tissue called the epiglottis closes over the throat when swallowing food to prevent it from entering the respiratory system.

The air passes through the larynx to the trachea. The trachea is held open permanently by the rings of cartilage that give it shape and structure.

The trachea divides into two bronchi (singular – bronchus), which lead into the left and right lungs. The bronchi are smaller than the trachea, but also contain rings of cartilage to keep them open. The bronchi split into a number of smaller ducts called

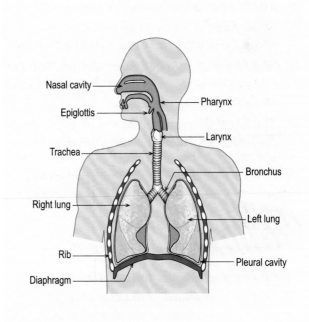

||||| Fig 12.1 Respiratory anatomy

bronchioles. As these continue to branch and divide they get smaller and smaller and do not contain cartilage. Each bronchiole ends in an air sac called an alveolus (plural – alveoli). Gaseous exchange takes place in the alveoli.

The alveoli are thin, elastic tissues, which can expand when they inflate with air. Each alveolus is wrapped in blood capillaries. Gaseous exchange occurs by diffusion.

When a mammal inhales air and it passes to the alveoli, it contains a high concentration of oxygen. This is higher than the oxygen concentration in the blood capillaries. Therefore, the oxygen diffuses from the alveoli into the capillaries and is transported to where it is needed. The capillaries also have a high concentration of carbon dioxide that is higher than the concentration in the inhaled air in the alveoli. The carbon dioxide diffuses from the capillaries into the alveoli, and from there it is exhaled.

☰ The Lungs

The lungs are located in the upper part of the mammalian body called the thoracic cavity. They are protected by the ribs. The movement of the ribcage outwards and upwards during inhalation is assisted by the intercostal muscles.

The lungs are separated from the abdominal cavity by the diaphragm, which flattens during inhalation to allow the lungs to expand.

During exhalation, the diaphragm returns to its normal position, which is concave in shape, and the ribcage moves downward and inwards, decreasing the space available to the lungs and forcing air out of them.

Summary

- The respiratory system allows the intake of oxygen to the body and the removal of carbon dioxide from the body, via the lungs.
- The intake of oxygen and the expulsion of carbon dioxide is known as gaseous exchange.
- Air is taken in through the mouth. It passes through the pharynx and larynx to the trachea.
- The trachea is kept open by rings of cartilage.
- The trachea splits into two bronchi, which lead into each lung. The bronchi split into bronchioles, which eventually end in air sacs called alveoli.
- Alveoli are surrounded by capillaries. The gaseous exchange of carbon dioxide and oxygen takes place in the alveoli when CO_2 passes from the capillaries to the alveoli and O_2 passes from the alveoli to the capillaries.
- The lungs are protected by the rib cage. The diaphragm lies below the lungs and moves downwards to allow the lungs to expand when an animal inhales air.

QUESTIONS

1. Where does air enter the respiratory system?
2. What gas is exhaled from a cow's lungs?
3. What name is given to the air sacs in the lungs?
4. Name the piece of tissue that prevents food from entering the respiratory system.
5. What is the function of the rings of cartilage?
6. How many bronchi are present in the respiratory system?
7. What is diffusion?
8. Explain gaseous exchange.
9. Name the muscles that aid movement of the ribcage.
10. What happens to the diaphragm when air is inhaled?

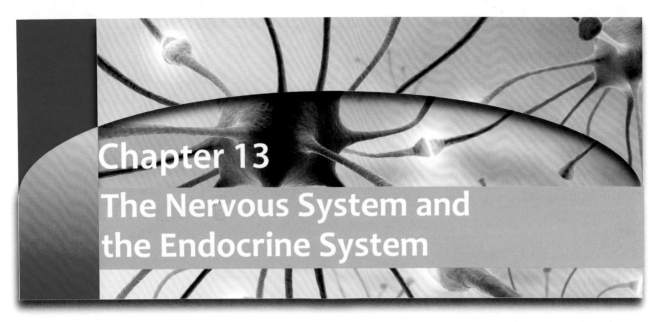

Chapter 13
The Nervous System and the Endocrine System

All animals have the ability to respond to a stimulus. Animals use their skeleton and muscles, their brain, nerves and hormones to respond to stimuli. The brain, nervous system and hormones (endocrine system) control the behaviour and actions of animals in a rapid response to a stimulus.

☰ The Nervous System

The nervous system in vertebrate animals consists of two parts: the central nervous system (CNS) and the peripheral nervous system (PNS).

The central nervous system (CNS)

The central nervous system consists of the brain and the spinal cord. The brain is protected by the skull and the spinal cord is protected by the vertebrae. The brain and spinal cord receive sensory information (sight, smell, touch, taste and sound) through nerves called the cranial nerves.

   The brain has a number of different regions, each with its own function.

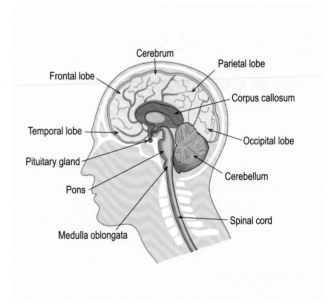

- ▨ **Cerebral hemispheres**: Each lobe of the cerebrum (see Fig 13.1) makes up part of the cerebral hemispheres. They are used for reasoning, memory, hearing and the other senses.

- ▨ **Corpus callosum**: Nerve fibres that connect the left and right hemispheres.

- ▨ **Cerebellum**: Regulates balance, movement and muscle coordination.

||||| Fig 13.1 The brain

- ▨ **Pituitary gland**: Secretes hormones (see The Endocrine System, page 104).

- ▨ **Pons**: Connects the cerebrum with the cerebellum.

- ▨ **Medulla oblongata**: Controls automatic functions such as breathing and heartbeat.

- ▨ **Spinal cord**: Nerve fibres that connect the brain to the peripheral nervous system (PNS).

The peripheral nervous system (PNS)

The peripheral nervous system consists of sensory nerves and motor nerves. The sensory nerves include the cranial nerves, which bring sensory information to the brain and spinal cord from sensory organs such as the ear or skin.

Other internal organs such as the lungs, heart and digestive system are monitored by the automatic nervous system and are not under the conscious control of the animal.

Nerves

A nerve cell is called a neuron.

- **Dendrites**: Contain receptors that accept impulses from other neurons.
- **Cell body**: Controls activity within the neuron.
- **Axon**: Nerve fibre running the length of the neuron over which the impulse is transmitted.
- **Schwann cell**: Surrounds the axon and provides insulation.
- **Synaptic knob**: Transmit the impulse to the dendrites of the next neuron, aided by a chemical transmitter. The space between the synaptic knob of one neuron and the dendrites of the next is known as a synapse.

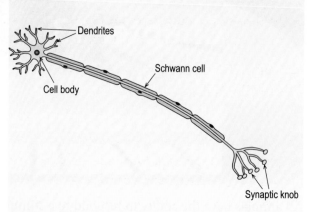

Fig 13.2 A motor neuron

The Endocrine System

Endocrine glands

Endocrine glands secrete hormones. However, unlike the circulatory system or lymphatic system, these hormones are not transported around the body in

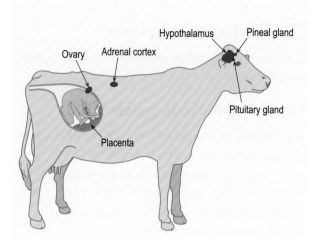

Fig 13.3 The endocrine system of a cow

specialised ducts. The glands secrete hormones into the bloodstream. Hormones are produced in very small quantities and are transported by the circulatory system to specific parts of the body, where they can stimulate or inhibit actions in the target organ or tissue.

There are many endocrine glands in the body (see Fig 13.3). Each gland secretes a different hormone, which controls a different response in the body.

Pituitary gland

The pituitary gland is located at the base of the brain below the hypothalamus. The hypothalamus is part of the fore-brain and controls the pituitary gland. It secretes chemicals that stimulate or inhibit hormone production in the pituitary gland. This has an important knock-on effect for the rest of the body, as the pituitary gland is responsible for the control of several other endocrine glands in the body. The brain sends information to the pituitary gland via the hypothalamus.

The pituitary gland is split into two parts: the anterior lobe and the posterior lobe. Each is responsible for specific functions and the production of specific hormones within the endocrine system.

Anterior lobe

Two of the most important hormones produced by the anterior lobe are the growth hormone and prolactin.

- The growth hormone is responsible for regulating the growth of bone and other tissues.
- Prolactin is responsible for the production of milk in mammals.
- Luteinizing hormone (LH) in females stimulates ovulation and the development of the corpus lutuem. In males, LH stimulates the production of testosterone, which is also a hormone.
- Follicle-stimulating hormone (FSH) in females promotes the development of a follicle that produces oestrogen. In males, FSH is responsible for the development of the testes and sperm production.

The anterior lobe is also responsible for the regulation of activity within the thyroid, adrenal and reproductive glands.

Posterior lobe

The posterior lobe is responsible for the secretion of oxytocin and the anti-diuretic hormone (ADH).

Oxytocin is responsible for contractions in the uterine wall during birth. Suckling in mammals stimulates the production of oxytocin; the udder sends a signal to the brain. The message is relayed to the posterior pituitary gland and oxytocin is secreted. This causes the milk ducts to contract and let down the milk to the young mammal.

One of the most important functions of the anti-diuretic hormone (ADH) is to regulate water retention in the body. The kidneys carry out this function where water is reabsorbed through the collecting ducts. Salt levels in the body can also be regulated by the reabsorption of sodium and chloride ions in the kidneys. ADH also has a role in raising blood pressure.

Thyroid glands

The thyroid glands are one of the biggest glands in the endocrine system. They are located in the neck just below the larynx. The main hormone secreted by the thyroid glands is thyroxine, which contains iodine. Thyroxine regulates metabolism in the body and is responsible for growth. A lack of thyroxine due to insufficient iodine can lead to goitre. Goitre is the enlargement of the thyroid glands as they try to produce more thyroxine. This condition is more common in humans than animals.

Lambs or calves born with congenital goitre are often born very weak or are stillborn. This can be avoided by giving the mother an iodine supplement in her diet prior to the birth.

Parathyroid glands

The parathyroid glands are embedded in the surface of the thyroid glands. They are responsible for controlling the level of calcium in the bones and in the blood.

Parathyroid hormone (PTH) is released into the body when blood calcium levels drop. Blood calcium levels are increased by the breakdown and release of calcium from the bones. Calcium can also be increased by absorption from the gut and storage of calcium by the kidneys. When the calcium levels in the blood are normal the parathyroid glands stop producing PTH.

There are problems associated with the parathyroid glands. For example, if the parathyroid glands are not producing PTH it can lead to low levels of calcium in the blood, which can lead to hypocalcaemia in cattle.

Thymus

The thymus is located in the neck below the thyroid glands and extends into the thoracic cavity. Lymphocytes that are necessary for immunity response are produced by the thymus.

Pancreas

The pancreas is a leaf-shaped organ that lies above the duodenum. While the pancreas produces digestive enzymes, which are secreted into the small intestines, it has a second role that involves the secretion of the hormone insulin into the bloodstream.

The islets of Langerhans produce insulin. This is secreted when there are high glucose levels in the body. Fatty tissue, liver and muscle cells are stimulated to take up the glucose. The liver and muscle then store the glucose as glycogen. Insulin also restricts the use of fat as an energy source.

The most common disease caused by a lack of insulin is Diabetes mellitus. A common symptom is glucose in the urine, which means a high glucose level in the body. The kidneys, as a result, excrete glucose, which means it is not being stored as glycogen in the liver. The body is unable to metabolise it.

Adrenal glands

The adrenal glands are located above the kidneys. The adrenal glands consist of two parts, the adrenal cortex and the adrenal medulla. Hormones are produced by the adrenal glands when the body is under stress.

The adrenal cortex produces a large number of hormones, which are responsible for salt and water regulation, and maintaining blood pressure.

The adrenal medulla is responsible for producing adrenalin. This increases heart rate and blood pressure when the body is under stress and in survival mode.

Gonads

Gonads are the organs that produce gametes. The term gonads can be used to refer to the testes in the male or the ovaries in the female. The hormones that are produced in the gonads are involved in reproduction.

Testes

The testes secrete hormones known as androgens. Androgens are hormones that are responsible for the development of male characteristics. Their production leads to the growth of muscle mass and strength and the development of sex organs. The best known androgen is testosterone.

Ovaries

The ovaries secrete the hormone progesterone. Progesterone has a variety of responsibilities, which include supporting pregnancy by allowing the uterus to grow during gestation, the inhibition of lactation and labour and the inhibition of the immune response to the embryo.

Freemartin condition: Occurs in mixed-sex twin calves (one heifer calf and one bull calf). In the uterus, hormones from the male twin pass to the female twin. The male hormones masculinise the female and the result is called a freemartin. The female calf will be infertile and cannot be used for breeding. Her genitals will be smaller. This is a common outcome in cattle where twin calves are born, each of a different sex. It also occurs in sheep and pigs but is not as common.

The ovaries also secrete oestrogen. This promotes the secondary sex characteristics in the female. It includes the development and growth of mammary glands.

Summary

- The nervous system in vertebrate animals consists of two parts: the central nervous system (CNS) and the peripheral nervous system (PNS).
- The central nervous system consists of the brain and the spinal cord.
- The peripheral nervous system consists of sensory nerves and motor nerves.
- A nerve cell is called a neuron.
- Endocrine glands secrete hormones into the bloodstream. Hormones are produced in very small quantities and are transported by the circulatory system to specific parts of the body, where they can stimulate or inhibit actions in the target organ or tissue.
- The pituitary gland is located at the base of the brain and consists of an anterior lobe and a posterior lobe.

Summary

▨ Growth hormones, prolactin, LH and FSH are produced in the anterior lobe.

▨ Oxytocin and the anti-diuretic hormone are produced in the posterior lobe. Oxytocin is responsible for milk let-down and contractions during birth. ADH regulates water retention in the body.

▨ Androgens are hormones responsible for male sex characteristics and are produced in the testes. Testosterone is an androgen.

▨ Freemartin condition occurs in twin calves where one is male and the other is female. Hormones pass from the male to the female in the womb, leaving the female infertile.

▨ Ovaries secrete oestrogen and progesterone. Oestrogen promotes the sex characteristics in females. Progesterone allows for the growth of the uterus during gestation.

QUESTIONS

1 Name the two parts of the nervous system.
2 Which two parts of the body make up the central nervous system?
3 What is the function of the cerebral hemispheres, cerebellum and medulla oblongata?
4 What is the function of the dendrites and the Schwann cell in a neuron?
5 Where is the pituitary gland located?
6 Name two hormones secreted by the pituitary gland.
7 Two hormones associated with reproduction are LH and FSH. What do the letters LH and FSH stand for?
8 Which hormone is needed for respiration?
9 Where is the thyroid gland located?
10 What hormone is produced in the thyroid gland? Name one condition that can be caused by a lack of this hormone.
11 What is the cause of hypocalcaemia in cattle?
12 What is adrenalin needed for?
13 List one symptom of diabetes.
14 Where is the growth hormone produced?
15 Name one female reproductive hormone and one male reproductive hormone.

EXAM QUESTIONS

1 Describe the physiological processes involved in the let-down of milk in farm animals. (LC, HL, 2010)
2 Explain the term 'freemartin condition'. (LC, HL, 2010)
3 Write notes on glycogen in the body of a mammal under the following headings: (a) its site of production, (b) its function. (LC, HL, 2008)
4 'Animal hormones are blood-borne messengers that regulate the actions of different parts of an organism'.
   (a) Name two reproductive hormones in animals.
   (b) Give one function for each of them.
   (c) Name the hormone involved in 'milk let-down' in animals.
   (d) Where in the body is the pituitary gland? (LC, OL, 2007)

Chapter 14

Reproduction in Animals

Reproduction is the method by which animals pass their genes on to their offspring, ensuring the survival of the species. There are two main patterns of reproduction: asexual and sexual.

Asexual Reproduction

Asexual reproduction only involves one parent. The offspring is identical to the parent in terms of its genetic make-up. An example of this occurs in aphids in spring, when only females are present in the population, so an unfertilised egg develops into a female identical to its mother.

Sexual Reproduction

Sexual reproduction takes place in vertebrates and involves sex cells known as gametes. Gametes produced by a female are called eggs and those produced by a male are called sperm.

When animals reproduce sexually the offspring produced inherits half of its genes from one parent and half from the other parent. The offspring will be genetically different from both its parents and this introduces variation into a species, which can be an advantage to the organism.

The genetic combination inherited by the offspring of a pair of animals may be superior to that of either parent; and they may be better adapted to the environment in which they live.

The term hybrid vigour (heterosis) is used when the offspring produced as a result of cross-breeding two dissimilar animals is genetically superior to either of its parents.

> **Hybrid vigour:** The advantage in performance of crossbred animals above the mid-parent mean of the two parent breeds.

The Male Reproductive System

Fig 14.1 shows the reproductive system of a bull. Reproductive organs that produce gametes (sex cells) are known as gonads. In the male reproductive system, the gonads are paired testes. Only one of the pair of testes is shown in Fig 14.1.

The testes are responsible for the production of the male gametes (sperm). The testes are suspended

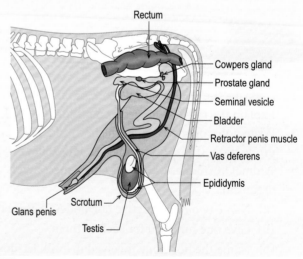

||||| Fig 14.1 A bull's reproductive organs

in the scrotum, which hangs outside the body cavity. This is to keep it at a lower temperature than the rest of the body. This is necessary to allow the sperm to develop and mature properly.

Sperm produced in the testes matures and is stored in the epididymis. It is also stored in a duct leading out of the epididymis called the vas deferens. As sperm travel along the vas deferens, three fluids are secreted from the seminal vesicle, the prostate gland and the Cowpers gland. These give the sperm mobility, and the combination of sperm and fluids is known as semen. These fluids are added to the sperm prior to ejaculation. The sperm is released into the vagina of the female by ejaculation during copulation (mating).

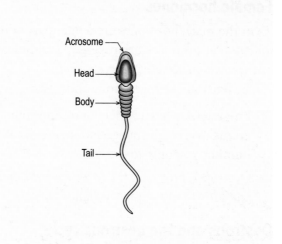

|||||| Fig 14.2 The sperm has a head which contains the genetic material and a tail (flagellum) which enables it to swim

Male hormones

Hormones play an important role in reproduction.
As was mentioned in Chapter 13, FSH (follicle-stimulating hormone) promotes sperm production and LH (luteinising hormone) controls the production of another male sex hormone, testosterone. Testosterone is responsible for the development of the male sex characteristics and the male sex organs.

☰ The Female Reproductive System

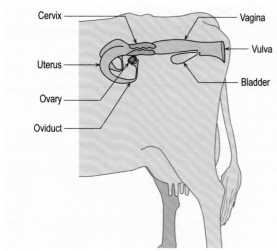

|||||| Fig 14.3 A cow's reproductive system

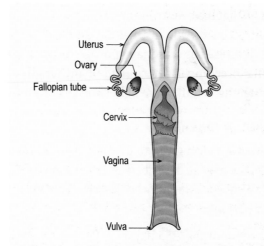

|||||| Fig 14.4 A cow's reproduction organs

Figures 14.3 and 14.4 show the cow's reproductive system. The gonads in a female are called the ovaries. Ovaries produce eggs (ova). The fallopian tubes (oviducts) connect the ovaries to the uterus. Fertilisation of eggs by sperm takes place in the fallopian tubes. The fertilised egg (zygote) then makes its way to the uterus (womb) where it implants itself in the uterine wall. As the cells divide in the zygote and it starts to develop, it is known as an embryo.

The uterine walls are muscular and can stretch to accommodate the developing foetus. The narrow opening at the end of the uterus is called the cervix, which dilates during birth. The vagina, which held the penis during copulation, serves as the birth canal when the young animal is born.

Female hormones

As in the male, hormones are a vital part of the reproductive cycle. FSH promotes the development of a follicle that produces oestrogen. LH stimulates ovulation and promotes the development of the corpus luteum, which secretes progesterone.

The hormones progesterone and oestrogen are produced in the ovaries.

- Progesterone has a variety of responsibilities that include supporting pregnancy by allowing the uterus to grow during gestation, the inhibition of lactation and labour, and the inhibition of the immune response to the embryo.
- Oestrogen promotes the secondary sex characteristics in the female. This includes the development and growth of mammary glands.

Oestrous and the oestrous cycle

The oestrous cycle in mammals (equivalent to the menstrual cycle in human females) is a recurring cycle that is driven by the hormones already mentioned. Once an animal has ovulated (comes into oestrous, comes into heat), the follicle from which the egg was released develops into the corpus luteum and begins to secrete progesterone. The function of progesterone is to build up the wall of the uterus. This is in preparation for the implantation of the embryo.

When fertilisation does not occur, the corpus luteum breaks down, removing the source of progesterone, and the lining of the uterus is reabsorbed (unlike in humans where it is shed).

The length of the oestrous cycle varies from species to species. In cattle and pigs it is every 21 days and in sheep it is 17 days.

The duration of oestrous (when a female is in heat) also varies. Oestrous last 18 hours in cattle, 36 hours in sheep and two to three days in pigs.

Animals that have oestrous cycles throughout the year are described as polyoestrous. Cows and pigs are both polyoestrous. Animals that have a number of oestrous cycles, but only during a certain time of the year, are described as seasonally polyoestrous or seasonal breeders. Sheep are seasonal breeders.

Seasonal breeding is determined by the length of day (photoperiod). Sheep are short day breeders, and breed when the length of daylight shortens (autumn and winter).

Gestation in mammals

Gestation is the term given to pregnancy in mammals. It is the period of time from conception to birth. A pregnant cow may be described as 'in calf', and if it is her first calf she may be described as 'an in-calf heifer'. Similarly a sheep (ewe) may be described as 'in lamb' and a pig (sow) as 'in farrow'. Listed below are their gestation periods:

- Cow: 9.5 months (283 days)
- Sheep: 5 months (149 days)
- Pig: 115 days (3 months, 3 weeks, 3 days).

☰ Birth

Hormones play an important role in the birth of an animal. Oxytocin is responsible for contractions in the uterine wall during birth and, subsequently, milk let-down after the birth. Suckling in mammals stimulates the production of oxytocin. Prolactin is responsible for the production of milk in mammals.

Birth in cows and sheep

The lamb is born
forelegs first

The lamb is born
hind legs first

|||||| Fig 14.5 Lamb birth showing normal presentation and hind leg presentation

A few days before the birth, the udder of the cow or ewe swells. At the birth, some of the membranes that cover the calf or lamb should come out. The membranes contain water, and this is commonly called the 'water bag'. The young animal's forelegs will then appear. Sometimes the hind legs will come first.

After the calf or lamb is born, the umbilical cord is cut and tied at both ends. The navel can be disinfected with iodine. The mother should be allowed to lick her calf or lamb clean. The remaining membranes will be expelled after this. It is important that they are removed from the uterus so that infection does not set in.

Summary

- Sexual reproduction in animals involves sex cells called gametes. Female sex cells are called eggs and male sex cells are called sperm.
- An organism inherits half of its genes from its mother and half from its father.
- The term hybrid vigour is used when the offspring produced as a result of cross-breeding two dissimilar animals is genetically superior to either of its parents.
- Sperm in the male is produced in the testes and stored in the epididymis.
- In the male, FSH promotes sperm production. LH controls the production of testosterone and testosterone is responsible for the development of the male sex characteristics.
- In the female, eggs are produced in the ovaries. Fertilisation of eggs takes place in the fallopian tubes.
- In the female, FSH promotes the development of a follicle that produces oestrogen. LH stimulates ovulation and promotes the development of the corpus luteum, which secretes progesterone.
- Progesterone supports pregnancy.
- Oestrogen promotes the secondary sex characteristics in the female.
- The oestrous cycle in animals is recurring and driven by hormones.
- The oestrous cycle in pigs and cattle is 21 days and 17 days in sheep.
- The duration of oestrous is how long a female is in heat. This lasts 18 hours in cattle, 36 hours in sheep and two to three days in pigs.
- Gestation is how long an animal is pregnant: 283 days in cattle, 149 days in sheep and 115 days in pigs.
- During birth, the hormone oxytocin is responsible for contractions in the uterus and milk let-down.
- Prolactin is responsible for the production of milk.

QUESTIONS

1 What is the difference between asexual and sexual reproduction?
2 What are gametes?
3 What does the term *hybrid vigour* mean?
4 Where is sperm produced in the male reproductive system?
5 Why are the testes located outside the male body cavity?
6 Where is sperm stored in the male?
7 Name two hormones associated with the male reproductive system.
8 Name two hormones associated with the female reproductive system.
9 Where are eggs produced in the female reproductive system?
10 Where does fertilisation take place?
11 State the length of the oestrous cycle and duration of oestrous in cattle, pigs and sheep.
12 Explain the terms *polyoestrous* and *seasonally polyoestrous*.
13 List one factor that has an effect on seasonal breeders.
14 What are the gestation periods for cows, pigs and sheep?
15 Which hormone causes contractions in the uterine wall?
16 Which hormone is responsible for milk production?

EXAM QUESTIONS

1 In the case of the pig, state:
   (a) The length of gestation
   (b) The length of the oestrous cycle. (LC, HL, 2010)
2 In relation to dairy cows state, in days, the length of each of the following:
   (a) Gestation
   (b) Oestrous. (LC, HL, 2009)
3 Explain the connection between shortening day length and the onset of oestrous in sheep.
   (LC, HL, 2009)
4 (a) Sheep are polyoestrous. What does the term *polyoestrous* mean?
   (b) What is the length of the oestrous cycle in sheep? (LC, OL, 2009)

●●●UNIT 4

Genetics

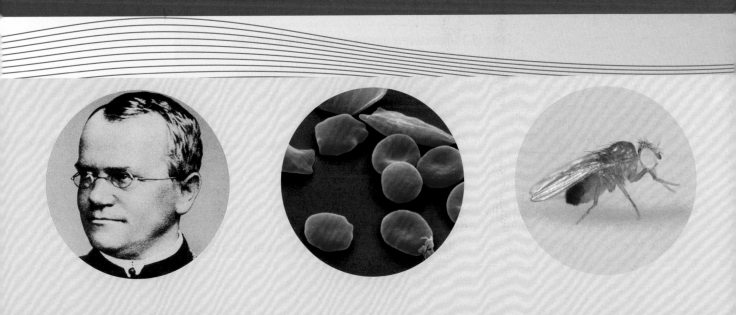

Chapter 15
Cell Division

Chromosomes

As described in Chapter 1, the nucleus of the cell contains genetic instructions in the form of DNA. When viewing cells under a light microscope, the nucleus appears as a dark mass composed of a material called chromatin. This is a mixture of DNA and protein. However, when the cell is about to divide, the chromatin forms structures called chromosomes. Chromosomes are composed of DNA and sections of this DNA code for the production of proteins. These sections are known as genes.

Chromosomes are composed of DNA and protein and are only visible during cell division.

A **gene** is a part of a chromosome that contains information to produce a protein.

A **diploid cell** is diploid or 2n when it has a full set of chromosomes.

To help you understand how chromosomes work, think of chromosomes being like a dictionary. A dictionary contains thousands of words; similarly chromosomes contain thousands of genes. Each word has a meaning or explanation, just as a gene contains a specific instruction in its sequence of DNA.

Chromosomes occur in pairs and therefore a cell with a complete set of chromosomes is known as diploid or 2n. Every species has its own chromosome number. Humans have a total of 46 chromosomes (or 23 pairs) in their body cells.

Table 15.1 shows a list of chromosome number for common agricultural animals.

Table 15.1 Chromosome number in agricultural animals	
Animal	**Diploid number**
Cattle	60
Sheep	54
Pigs	38
Chickens	78

In order for animals and plants to grow, repair and replace dead and worn-out cells, and to reproduce, cell division must occur. There are two types of cell division: mitosis and meiosis. Mitosis occurs in normal body cells, referred to as somatic cells. Meiosis occurs in the testes and ovaries to produce gametes.

Mitosis

During mitosis a cell divides to produce two genetically identical daughter cells. Before cell division, the cell prepares itself for mitosis by gradually getting bigger and producing additional organelles such as mitochondria. This stage is called interphase.

Once cell division actually commences it can be divided into four main stages: prophase, metaphase, anaphase and telophase.

Prophase

During the prophase stage, the chromosomes become visible in the cell. Each chromosome duplicates itself, so that the chromosomes appear as two strands (called sister chromatids) joined in the centre. The old chromosome is attached to an identical copy of itself.

The nuclear membrane surrounding the nucleus and other cell organelles disappear. Spindle fibres start to form in the cell and centriole pairs migrate to opposite poles of the cell.

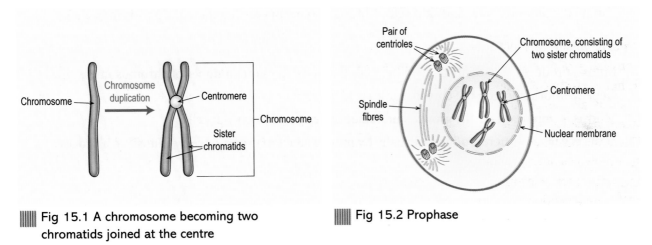

||||| Fig 15.1 A chromosome becoming two chromatids joined at the centre

||||| Fig 15.2 Prophase

Metaphase

During the metaphase stage, the chromosomes line up in the centre of the cell. The spindle fibres attach themselves to the centromere of the chromosome.

Anaphase

During the anaphase stage, the spindle fibres contract, separating the duplicated chromosome from its copy. Each separated strand is once again called a chromosome. The chromosomes are pulled to opposite poles of the cell.

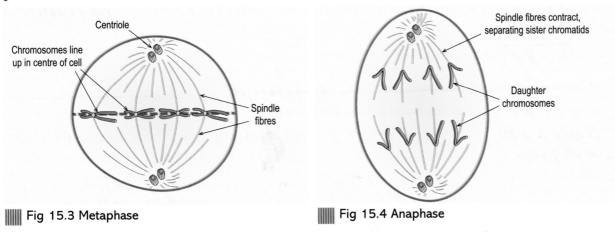

||||| Fig 15.3 Metaphase

||||| Fig 15.4 Anaphase

Telophase

Telophase is the final stage in cell division. During this phase the cytoplasm divides to form two cells each with its own set of chromosomes, this process is called cytokinesis. The chromosomes begin to uncoil to form chromatin and the nuclear membrane reforms around the chromatin. In plant cells, a cell plate grows between the two new cells and from this a new cell wall develops, thus separating the two cells.

Cleavage furrow

Nuclear membrane starts to reform and chromosomes start to uncoil

||||| Fig 15.5 Telophase

Locations of mitosis

In plants, cell division by mitosis is continuously occurring in the tips of shoot and roots. Meristematic tissues in these locations are constantly producing new cells by mitosis to allow for plant growth.

In animals, mitosis is continuously occurring in the bone marrow to produce new red blood cells, the cells lining the digestive tract and skin cells. Mitosis also occurs during metamorphosis in insects.

The significance of mitosis

▤ Mitosis produces two identical daughter cells that have the same number of chromosomes.

▤ Genetic information on the chromosomes is identical.

▤ Mitosis is important for the growth and repair of dead and worn-out cells.

▤ Some organisms can reproduce asexually by mitosis. Bacteria reproduce by mitosis in a process known as binary fission.

☰ Meiosis

Meiosis, also known as reduction division, occurs in the testes and ovaries of animals and produces four non-identical cells that have half the number of chromosomes of the parent. These cells are called gametes or sex cells (egg and sperm). As these cells have only half a set of chromosomes, they are called haploid or n.

A **haploid cell** is haploid or n when it has half a set of chromosomes. Gametes are haploid.

During meiosis, crossing over can occur between a pair of chromosomes. During this process the pair of chromosomes will swap DNA. This process brings about variation in the combination of genes on the resulting chromosomes and consequently in the gametes produced. Remember that chromosomes occur in pairs, and because of meiosis, each gamete has one chromosome from each pair.

In humans, the gametes have 23 chromosomes. On fertilisation, the diploid number of chromosomes is restored. If meiosis did not occur, then offspring would have double the number of chromosomes that the parent had.

The significance of meiosis

▤ Meiosis reduces the chromosome number in the cell by half.

▤ Chromosome diploid number is restored on fertilisation.

▤ Crossing over during meiosis produces new combinations of genes, which leads to new variations in the offspring.

Table 15.2 Summary of mitosis and meiosis		
Significance	**Mitosis**	**Meiosis**
Chromosome number	Same as parent cell	Reduced by half
Importance	Growth, repair and asexual reproduction	Production of gametes. Reproduction in some organisms
Genetic information	Identical to parent cell	Different, new combination of genes due to crossing over between pairs of chromosomes
Location of cell division	Somatic cells	Reproductive organs
Produces	Two diploid daughter cells	Four haploid daughter cells

Activity 15.1

Try making posters of each stage of mitosis to hang in your classroom or use pipe cleaners or plasticine as chromosomes to demonstrate the stages of mitosis and crossing over in meiosis.

Summary

- Chromosomes are composed of DNA and protein and are only visible during cell division.
- A gene is a part of a chromosome that contains information to produce a protein.
- Chromosomes occur in pairs. A complete set of chromosomes is diploid or 2n.
- During mitosis a cell divides to produce two genetically identical daughter cells.
- Mitosis is divided into four main stages: prophase, metaphase, anaphase and telophase.
- Mitosis occurs in the tips of shoot and roots in plants.
- In animals, mitosis occurs in the bone marrow to produce red blood cells, the cell's lining, the digestive tract and skin cells.
- Bacteria can reproduce asexually by mitosis.
- Meiosis produces four non-identical cells that have half the number of chromosomes of the parent.
- Cells with half a set of chromosomes are haploid or n.
- Meiosis occurs in the testes and ovaries of animals to produce gametes.
- On fertilisation, the diploid number of chromosomes is restored.

QUESTIONS

1 What are chromosomes made of?
2 Explain the meanings of the following terms: *diploid*, *haploid*, *mitosis* and *meiosis*.
3 The following is the diploid number of chromosomes for some agricultural animals. Calculate the number of chromosomes present in the gametes of these animals.
   (a) Cow: 60 chromosomes
   (b) Chicken: 78 chromosomes
   (c) Sheep: 54 chromosomes.
4 The following diagrams are the four stages of mitosis in a random order.

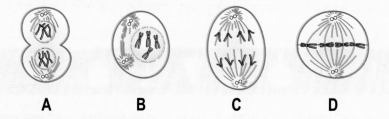

A   **B**   **C**   **D**

||||| Fig 15.6

   (a) Put the stages A–D in the correct order.
   (b) Briefly explain what is happening at each stage.
   (c) What is the significance of mitosis in the growth of organisms?
5 Identify one location in (a) an animal's body and (b) a plant where mitosis takes place.
6 Some organisms asexually reproduce by mitosis. Give an example of an organism that reproduces by mitosis.
7 Meiosis is often described as **reduction division**. Explain the meaning of the highlighted term.
8 Where in an animal's body does meiosis occur?
9 What process is responsible for the production of new combinations of genes during meiosis?
10 If meiosis did not occur during gamete formation, what consequence would this have on the number of chromosomes that offspring would have compared to the parents?

EXAM QUESTIONS

1 This is an image of a chromosome.
   (a) Where in a cell would you find a chromosome?
   (b) There are 38 chromosomes in a body cell of a pig. How many chromosomes are there in a gamete of a pig? (LC, OL, 2007)
2 Write a short note on mitosis and meiosis. (LC, HL, 2008)
3 Outline the significance of meiosis in reproduction (LC, HL, 2006)

||||| Fig 15.7

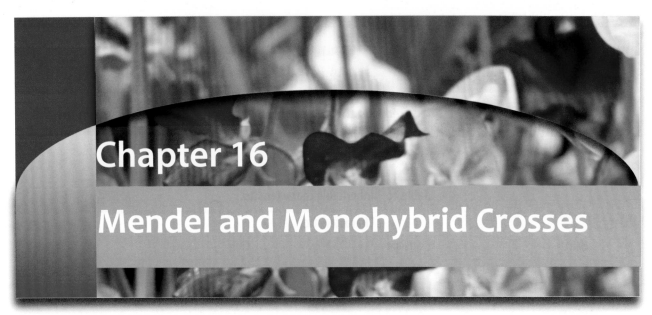

Chapter 16

Mendel and Monohybrid Crosses

≡ Genetics

Genetics is the study of inheritance. Individuals within a species are not all identical; there is considerable variation within a population. However, some of these variations are more desirable than others are. Animals and plants pass on these traits to their offspring. For centuries,

> **Artificial selection**: A process by which humans breed plants and animals to ensure certain desirable traits.

farmers have recognised this, and have artificially selected animals and plants with desirable characteristics. These animals are mated or crossed to produce offspring with these traits.

Farmers have artificially selected characteristics such as good milk production in cattle, resistance to disease in crops and good conformation in beef animals.

Artificial selection is mainly carried out by selective breeding, which is dealt with in detail in Chapter 18, Applied Genetics. To understand the existence of variations within a population we will look at variations within the human population. For example, individuals in the human population have the ability to write, but not everyone writes with their right hand. Some people write with their left hand. This is an example of a characteristic or trait where there is a variation. Some other examples of easily identifiable variations in the human population are listed in Table 16.1.

Project link

For the practical examinations, students are required to have carried out a genetics' investigation. Activity 16.1 is an example of a genetics' investigation.

||||| Fig 16.1 Writing with your left hand is a genetic trait

Activity 16.1

Conduct a class survey. Each student records the characteristic that he/she possesses from the table below. At the end count the results and record the characteristics that are most common within the class.

Table 16.1 Inheritable characteristics		
Characteristics		
Hair	Straight	Curly
Ear lobes	Attached	Unattached
Tongue rolling	Can roll tongue	Cannot roll tongue
Handwriting	Left-handed	Right-handed
Thumb	Straight	Hitchhikers
Hand clasping	Left thumb on top	Right thumb on top
Dimples	Present	Absent
Hair line	Straight	Widow's peak

Other interesting genetic tests

Sensitivity to the bitter compound phenylthiocarbamide (PTC)
People who can taste PTC compounds are referred to as tasters (dominant) and those who cannot are non-tasters (recessive). PTC compounds are found in cucumbers, cabbage, brussel sprouts and broccoli. People who can taste PTC do not usually like these vegetables as they taste bitter to them.

Sulfur excretors
Try eating some asparagus and later check for an odour from your urine. A sulfur-containing compound in asparagus is excreted in the urine of some individuals (excretors) and not in others (non-excretors). This test has one limitation, as some people are unable to smell odorous urine.

Results
After you have counted your results, you should notice that some characteristics are more common than others. For example, most individuals can roll their tongue, have unattached ear lobes, can write with their right hand and have dimples.

Dominant characteristics

Characteristics that are more common within populations are said to be dominant. The reason for this is explained in our genetic make-up. If you recall from Chapter 15 our chromosomes carry all our genetic information in the form of genes. As chromosomes occur in pairs, so do genes. Chromosome pairs have similar genes. All individuals have two genes for handwriting. However, the gene comes in two different forms, one form for people writing right-handed and another form for left-handed people.

When genes exist in different forms, they are called alleles. Normally when different alleles exist for a gene, one of the alleles will be dominant and the other will be recessive. Dominant genes are those that appear regularly within a population, while recessive genes only occur occasionally. Gregor Mendel was one of the first scientists to investigate this concept of dominant and recessive alleles and how they control inheritance.

> **Alleles** are alternative forms of the same gene.

Gregor Mendel (1822–84)

Gregor Mendel was a scientist and an Augustinian monk with an interest in the inheritance of characteristics in the garden pea plant. He chose seven different characteristics to study, each characteristic existing in two alternative forms, which were controlled by what Mendel called 'factors'. Today these factors are called genes. He performed several thousand crosses over the course of about two years. He kept accurate records of the results of these crosses and performed a statistical analysis on his results. From his results, he identified patterns of inheritance.

The following table is a list of some of the characteristics Mendel studied and their alleles. In each case, one of the alleles is dominant and the other is recessive.

||||| Fig 16.2 Gregor Mendel

Table 16.2 Genetic traits in pea plant		
Characteristics (gene)	**Dominant allele**	**Recessive allele**
Shape of seed	Round	Wrinkled
Colour of seed	Yellow	Green
Length of stem	Tall	Dwarf
Flower colour	Purple	White

Monohybrid Cross

Monohybrid crosses study the inheritance of one characteristic. Mendel identified that in the adult pea plant each characteristic was governed by a pair of 'factors' or genes. When a plant produces its gametes, only one gene from a pair of genes may go into the gamete. The pair of genes for the characteristic is separated during meiosis.

Study Fig 16.4 overleaf. The first cell contains a pair of chromosomes. Each chromosome has a gene for height in pea plants. T represents the allele for tall and t represents the allele for dwarf. Upon meiosis, the pair of chromosomes are separated so that only one chromosome from the pair occurs in the gametes (egg and sperm cell). As a result, the alleles are separated with each gamete having only one of the alleles present.

||||| Fig 16.3 Pea plant (*Pisum sativum*)

This became Mendel's first law of inheritance known as the Law of Segregation.

> Mendel's **Law of Segregation** states that when gametes are formed only one allele from a pair of alleles is carried in the gamete.

Mendel established true breeding lines before he commenced crossing plants with alternative traits. True breeding plants are **homozygous** or have two of the same alleles present on their chromosomes. If a plant has two dominant alleles for plant height, they are **homozygous dominant** and represented by the letters TT. The presence of the dominant gene T dictates that this plant will be tall. If a plant has two recessive genes for height, they are called **homozygous recessive** and this is represented by the letters tt. As the dominant gene T is absent here, this plant will be dwarf.

The **genotype** of an organism is the alleles present in an organism for a particular characteristic and it is always represented by letters, for example TT or tt. The physical appearance of an organism as a result of the genotype is referred to as the **phenotype**.

Fig 16.5 gives a step-by-step account of how to carry out a monohybrid cross between a homozygous tall plant with a homozygous recessive dwarf plant.

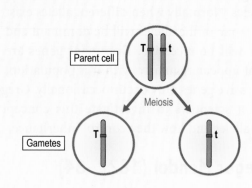

Fig 16.4 gamete formation

Homozygous: The alleles present in the genotype are the same, e.g. TT or tt.
Dominant: Expressed in the phenotype when present in the genotype and it is normally represented by a capital letter, e.g. T.
Recessive: Expressed only when an individual has no dominant gene present and it is usually represented with a lower-case letter, e.g. t.

Parents: TT × tt	**Step 1:** Write down the genotype of the parents.
Gametes: (T) (T) × (t) (t)	**Step 2:** To identify the gametes, separate the alleles in the parents and put a circle around them.

When fertilisation occurs, each gamete from the first parent has a chance of combining with either of the gametes from the second parent. The easiest way of showing this is to draw a punnet square. Place the first parent's gametes down the side, one gamete per box; and the other parent's gametes across the top, one gamete per box.

	t	t
T		
T		

Step 3: Draw a punnet square.

	t	t
T	Tt	Tt
T	Tt	Tt

Step 4: Now complete the box and fill in the spaces by combining one allele from the left with one allele from the top for each square.

Note: When filling in the punnet square always write the dominant allele, capital letter first.

F1 Genotype: 100% Tt

Step 5: List the genotypes produced by the cross. In the above cross, all the genotypes of the offspring are the same. The first generation of offspring produced by a cross is called the F1 (first filial) generation. In the above cross, all four boxes in the punnet square are of genotype Tt.

Phenotype: 100% tall

Step: 6: Write down the phenotype or what the offspring will look like from this cross. As T is dominant and the offspring have a T, this will result in all the offspring being tall.

▓ Fig 16.5 Homozygous tall plant × recessive dwarf plant cross

The cross between the homozygous tall plant and the homozygous recessive plant has produced a **hybrid**. This organism contains two different alleles in its genotype and it is called **heterozygous**. Even though a recessive allele is present in the genotype of this organism, it is not expressed in the phenotype. The reason is that the recessive allele is being masked by the dominant allele. When Mendel carried out this cross he found that all the F1 were tall.

Heterozygous: The alleles present in the genotype are not the same, e.g. Tt.

Mendel carried out a second cross where he crossed two of the F1 offspring with each other to produce the second generation (F2). Here, a heterozygous tall plant was crossed with another heterozygous tall plant.

Parents (F1):   Tt × Tt

Gametes: (T)(t) × (T)(t)

Punnet square

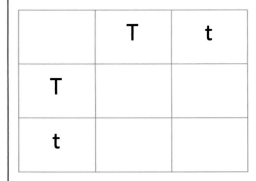

Note: In this cross both parents produce two different types of gametes. Place these in a punnet square like before and fill in the spaces.

	T	t
T	TT	Tt
t	Tt	tt

The result of this cross has produced three different types of genotypes: TT, Tt and tt.

F2 Genotype: 25% TT, 50% Tt and 25% tt

F2 Phenotype: 75% Tall and 25% dwarf

Finally, write out the genotype and the phenotype of the second generation (F2). Group genotypes that will give the same phenotype together. For example, TT and Tt will both produce tall offspring.

▥ Fig 16.6 Heterozygous tall plant × heterozygous tall plant

Above are the results that Mendel got when he crossed two plants that were heterozygous tall. The offspring in the F2 occurred in a 3:1 ratio of tall to dwarf. The punnet square is extremely important in this cross as it illustrates the random nature in which gametes combined at fertilisation.

Another important point to note in the above cross is that a homozygous dominant tall plant (TT) and a heterozygous plant (Tt) will both give the same phenotype. The recessive characteristic is also present in the phenotype, as one quarter of all the offspring will inherit both recessive alleles (tt) from their parents. The only time the recessive characteristic will appear in the phenotype is when the offspring has inherited one recessive allele from both parents.

The key to carrying out and interpreting genetic crosses is to understand the terms used. Below is a summary of the terms and their meanings in genetics, using plant height of peas as an example.

Table 16.3 Summary of genetic terms		
Terms	**Genotype**	**Phenotype**
Homozygous dominant	TT	Tall
Heterozygous	Tt	Tall
Homozygous recessive	tt	Dwarf

Always read genetic problems with care and highlight the term used to help you to solve the problem. Look at the following example.

In corn plants, yellow seed (Y) is **dominant** over green seed (y). A **heterozygous** corn plant was crossed with a plant with green seeds. Outline the gametes, genotype and phenotype of the offspring (F1).

First, the heterozygous plant must have both a dominant (Y) and recessive allele (y) in its genotype; therefore it is Yy. The plant with green seeds must have a genotype of yy, in order for the recessive green colour to be visible in the phenotype. Therefore the cross is:

Parents: Yy   ×   yy

Now the most difficult part of any cross is complete. From here write out the gametes, genotype and phenotype of the cross. What ratio of yellow to green seeds did you get?

Back cross

A back cross involves the mating of a hybrid with a purebreeding recessive parent. It is used to verify if an organism is homozygous dominant (BB) or heterozygous (Bb). For example, in peas a purple flower (P) is dominant over a white flower (p). A plant that has purple flowers could be PP or Pp. The only way to determine its actual genotype is to cross it with a white flowering plant. Two scenarios can arise from this cross.

1   If the original plant is homozygous dominant PP, then when it is crossed with the white flowering plant (pp) all the offspring will be purple flowering plants.

2   If the original plant was heterozygous Pp, then when it is crossed with the white flowering plant (pp) 50 per cent of the offspring will be purple flowering plants and 50 per cent of the offspring will be white flowering plants. Try both crosses for yourself and examine the outcome.

Use of peas in Mendel's studies

Mendel chose peas as the subject for his inheritance studies for a number of reasons. Firstly, the traits that he chose had easily distinguishable alternatives and he concentrated on the inheritance of one characteristic at a time. He controlled pollination of the pea plants, crossing plants with alternative traits by hand. Peas are easy to grow and produce large numbers of seeds.

Mendel also had a little bit of luck on his side. The traits he chose to study were located on different chromosomes and, as we will see in the next chapter, they had the ability to sort independently into the gametes.

Incomplete dominance

In all of Mendel's crosses, one allele for a particular characteristic was dominant over the other allele. However, this is not always the case. In snapdragons, red flowers are homozygous RR and white flowers are homozygous rr. When a red flowering snapdragon is crossed with a white flowering snapdragon all the offspring are pink.

This is an example of incomplete dominance. In this case, neither the allele for red nor the allele for white is dominant. Thus, when both alleles occur together in the offspring a blending occurs in the phenotype.

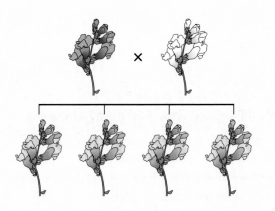

> **Incomplete dominance** occurs when two alleles are equally dominant, and when both occur together in the genotype the resulting phenotype is a blend of the two.

||||| Fig 16.7 Incomplete dominance snapdragons

Fig 16.7 illustrates what happens when a homozygous red snapdragon is crossed with a homozygous white snapdragon.

Parents: Red flower × White flower

Step 1: As this is incomplete dominance, the parent's genotype is easily determined from the phenotype.

Parents genotype: RR × rr

Gametes: (R) × (r)

Step 2: Identify the gametes. When both gametes for a parent are the same, you only need to write down one.

F1 Genotype: 100% Rr

F1 Phenotype: 100% pink

Step 3: Join the two gametes together. All the offspring will be Rr and as a result pink in colour.

What happens if you cross two F1 plants?

F1 Pink flower × Pink flower

Step 4: Cross two F1 offspring. Identify the gametes.

Genotype: Rr × Rr

Gametes: (R)(r) × (R)(r)

F2 Punnet square

	R	r
R	RR	Rr
r	Rr	rr

Step 5: Draw a punnet square, insert gametes and fill in the spaces by combining the alleles.

F2 Genotype: 25% RR, 50% Rr and 25% rr

F2 Phenotype: 25% red, 50% pink and 25% white

Note: The reappearance of the red and white flowering plants in the F2 generation. White and red flowering plants will only appear in the homozygous state (RR and rr). The flowers will always be pink if the plant is heterozygous (Rr).

||||| Fig 16.8 Incomplete dominance cross in snapdragons

A similar situation occurs with dairy Shorthorn cattle. Coat colour in Shorthorn cattle is controlled by two alleles. Red-coat colour is RR and a white-coat colour is rr. When a red-coated cow (RR) is crossed with a white-coated bull (rr), all the offspring will be Rr. This means the offspring's coat is a mix of red and white hairs, which is called a roan coat.

Multiple alleles

In all of the characteristics we have examined so far, a characteristic or trait has been controlled by the presence of two alternative alleles. However, some characteristics are controlled by more than two alleles; when this occurs the characteristic is said to have multiple alleles.

> **Multiple alleles:** When a characteristic is controlled by two or more alleles, the alleles are called multiple alleles.

For example, blood groups in humans are controlled by three alleles, A, B and O. The alleles A and B are equally dominant or co-dominant, while the allele for O is recessive. The presence of the three different alleles within the human population means that there are four possible blood groups depending on the alleles present in the individual. However, an individual can only have two of the alleles present in their genotype. Table 16.4 below lists the genotype and phenotypes of the four blood types.

Table 16.4 Genotypes and resulting blood types in humans	
Genotype	**Phenotype (blood group)**
AA and AO	Blood type A
BB and BO	Blood type B
AB	Blood type AB
OO	Blood type O

☰ Continuous Variation

In animals, characteristics such as milk yield, growth rate and carcass quality are not controlled by a pair of genes. In fact, these characteristics are controlled by a number of genes that all interact with each other to produce a phenotype that does not fall into two distinct categories, but gives a range of phenotypes. For example, in humans height is controlled by a number of genes and, as a result, there is more than just tall and short people, but an intermediate range between tall and short. Milk yield within a breed of dairy cows is also controlled by a number of genes, and this coupled with environmental factors such as diet, the quality of pasture and housing conditions will ultimately determine the quantity of milk that the cow produces.

Table 16.5 Summary of genetic terms	
Term	**Meaning**
Gene	Part of a chromosome that contains information to produce a protein
Alleles	Alternative forms of the same gene, e.g. height in pea plants; Tall (T) and dwarf (t)
Gamete	Sex cell (egg and sperm). Gametes are haploid (n)
Genotype	The genes present in the organism whether they are expressed or not, e.g. TT, Tt and tt
Phenotype	Outward appearance of the organism
Dominant	Expressed in the phenotype when present in the genotype and normally represented by a capital letter, e.g. T
Recessive	Expressed only when an individual has no dominant gene present and is usually represented with a lower-case letter, e.g. t

Table 16.5 Summary of genetic terms

Term	Meaning
Homozygous	The alleles present in the genotype are the same, e.g. TT (homozygous dominant) or tt (homozygous recessive). True breeding
Heterozygous	The alleles present in the genotype are not the same, e.g. Tt. This organism has one dominant and one recessive gene. Commonly known as a hybrid
Incomplete dominance	Neither allele present in the genotype is dominant. This results in a blend of the two alleles in the phenotype, e.g. Shorthorn cattle, red x white = roan
Multiple alleles	When a characteristic is controlled by two or more alleles, the alleles are known as multiple alleles, e.g. blood groups in humans
Continuous variation	When a characteristic is controlled by a number of genes interacting with each other to give a range of phenotypes rather than two distinct groups

Summary

- Artificial selection is a process by which humans breed plants and animals to ensure certain desirable traits.
- Characteristics that are more common within populations are said to be dominant.
- Chromosome pairs have similar genes.
- Alleles are different forms of the same gene.
- Dominant genes are those that appear regularly within a population, while recessive genes only occur occasionally.
- The dominant form of the gene is represented by a capital letter (T) and the recessive form of the gene is represented by a lower-case letter (t).
- Monohybrid crosses study the inheritance of one characteristic.
- Mendel used peas in his study of inheritance as he could control pollination and they produce large number of offspring.
- Mendel's Law of Segregation states that when gametes are formed only one allele from a pair of alleles is carried in the gamete.
- True breeding plants are homozygous. They have two of the same alleles present on their chromosomes.
- The genotype of an organism is the alleles present in an organism.
- The physical appearance of an organism is called the phenotype.
- An organism that has two different alleles in its genotype for the same gene is heterozygous.
- Incomplete dominance occurs when two alleles are equally dominant and when both occur together in the genotype; the resulting phenotype is a blend of the two.
- When a characteristic is controlled by two or more alleles, the alleles are known as multiple alleles.
- In animals, characteristics such as milk yield, growth rate, and carcass quality show continuous variation. These traits are controlled by a number of genes which all interact with each other to produce a phenotype that does not fall into two distinct categories but gives a range of phenotypes.

QUESTIONS

1   Look at the following genotypes and decide whether they are homozygous dominant, heterozygous or homozygous recessive:
    (a) BB
    (b) Bb
    (c) YY
    (d) aa
    (e) Aa
    (f) tt.

2   Distinguish between each of the following pairs of terms:
    (a) Homozygous and heterozygous
    (b) Dominant and recessive
    (c) Genotype and phenotype
    (d) Monohybrid cross and back cross.

3   In mice, brown fur (B) is dominant over white fur (b). A homozygous brown mouse was crossed with a white mouse. Outline the cross showing the gametes, genotypes and phenotypes of the F1.

4   In peas, the allele for round seed (R) is dominant over the allele for wrinkled seed (r). A heterozygous round seeded plant is crossed with a wrinkled seeded plant. Outline the gametes produced, the genotype and the phenotype of the F1.

5   In poultry, feathered legs (F) are dominant over clean legs (f). What will be the genotype and phenotype of the offspring resulting from the following crosses?
    (a) A homozygous dominant male crossed with a cleaned leg female.
    (b) A heterozygous feathered male crossed with a heterozygous feathered female.
    (c) A heterozygous feathered male crossed with a cleaned leg female.

6   Explain the meaning of a back cross and give an example of when such a genetic cross could be used.

7   Coat colour in Shorthorn cattle is controlled by two alleles that show incomplete dominance.
    (a) Explain the meaning of the term *incomplete dominance*.
    (b) A red-coated (RR) bull was crossed with a white-coated cow (rr) and all the F1 offspring were roan-coated. Write down the genotype of the F1.
    (c) Another roan-coated bull was crossed with a female from the F1. Show by means of a cross, the gametes produced, the genotype and phenotype of the F2.

8   Explain the meaning of the term *multiple alleles* and describe, using an example, how multiple alleles can give a range of phenotypes.

9   Describe, using an example, how continuous variation leads to a range of phenotypes within a population of cattle.

EXAM QUESTIONS

1   In maize, G represents green and g represents albino. 55 maize seeds are sown and the results show 42 green plants and 13 albino plants. Show by means of suitable cross how this result might occur, starting with homozygous parents. (LC, HL, 2009)

2   In poultry, the allele for feathered legs (F) is dominant over the allele for clean legs (f). Copy the following into your answer book and complete the cross by filling in the possible gametes, genotype and phenotype of the offspring. (LC, OL, 2009)

Genotype of parents   (FF)   ×   (Ff)
Gametes produced   ( )   ×   ( )   ( )
Genotype of offspring   ( )   ( )
Phenotype of offspring _____

3   Red flower colour in sweet pea plants is a homozygous dominant condition (RR). Pink flowering sweet pea plants were crossed with pink flowering sweet pea plants. The seeds from these plants were collected and sown, and the new plants produced flowers as follows:

■ Number of plants with red flowers: 27
■ Number of plants with pink flowers: 56
■ Number of plants with white flowers: 29

(a) State the genotype of the original pink flowering parents.

(b) Explain how the three flower types shown above resulted from a cross between two pink flowered plants.

(c) What offspring would result if a pink flowering sweet pea plant was crossed with a red flowering sweet pea plant? Describe the cross and state the genotype and phenotype of the offspring produced.

(d) State one advantage for using plants in the studies in genetics. (LC, HL, 2003)

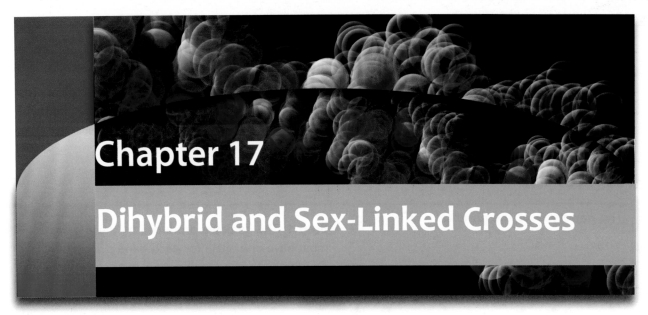

Chapter 17

Dihybrid and Sex-Linked Crosses

☰ Independent Assortment

It was by chance that the characteristics Mendel studied occurred on separate chromosomes. As a result, when gametes were formed by meiosis the separation of the alleles occurred randomly. Mendel observed this in his dihybrid crosses and formulated his second law of inheritance called the Law of Independent Assortment.

> The **Law of Independent Assortment** states that during gamete formation, members of a pair of alleles segregate and move into the gametes independently of any other pair of alleles.

To understand how independent assortment happens look at Figures 17.1 and 17.2.

▦ The first cell is diploid (2n). Chromosome pair number 1 contains a pair of genes for plant height, with one chromosome carrying the allele for tall (T) and the other chromosome carrying the allele for dwarf (t).

▦ Chromosome pair number 2 carries a gene pair for the shape of the seed. One chromosome carries the allele for round seed (R), while the other chromosome carries the allele for wrinkled seed (r).

▦ During meiosis, one chromosome from each pair must pass into the gamete, therefore reducing the chromosome number from four in the diploid cell to two chromosome in the gametes. As a result, only one allele for each characteristic will be present in each gamete.

▦ Taking one chromosome from each pair, count the number of combinations of alleles produced from the diploid cell in Fig 17.1. Remember that each gamete must have one allele from each pair of alleles (one for height and one for seed shape).

If you came up with four possible combinations of alleles, you are correct. Look at Fig 17.2 to see these combinations. As the alleles are on separate chromosomes, they can travel independently into the gamete.

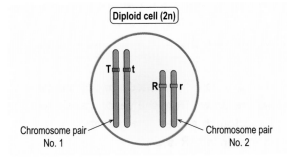

||||| Fig 17.1 Alleles present in diploid cell

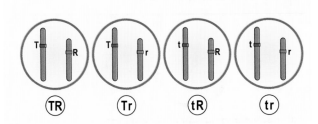

||||| Fig 17.2 Gametes formed from a diploid cell

☰ Dihybrid Crosses

Dihybrid crosses involve the inheritance of two characteristics. The following example is a typical cross that Mendel completed, involving a tall pea plant with round seeds crossed with a dwarf pea plant with wrinkled seeds. Tall (T) and round (R) were dominant and dwarf (t) and wrinkled (r) were recessive. True breeding parents are used to start the cross.

First cross parents

The genotype of the parents: TTRR × ttrr

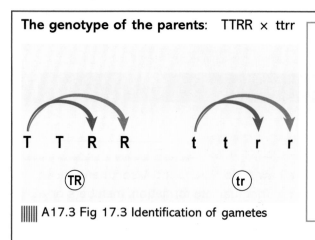

|||||| A17.3 Fig 17.3 Identification of gametes

Step 1: The gametes produced by these parents must have one allele for each gene pair present. To identify the gametes arrows are used to pair up the alleles. An arrow is drawn from the first allele to each of the third and fourth. The allele pairs from this are TR and tr. A circle is put around each pair to identify them as gametes.

Note: If two or more gametes are the same, it is only necessary to write them down once.

Genotype of the F1: TtRr
Phenotype of the F1: Tall with round seeds

Step 2: On fertilisation the gamete TR will fuse with the gamete tr to produce the F1.

All the offspring in the F1 are tall and round as they all have a dominant allele for tall and round. The recessive alleles do not appear in the phenotype. Mendel now crossed two of the F1 offspring.

Second cross F1 × F1

Genotype of the parents: TtRr × TtRr

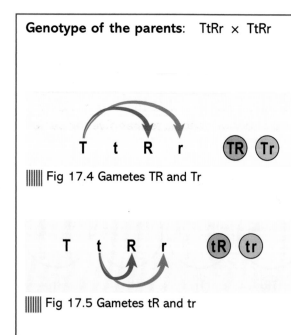

|||||| Fig 17.4 Gametes TR and Tr

|||||| Fig 17.5 Gametes tR and tr

Step 3: As the genes for the plant height and seed shape occur on different pairs of chromosomes, the alleles will behave according to Mendel's Law of Independent Assortment. Arrows are used to identify all the possible combinations of alleles that could arise in the gametes. First, an arrow is drawn from the first allele to the third and the fourth alleles. These are then circled, TR and Tr.

Step 4: The process is repeated, except this time the arrows are drawn from the second allele to the third and fourth alleles. The gametes produced are circled tR and tr.

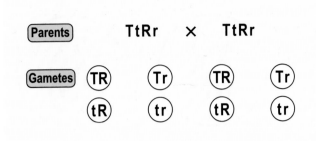

Parents   TtRr   ×   TtRr

Gametes   (TR)   (Tr)   (TR)   (Tr)
          (tR)   (tr)   (tR)   (tr)

|||| Fig 17.6 Parents and gametes from F1 cross

As both parents are heterozygous for both characteristics here, each parent has produced four different types of gametes.

	TR	Tr	tR	tr
TR	TTRR	TTRr	TtRR	TtRr
Tr	TTRr	TTrr	TtRr	Ttrr
tR	TtRR	TtRr	ttRR	ttRr
tr	TtRr	Ttrr	ttRr	ttrr

|||| Fig 17.7 Punnet square for dihybrid cross

Step 5: Finally, a punnet square is used to identify all the possible genotypes produced from this cross. One parent's gametes are placed across the top of the punnet square and the other parent's genes are placed down the side.

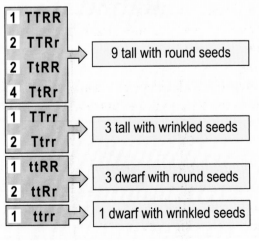

1 TTRR
2 TTRr
2 TtRR   → 9 tall with round seeds
4 TtRr

1 TTrr
2 Ttrr   → 3 tall with wrinkled seeds

1 ttRR
2 ttRr   → 3 dwarf with round seeds

1 ttrr   → 1 dwarf with wrinkled seeds

|||| Fig 17.8 Genotype F2 and phenotype F2

Step 6: Identical genotypes are grouped together. Ticking them off as you go through them is a good way of keeping track. Count the number of genotypes that give the same phenotype and record this.

Try some of the questions at the end of the chapter.

☰ Sex Determination

Humans have 23 pairs of chromosomes; 22 pairs are known as autosomes and one pair of chromosomes are called the sex chromosomes (X and Y). The sex chromosomes determine the sex of an individual. Females have two X chromosomes and males have an X and a Y chromosome. Look at Fig 17.9. What observation can you make about the Y chromosome?

The Y chromosome is much smaller than the X chromosome. Therefore, we can conclude that the Y chromosome does not have the same amount of information on it as the X chromosome. This has important consequences when we examine some of the genes that are carried on these sex chromosomes. As males have two different sex chromosomes, the X and the Y chromosome, they are responsible for the sex determination of their offspring. When meiosis occurs, females produce gametes that all contain an X chromosome. However, half of the male's gametes contain the X chromosome and half carry the Y chromosome. Examine Fig 17.10.

On fertilisation, the egg cell contributes an X chromosome, while the male sperm determines the sex of the offspring. If an X sperm cell fertilises the egg the offspring will be female, while if a Y sperm cell fertilises the egg the offspring will be male.

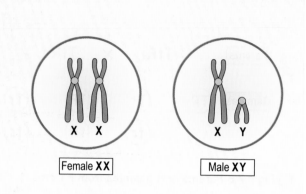

||||| Fig 17.9 Male and female sex chromosomes

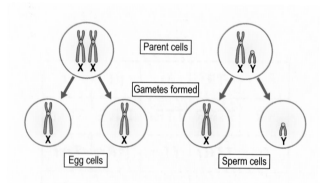

||||| Fig 17.10 Sex chromosomes and the gametes produced

Sex linkage

In 1907, Thomas Hunt Morgan was conducting genetic crosses with the fruit fly (*Drosophila melanogaster*).

||||| Fig 17.11 Thomas Hunt Morgan

||||| Fig 17.12 Red-eyed and white-eyed fruit flies

Initially Morgan was using these fruit flies to reproduce Mendel's monohybrid crosses. Fruit flies usually have red eyes. However, Morgan noticed a white-eyed male in one of his crosses (see Fig 17.13). He crossed this white-eyed male with a red-eyed female and all of the F1 produced had red eyes. Naturally, he presumed that red eyes were dominant and white eyes were recessive. He continued his investigation and crossed a F1 male with a F1 female. He presumed that he would get a Mendelian ratio of 3 red-eyed flies to 1 white-eyed fly in the F2 generation. On examination of the results of the cross, he recorded that all the F2 females and 50 per cent of the males had red eyes while the other 50 per cent of the males had white eyes.

Morgan concluded that the inheritance of eye colour in fruit flies was related to the sex of their offspring. What Morgan had discovered was that the gene for determining eye colour in fruit flies was located on the sex chromosomes.

The X chromosome carries a number of genes that are not related to sex determination. For example, in fruit flies the gene for eye colour is located on the X chromosome and in humans the gene for blood clotting and colour vision are carried on the X chromosome. These genes are known as sex-linked genes or X-linked as they are only found on the X chromosome and there is no gene for these characteristics on the Y chromosome.

> **Sex-linkage or X-linkage:** A gene that is found on the X chromosome but there is no copy on the Y chromosome.

White eye, haemophilia and colour blindness are all caused by recessive genes. Normally, the inheritance of two recessive genes is required for these characteristics to be expressed in the phenotype. However, as these genes are carried on the X chromosome and males have only one X chromosome, these sex-linked disorders occur more commonly in males than in females. In order for a female to be affected by a sex-linked characteristic, she would have to inherit two copies of the recessive gene and the chances of this happening are low.

Examine Fig 17.13 below showing the inheritance of white eye colour in male fruit flies.

Genotype of parents: $X^R X^R$ × $X^r Y$

An homozygous red-eyed female is crossed with a white-eyed male. The male is white-eyed because he has only one gene and the recessive one is expressed.

Gametes: (X^R) (X^R) × (X^r) (Y)

In the gametes, the X chromosomes carry the gene and the Y is left blank to show that it does not have a gene for eye colour.

F1

	X^r	Y
X^R	$X^R X^r$	$X^R Y$
X^R	$X^R X^r$	$X^R Y$

F1 Genotype and phenotype: Both males and females have red eyes. The males and females inherited the red-eyed gene from their mother. However, the females have inherited the white-eye gene from their father, but it is not expressed as the gene for red eyes is dominant. In this case, the females are called carriers.

F1 cross: $X^R X^r$ × $X^R Y$

Gametes: (X^R) (X^r) × (X^R) (Y)

> In the second cross, notice how the female produces two different types of X gametes. One gamete is carrying the normal gene for red eye and the other is carrying the gamete for white eye.

F2

	X^R	Y
X^R	$X^R X^R$	$X^R Y$
X^r	$X^R X^r$	$X^r Y$

> The only flies that have white eyes in the phenotype are those with genotype $X^r Y$. As there is no gene for eye colour on the Y chromosome, the white-eye gene on the X chromosome is expressed.

F2 Genotype: $X^R X^R$, $X^R X^r$, $X^R Y$ and $X^r Y$

F2 Phenotype: All females have red eyes, 50% of males have red eyes and 50% of males have white eyes

||||| Fig 17.13 Inheritance of white eyes in fruit flies

There is a very rare sex-linked characteristic in Holstein cattle. Male calves can be born with very little hair and with no incisors. This is more likely to happen if closely related animals are crossed.

Use of fruit flies in genetics

There are many advantages to using fruit flies when studying genetics.

- Fruit flies are easy to keep.
- They produce large numbers of offspring, which is good for statistical analysis.
- They produce a new generation every two weeks.
- They have only four pairs of chromosomes.
- They have well documented mutations, e.g. inheritance of white eyes in male fruit flies.

Mutations

The appearance of the white-eye allele in fruit flies was caused by a mutation in the gene for eye colour. A mutation is a permanent change in the DNA sequence of a gene. Mutations in genes are a source of new alleles. However, mutations are rare and random events. One well-known example of a mutation is sickle-cell anaemia.

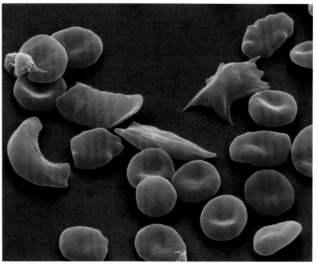

Here the mutation occurs in the gene for the production of the haemoglobin molecule in red blood cells. This produces red blood cells that are an abnormal, rigid sickle shape. Mutations can also lead to changes in chromosome numbers, and result in the formation of cells that are polyploidy (see page 144). Factors that cause mutations are known as mutagens. They interact with the DNA and cause changes to the DNA sequence. X-rays, radiation, UV light, radon and colchicines are all factors that cause mutations.

||||| Fig 17.14 Sickle red blood cell

Summary

- The Law of Independent Assortment states that during gamete formation, members of a pair of alleles segregate and move into the gametes independently of any other pair of alleles.
- After meiosis, only one allele for each characteristic will be present in each gamete.
- Dihybrid crosses involve the inheritance of two characteristics.
- When both parents are heterozygous for a characteristic, each parent will produce four different types of gametes.
- A ratio of 9:3:3:1 is produced in a dihybrid cross when both parents are heterozygous for both characteristics.
- A punnet square is used to identify all the possible genotypes produced from a cross.
- The sex chromosomes determine the sex of an individual. Females have two X chromosomes and males have an X and a Y chromosome.
- The Y chromosome is much smaller than the X chromosome and does not have the same amount of information on it as the X chromosome.
- Females produce gametes that all contain an X chromosome.
- Half of the male's gametes contain the X chromosome and half carry the Y chromosome.
- Sex-linkage or X-linkage is a gene that is found on the X chromosome but there is no copy on the Y chromosome.
- Fruit flies are used to study genetics because they are easy to keep, produce large numbers of offspring and produce a new generation every two weeks.
- A mutation is a permanent change in the DNA sequence of a gene.
- X-rays, radiation, UV light, radon and colchicines are all factors that cause mutations.

QUESTIONS

1 Define Mendel's second law of inheritance, the Law of Independent Assortment.
2 In lilies, the allele for straight stamens (S) is dominant to the allele for incurved stamen (s) and the allele for yellow petals (Y) is dominant to the allele for white petals (y). A homozygous straight stamen yellow flowering plant is crossed with an incurved stamen white flowering plant.
    (a) State the genotypes of the parents.
    (b) State the genotype and phenotype of the F1 offspring formed.
    (c) If two of the F1 plants were crossed, state the gametes formed, the genotype and phenotype of the F2.
3 In potato plants, the allele for purple stems (P) is dominant to the allele for green stems (p) and the allele for green fruit (G) is dominant to the allele for yellow fruit (g). A potato plant heterozygous for both characteristics is crossed with a potato plant with green stems and yellow fruit.
    (a) What are the genotypes of the parents?
    (b) State the genotype and the phenotype of the F1.
    (c) What proportion of the offspring will have green stems and yellow fruit?
4 During Mendel's investigations on peas, he discovered that purple flowers (P) were dominant to white flowers (p) and green pods (G) were dominant to yellow pods (g). Mendel crossed a pea plant homozygous for purple flower and green pod with a plant that was homozygous for white flower and yellow pod.
    (a) State the genotype and phenotype of the F1 plants produced from this cross.
    (b) Mendel went on to cross two of the F1 plants. Describe this cross and state the gametes formed, genotype and phenotype of the F2 offspring produced.
    (c) State the ratio of phenotypes found in the F2.
5 Explain the meaning of the following terms: *mutation* and *sex-linkage*.
6 Identify two factors that cause mutations.
7 Give three reasons why fruit flies are used in the study of genetics.
8 Explain, using examples, why some genetic disorders are more commonly seen in males than in females.
9 Outline a cross to explain the inheritance of white eyes in male fruit flies when a female heterozygous for red eyes is crossed with a red-eyed male.
10 Determine the genotype and phenotype of the F1 when a heterozygous red-eyed female fruit fly is crossed with a white-eyed male.

EXAM QUESTIONS

1 In poultry, feathered legs (F) is dominant over clean legs (f) and white plumage (W) is dominant over black plumage (w). What will be the genotype and phenotypes of the offspring of each of the following crosses?
    (a) FFWW x ffww
    (b) FFww x ffWW
    (c) FfWw x FFWW. (LC, HL, 2001)
2 The gender of offspring is determined by the male parent in mammals. Illustrate this statement in terms of chromosomes. (LC, HL, 2008)

Chapter 18

Applied Genetics

Applied genetics involves the manipulation of hereditary characteristics in order to improve or produce desirable characteristics in offspring. Desirable characteristics might include improved fertility, increased milk production or better growth rates in breeds of cattle.

For centuries, farmers have used controlled breeding, also known as selective breeding, in plants and animals to concentrate desirable traits in offspring by careful selection of parents with those traits. However, with the advent of artificial insemination (AI) and embryo transplantation, the number of offspring from genetically superior parents can be increased far beyond the numbers that would be possible by natural means.

In addition, genetic engineering allows the production of new plant species that contain genes from unrelated organisms, giving us a new generation of plants known as transgenic species.

In this chapter, we will divide the genetic manipulation of plants and animals into two categories: selective breeding and reproductive technologies.

≣ Selective Breeding

The selective breeding of plants and animals can be divided into inbreeding and crossbreeding. Inbreeding in animals involves the mating of genetically related individuals such as mother and son or father and daughter.

Inbreeding

Inbreeding has the advantage of fixing desirable genetic traits such as high milk yields in purebred dairy cattle, e.g. Holsteins. However, the disadvantage is that it also concentrates undesirable recessive traits. Studies have shown that inbreeding in Holsteins decreases the length of the cow's productive life and increases calving intervals.

> **Inbreeding:** The mating of closely related animals, which increases the chances of the offspring being affected by undesirable recessive traits.

Most animals carry undesirable traits. However, the genes for these traits tend to be recessive. Closely related animals have many similar genes. Undesirable recessive genes are usually hidden by the presence of the dominant, normal gene. However, inbreeding increases the inheritance of similar genes, leading to an increase in homozygous genotypes (BB or bb).

In cattle, mulefoot is a recessive trait that is caused by the inheritance of two recessive genes, one from each parent. This causes the two toes on the front feet of the calf to be fused together. The offspring here is homozygous (bb) for the trait.

Some cases of homozygous recessive genes can be fatal, leading to a failed conception in a cow. In these circumstances, the recessive genes are called lethal genes, as they cause the death of the organism. Most animal species carry some recessive, lethal genes, which have no effect on an organism when they are present as a heterozygous genotype (Bb). All purebred animals are inbred to some extent.

Inbreeding in plants is extensively used to produce stock or purebred lines. These purebred lines produce F1 hybrids. Inbreeding in plants can occur naturally or artificially by self-fertilisation.

Crossbreeding

Crossbreeding (or outbreeding) involves the mating of animals or plants from two different breeds, varieties or species. The offspring often inherit favourable genes from both parents, which leads to better health traits than either parent would have had. This is referred to as heterosis or hybrid vigour.

> **Heterosis (hybrid vigour):** The increased productivity displayed by offspring from genetically different parents.

Crossbreeding is the opposite of inbreeding as it reduces the risk of harmful recessive genes appearing in the phenotype by increasing the number of heterozygous pairs of genes.

In its extreme, it can involve the crossing of two different species. For example, when a female horse is crossed with a male donkey, the resulting offspring is called a mule. Mules demonstrate hybrid vigour as they have greater strength, are hardier animals with greater disease resistance and have a longer lifespan than their parents. The only drawback is that mules tend to be infertile and therefore are unable to reproduce.

Fig 18.1 A horse

Fig 18.2 A donkey

Fig 18.3 A mule

Countries such as New Zealand, Canada and the United States have conducted much research into the benefits of crossbreeding in dairy herds. Successive generations of inbreeding among purebred dairy cows, such as Holsteins, had led to decreased fertility rates and decreased productivity over the lifespan of the cow. In addition, the dairy industry was changing, with farmers' milk payments increased by its high milk solids content (protein and butterfat) and decreased for high water content of milk.

Purebred Holstein cows are the highest milk producers. However, milk protein and fat is low in comparison to the volume of the milk produced. Jersey cows, on the other hand, have the highest milk solids in their milk, but low milk yields. When Holsteins are crossed with Jerseys, the offspring have increased milk production from the Holstein and increased milk solids (protein and butterfat) from the Jersey. In addition, the offspring have increased fertility, health and lifespan in the dairy herd, which reduces the replacement rate.

|||| Fig 18.4 Holstein cow

|||| Fig 18.5 Jersey cow

|||| Fig 18.6 Holstein Jersey cross

Crossbreeding in F1 hybrid seed varieties

The production of F1 hybrid seed varieties uses crossbreeding extensively. These hybrid crosses are often stronger, have greater disease resistance and higher yields than their purebred parents do.

F1 hybrid seeds are derived from the crossing of two genetically different parent cultivars. For simplicity, we will refer to these parent plants as cultivar A and cultivar B. These parent plants have been inbred by repeated self-pollination over several generations, so that they are practically homozygous for their traits. These parent plants are called breeding stock. The two different cultivars A and B are crossed by hand pollination. This involves the removal of the immature anthers, which produce the pollen from cultivar A and then dusting cultivar A's stigma with the male pollen from cultivar B. This produces the seeds that are the hybrid AB.

|||| Fig 18.7 F1 seed variety packets

The F1 hybrids benefit from hybrid vigour. The production of F1 hybrid seeds is an expensive process, as in order to obtain the uniform phenotype of the F1 plants, the parent plants' cultivars A and B must be crossed every year. If the F1 hybrids are crossed for an F2 generation, the offspring have greater variability compared to the F1 and, as a result, lose some of the hybrid vigour of the F1.

≡ Reproductive Technologies

The following section focuses on how biotechnology has led to the increase in the number of offspring that can be produced from plants and animals of superior genetic merit.

Artificial insemination (AI)

As mentioned earlier in this chapter, farmers have been improving the genetic merit of their cattle herds by selective breeding. In order to do this, cows of good genetic merit are crossed with superior bulls.

Keeping a bull on a farm has a number of implications: they are dangerous, expensive to keep and must be changed on a regular basis to prevent high levels of inbreeding within the herd.

In Ireland, the most popular method of increasing the genetic merit of a herd of cattle is by using artificial insemination and, as a result, this has become a routine procedure on dairy farms in particular. Another advantage of using AI is that the bulls have been both performance and progeny tested.

The production of AI straws involves the initial collection of the bull's semen. The semen is diluted with an extender, which protects and nourishes the sperm during storage. The extender usually consists of milk or egg yolk, which protects against cold shock, glucose, which is a source of energy for the sperm, and glycerol, which prevents damage to the sperm during freezing. In addition, diluting the sperm increases the number of female cows that can be serviced by one ejaculation.

By natural methods, a bull can service between 50–60 cows per year. Using AI, one bull can service thousands of cows per year.

Finally, the diluted sperm is packed into a plastic straw and stored in liquid nitrogen at −196°C. Before insemination, the straws are thawed in warm water. Table 18.1 shows the advantages and disadvantages of AI.

Performance testing: The evaluation of a bull's performance by comparing its weight gain and food conversion ratio with other bulls kept under similar feed and housing conditions.
Progeny testing: The evaluation of the performance of a bulls' offspring compared to other bulls' offspring under similar feed and housing conditions.

Table 18.1 The advantages and disadvantages of AI

Advantages	Disadvantages
Allows maximum use of superior bulls	Successful heat detection is crucial
Farmers have a choice of bulls that have been performance and progeny tested	More labour and management skills required than natural service
AI prevents the spread of sexually transmitted diseases	
The cost of a straw is small in comparison to the cost of purchasing, feeding and housing a bull	

Embryo transplantation

In embryo transplantation, the embryos from a donor animal are collected and implanted into a recipient female, who serves as a surrogate mother. Only animals with a good breeding history and superior genetic merit are selected.

The breeding of pedigree sheep and cattle uses this technique. It allows the production of large numbers of offspring, which would not be possible by natural means.

The surrogate mother does not have to be a pedigree animal, but must be in excellent health and have good mothering abilities. Table 18.2 outlines a typical programme for embryo transplantation in sheep.

Table 18.2 Timeline for embryo transplantation

Day	Event
0	Both donor and recipient ewe are sponged with progesterone impregnated sponges. This allows synchronisation of the reproductive cycles of both the donor ewes and the recipient ewes. The recipient must be at the correct stage of her reproductive cycle in order to receive an embryo
10	Hormone injections are given to the donor ewes to increase the number of eggs that are released at ovulation. This is known as super ovulation

Day	Event
	Table 18.3 Timeline for embryo transplantation
12	The sponges are removed from both the donor and the recipient ewes
13	Heat detection of both the donor and the recipient ewes is carried out. The introduction of teaser rams with raddles will identify ewes in standing heat. Ewes should come into heat 36-48 hours after sponges are removed
14	The donor ewes are inseminated by AI. Using a laparoscope (an optical device), a small incision is made in the abdomen of the donor ewe and semen is inserted into the left and right horn of the uterus. If fresh semen is being used, only one insemination is required. If the semen has been frozen, use two inseminations as required (7 hours apart) to increase the chances of the eggs being fertilised
20	The embryos are flushed from the donor ewes. A small surgical procedure is required and a catheter is placed in the horn of the uterus and the uterus is flushed with sterile solution. The embryos are collected and graded. The embryos are then transferred to the surrogate mother, inserting two embryos into the horn of the uterus After removing the embryos from the donors, the ewes are given an injection of hormones, which brings them back into 4 days later, and they are serviced naturally by a ram

Embryo transplantation in cattle is slightly different to sheep, but both have the same basic procedure, involving the synchronisation of reproductive cycles, followed by hormone injections to cause super ovulation in the donor cow.

Fertilisation of the eggs can take place inside the cow, or the eggs can be flushed out and fertilised *in vitro* (in a test tube). The fertilised eggs are then transferred to a surrogate cow, which will carry and give birth to the calf.

|||||| Fig 18.8 Laparoscopic AI

Micropropagation

Micropropagation allows the rapid multiplication of plants and it is often used to produce large numbers of potato seed tubers. Micropropagation is often referred to as tissue culture propagation, as it produces plants asexually from very small pieces of plant tissue. The plants used for propagation must be disease-free.

In the production of potatoes, the plants sprout. The sprouts are removed and are sterilised with bleach or alcohol and finally with sterilised water. A small portion of the sprout (10 mm section) is placed on a growth medium containing sucrose, as a source of energy, and plant hormones. The medium is sterilised before use to prevent contamination by bacteria and fungi and is often thickened with agar. The plant cultures are incubated under low-light conditions at 25°C. Three weeks after inoculation, the shoots are removed from the culture, divided into sections and re-inoculated onto a fresh medium. This procedure is repeated every three weeks until finally the plantlets are transferred to soil and are grown in greenhouses.

A single plant can produce thousands of clones, all genetically identical to each other and to the parent plant.

≡ Genetic Modification

Genetic engineering allows scientists to insert beneficial genes into the chromosomes of plants and animals from unrelated species. Plants and animals that are produced by genetic engineering are called transgenic species or genetically modified organisms (GMOs). Some of the benefits of this technology in plants include:

- Increased crop yields.
- Increased resistance to pests and diseases.
- Increased tolerance to cold conditions.

Genetically modified maize contains a gene from a *Bacillus thuringiensis* that codes for a toxin. This toxin is poisonous to insect pests and in particular to the corn borer caterpillar. The plant can now produce its own pesticide so that the caterpillars die when they eat the plant. This reduces the need to spray crops with pesticides.

‖‖ Fig 18.9 Maize crop

Some varieties of maize have also been genetically engineered so that they can tolerate herbicides such as Roundup. Farmers can then spray crops with herbicides to kill competing weeds without killing the maize crop.

There is considerable controversy surrounding genetically modified plants. Some disadvantages of this new technology are that GMOs could cause allergies in people consuming the plants and, potentially, these genes could escape into other plants by cross-fertilisation to produce 'super weeds', which are resistant to herbicides.

GMOs are not currently available to grow in Ireland, but are widely used in the United States and to a lesser extent in Britain and Australia.

≡ Polyploidy

Polyploidy describes cells that contain more than two sets of chromosomes. Most organisms are diploid (2n, two sets of chromosomes), with gametes (egg and sperm) being haploid (n, one set of chromosomes). Polyploidy occurs due to abnormal cell division and is most commonly found in plants. Several strains of wheat are polyploidy. For example, durum wheat is a tetraploid (4n, four sets of chromosomes) and some strawberry plants are decaploid (10n, ten sets of chromosomes).

Polyploidy can be induced by exposing cells to some chemicals, thus causing mutations that lead to an increase in the chromosome number of a plant.

Colchicine is a natural product that inhibits chromosome segregation during meiosis, causing all the chromosomes to pass into one gamete.

Some polyploidy crops are sterile (especially those with an odd set of chromosomes, e.g. 3n and 5n), which is advantageous in the production of fruits, e.g. seedless grapes and watermelons. Polyploidy plants have larger cells, due to the greater amount of DNA present, and often produce much larger plants.

Polyploidy is much rarer in animals. However, it has been found in some insects, fish (salmon), amphibians and reptiles.

Summary

- Applied genetics involves the manipulation of hereditary characteristics in order to improve or produce desirable characteristics in offspring.

- Inbreeding involves the mating of closely related animals, which increases the chances of the offspring being affected by undesirable, recessive traits.

- Inbreeding increases the inheritance of similar genes, leading to an increased risk of inheriting genetic disorders controlled by recessive genes.

- Inbreeding in plants is used to produce purebred lines; these are then used to produce F1 hybrids.

- Hybrid vigour is the increased productivity displayed by offspring from genetically different parents.

- Crossbreeding is the opposite of inbreeding as it reduces the risk of harmful recessive genes being displayed in the phenotype.

- Hybrid offspring are often stronger, have greater disease resistance and higher yields than their purebred parents do.

- Keeping a bull on a farm has a number of implications: they are dangerous, expensive to keep and must be changed on a regular basis to prevent high levels of inbreeding within the herd.

- Artificial insemination (AI) is a popular method of increasing the genetic merit of a herd of cattle.

- Performance testing is the evaluation of a bull's performance by comparing its weight gain and food conversion ratio with other bulls kept under similar feed and housing conditions.

- Progeny testing is the evaluation of the performance of a bull's offspring compared to other bulls' offspring under similar feed and housing conditions.

- Embryo transplantation involves the collection of a donor animal's embryos and transferring these into a recipient female, which serves as a surrogate mother.

- Micropropagation allows the rapid multiplication of plants and is often used to produce large numbers of potato seed tubers.

- Genetic engineering allows scientists to insert beneficial genes into the chromosomes of plants and animals from unrelated species.

- Plants and animals that are produced by genetic engineering are called transgenic species or genetically modified organisms (GMOs).

- Polyploidy describes cells that contain more than two sets of chromosomes.

- Polyploidy can be induced by exposing cells to some chemicals, thus causing mutation that leads to an increase in the chromosome number of a plant.

QUESTIONS

1   Explain the term *applied genetics*.
2   Distinguish between inbreeding and crossbreeding. Outline the advantages and disadvantages of both.
3   Explain the meaning of the term *heterosis*.
4   Briefly describe, using examples, why dairy farmers are increasing the number of crossbred cows compared to purebred animals in their dairy herd.
5   Describe the production of F1 seed varieties.
6   Distinguish between performance and progeny testing.
7   What do the letters AI stand for? What benefits are there to a farmer of using AI?
8   Briefly explain the function of each of the following in the production of AI straws:
    (a) Addition of an extender.
    (b) Presence of glycerol in the extender.
    (c) Presence of glucose in the extender.
9   Write notes on each of the following:
    (a) Polyploidy
    (b) Genetic modification
    (c) Micropropagation.

EXAM QUESTION

1   (a) Briefly outline the principal stages in embryo transfer in cows.
    (b) Explain lethal gene. (LC, HL, 2009)
2   (a) Explain how polyploidy arises in plants.
    (b) Name and give an example of one type of polyploidy.
    (c) Explain artificial selection. (LC, HL, 2010)
3   Distinguish between each of the following:
    (a) Inbreeding and crossbreeding
    (b) Performance testing and progeny testing. (LC, HL, 2007)

●●●●● UNIT 5

Soil Science

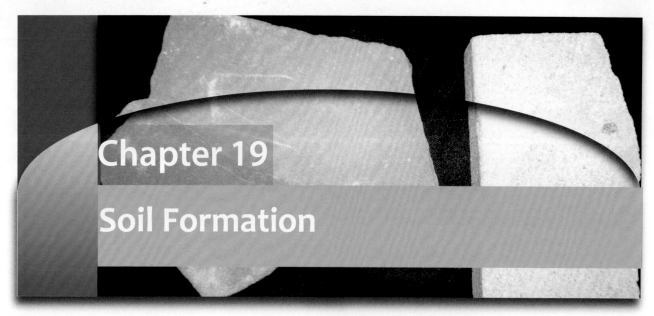

Chapter 19

Soil Formation

What is Soil?

Soil is the top layer of the earth's surface. It consists of mineral and rock particles, organic matter, water and air. Soil has developed over millions of years through weathering. The soils of Ireland are considered young, as they were only formed after the last Ice Age.

Much of the parent material from which the soils developed was transported, deposited and broken down by the glaciers. This is known as parent rock material. Plant residues, known as organic parent material, also contribute to soil formation.

Agriculture could not exist without soil. Crops are grown in soil, and the type of soil on a farm

|||| Fig 19.1 Glaciers, similar to the one in the picture, transported much of the parent rock material responsible for soil formation in Ireland

determines which crops can be grown. Poor yields of crops can result from growing a crop in an unsuitable soil. This chapter looks at the materials and the factors that contribute to soil formation.

Rock Types

Rocks are divided into groups based on how they are formed. There are three groups of rocks, all of which are found in Ireland. The three groups are igneous, sedimentary and metamorphic rocks. All three groups provide the parent material from which the mineral matter in our soils originates.

Igneous rock

Magma is a liquid found underneath the earth's crust. Magma is molten (melted) rock. When magma cools it solidifies and forms rock. When magma appears above the earth's surface it is called lava. This also cools to form rock. The type of rock that is formed when magma or lava solidifies is called igneous rock.

As magma cools, it forms crystals, which consist of minerals. If magma cools quickly, the crystals will be small but if it cools slowly, the crystals formed are large. The three most common crystals formed are quartz, feldspar and mica. Their properties determine the characteristics of the rock in which they are found and in turn the soil that is formed when that rock is weathered. Quartz is acidic in nature, while feldspar is alkaline.

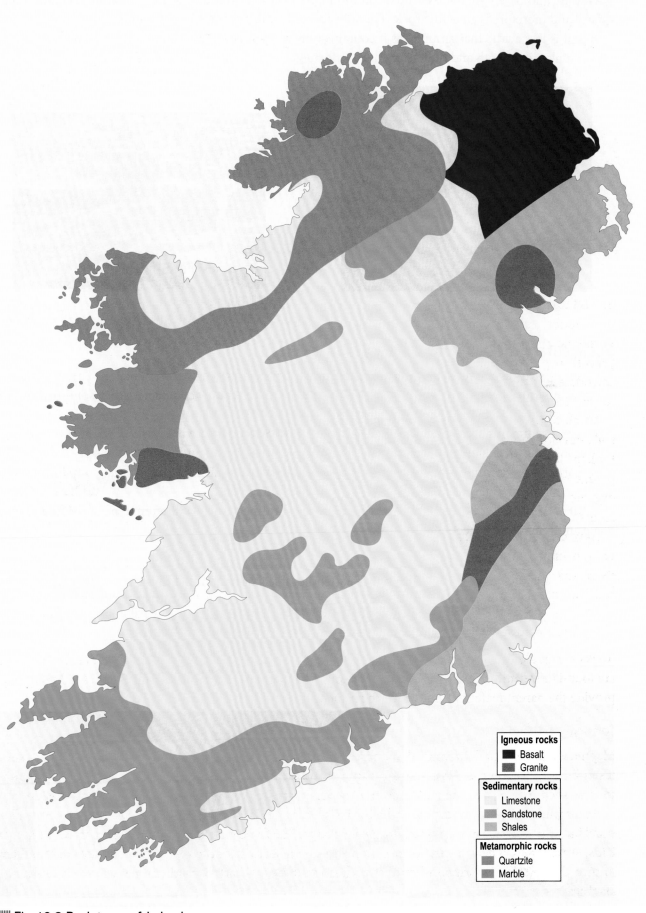

Igneous rocks
- Basalt
- Granite

Sedimentary rocks
- Limestone
- Sandstone
- Shales

Metamorphic rocks
- Quartzite
- Marble

|||||| Fig 19.2 Rock types of Ireland

Granite and basalt are the two most common igneous rocks found in Ireland. Granite contains a lot of quartz and therefore is an acidic rock. The soils formed from granite are also acidic.

Basalt is less acidic than granite, as it contains only a small amount of quartz. It does contain feldspar, which makes it smooth and fine-grained. Soils formed from basalt take the same form.

▌▌▌ Fig 19.3 Granite

▌▌▌ Fig 19.4 Basalt

Sedimentary rock

Millions of years ago, layers of sediment were deposited at the bottom of seas and lakes. These layers built up over millions of years and slowly compacted in the process. As they compacted, they solidified to form sedimentary rock.

Mineral sediments are different sizes. The largest particles (quartz) were washed up on shores and are commonly known as sand. Smaller particles known as clay were brought further out to sea for deposition. Clay particles are a result of the weathering of igneous rock. The shells of fossils that contain lime were deposited in deep water.

Each of the three types of sediment was compacted over time to form a different type of rock: sandstone, shale and limestone respectively.

Table 19.1 Characteristics of sedimentary rocks		
Particle type	Rock formed	pH
Sand (quartz)	Sandstone	Acidic
Clay	Shale	Less acidic
Fossils and shells	Limestone	Alkaline

▌▌▌ Fig 19.5 Sandstone

▌▌▌ Fig 19.6 Shale

▌▌▌ Fig 19.7 Limestone

Metamorphic rock

Metamorphic rocks are formed from igneous or sedimentary rocks. Heat or pressure brings about a change in the rock and its mineral content. Metamorphic rocks such as igneous and sedimentary rocks have an influence on the acidity or alkalinity of the soils formed from them. If the metamorphic rock is acidic, the soil formed when it is weathered will also be acidic.

Table 19.2 Metamorphic rock formation		
Rock type	Rock group	Metamorphic rock formed
Limestone	Igneous	Marble
Shale	Sedimentary	Slate
Granite	Igneous	Gneiss
Sandstone	Sedimentary	Quartzite

|||||| Fig 19.8 Gneiss rock in Greenland, formed by heat and pressure on granite rock

|||||| Fig 19.9 Limestone is converted to marble by intense heat

|||||| Fig 19.10 Slate is formed by intense pressure on shale

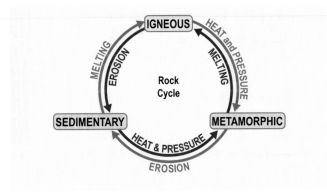

|||||| Fig 19.11 Rock cycle

☰ Weathering and Decomposition of Rocks

Weathering of rock takes place when rock is broken down by physical (mechanical) or chemical means. Physical weathering involves the breakdown of rocks into sediments. Chemical weathering brings about a chemical change during the decomposition process. The main methods of physical and chemical weathering are outlined next.

Physical weathering

There are different types of physical weathering, each of which breaks down rock into smaller and smaller particles.

- **Heating and cooling**: Increased temperatures can cause minerals in rock to expand. Minerals expand at different rates, causing rock to shatter and disintegrate. Minerals also contract as they cool, contributing to the weathering process.

- **Freezing (frost action)**: Water fills cracks in the rock. As it freezes and turns to ice, it expands, causing the rock to shatter and break, leading to more cracks in the rock, which will subsequently fill with water and undergo the same process.

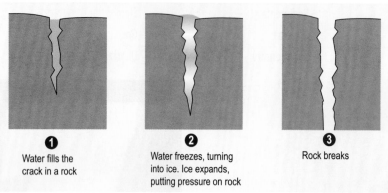

❶ Water fills the crack in a rock

❷ Water freezes, turning into ice. Ice expands, putting pressure on rock

❸ Rock breaks

||||| Fig 19.12 Frost action

- **Activity of roots**: Roots of trees penetrate cracks in rock. They put pressure on rock as they grow, causing the rock to break.

- **Activity of animals**: Animals digging and burrowing contribute to rock breakdown.

- **Grinding action**: Glaciers levelled hills and moved boulders and rock over long distances by grinding action. Rocks and rock particles are also moved by water (rainfall and rivers), wind (sand) and gravity. The movement of rock particles through this grinding action further contributes to the breakdown of rocks.

||||| Fig 19.13 Rock showing the effects of weathering

Project link

As part of the Leaving Certificate Practical Assessment, students must carry out a range of experiments and provide (written) evidence of having completed the experiments. Soil is one of the topics on the course on which at least one experiment must be completed. Any of the soil experiments in the following five chapters would be suitable for this part of the coursework. While students must complete a minimum of one experiment, it is recommended that students should complete as many as possible.

Experiment 19.1

To show the effects of heating and cooling on rock

Materials

Small samples of granite rock, tongs, Bunsen burner, beaker/water trough and water
Safety: Wear goggles during this experiment.

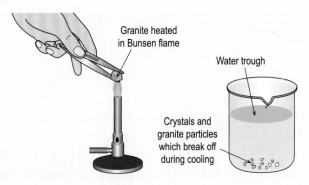

||||| Fig 19.14 To demonstrate the effects of heating and cooling on granite

Method

1   Pick up a small piece of granite with metal tongs and hold it in the Bunsen flame until it starts to glow.

2   Remove it from the flame and place it in the water trough to cool.

3   When the granite has cooled, remove it from the water with the tongs and repeat the procedure.

4   Each time the granite is removed from the water, look in the bottom of the trough for crystals and particles of granite that have broken off.

Note: The heating and cooling action that takes place in the experiment imitates the conditions that rock is exposed to on a daily basis. Rock is heated by the sun during the day and cools down at night.

Chemical weathering

Chemical reactions with rock bring about a change in rock minerals. There are a number of ways that rock is weathered chemically.

Hydrolysis

Hydrogen ions in water react with rock minerals. The result is that hydroxide compounds are formed which in turn release minerals such as potassium into the soil. An example of this is the reaction of the rock mineral potassium feldspar with water.

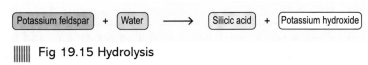

||||| Fig 19.15 Hydrolysis

▨   Clay is formed from silicic acid.

▨   Potassium ions (K^+) are released into the soil from the potassium hydroxide.

Oxidation and reduction

Oxidation is loss of electrons; reduction is gain of electrons (OIL RIG). Oxidation is also the addition of oxygen to a substance and reduction is the removal of oxygen from a substance. Oxidation of iron in rock is a common occurrence and takes place in dry conditions. Haematite is a mineral formed by oxidation.

Reduction takes place in wet conditions where oxygen is absent. In these conditions, manganese and iron may be dissolved and removed from rock.

Hydration

Hydration is the addition of water to a rock mineral. This takes place frequently after oxidation where iron oxide is produced. When water molecules combine with the iron oxide, they cause the rock to expand and decompose.

Solution and carbonation

Water is a natural solvent and it dissolves minerals in rock as it percolates through the rock. Metal ions such as potassium, sodium and calcium are highly soluble in water.

If water reacts with carbon dioxide gas, it forms carbonic acid. The carbonic acid dissolves the alkaline minerals in rock faster than water. Limestone, in particular, is weathered quickly by carbonic acid.

Experiment 19.2

To show the effects of chemical weathering on rock

Materials
Sample of sandstone, limestone, dilute hydrochloric acid, petri dishes, droppers
Safety: Wear safety goggles and glasses as acid is corrosive.

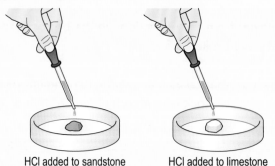

HCl added to sandstone   HCl added to limestone

||||| Fig 19.16 To demonstrate the effect of carbonation on limestone

Method
1   Place a sample of sandstone in a petri dish.
2   Use a dropper to add a few drops of dilute hydrochloric acid to the sandstone.
3   Wait a few minutes and observe any reaction. Record your findings.
4   Place a sample of limestone in a petri dish and add hydrochloric acid to the limestone.
5   Record any observations.

Results
Sandstone is acidic and does not react with the HCl solution. Limestone is alkaline and contains calcium carbonate ($CaCO_3$). As it reacts with the HCl it releases carbon dioxide gas. Evidence of this will be seen by bubbling and frothing on the surface of the rock where the acid was added.

≡ Biological Decomposition of Rocks

Micro-organisms have their role to play in the decomposition of rock. Bacteria, fungi and lichens (a lichen consists of an algae and a fungus) colonise bare rocks. Some of these micro-organisms utilise nitrogen and carbon dioxide from the atmosphere. These micro-organisms produce acids, which dissolve mineral nutrients such as calcium and phosphorus in rock. This leads to the decomposition of rock and contributes to soil formation.

Organic parent material

Organic parent material consists of the remains of plants that have partially decomposed. These remains accumulate in wet, waterlogged conditions and often in lakes.

Oxygen is necessary for the decomposition of the plant material. The wet, waterlogged conditions in which these plant remains are found lack the oxygen necessary for this process to occur.

Peat is the main material that is produced from these plant remains. An area where peat accumulates is known as a bog. There are three types of bog in Ireland: basin peats also called fens, raised bogs and blanket bogs (see Table 19.3).

Basin peats (fens) are flat bogs that have developed in hollows in the landscape such as in lakes and waterlogged areas where there is a mineral-rich water supply (see Fig 19.17). When the water supply no longer exists, and more material accumulates on top of the basin peat, a raised bog forms. The basin peats or fens are only slightly acidic, but as they form raised bogs they become more acidic as their pH lowers.

Blanket bogs develop in areas of high rainfall and low evaporation in anaerobic conditions (absence of oxygen). They are found in mountainous areas along the west coast of Ireland from Donegal to Clare and in the lowlands of Kerry. They are not as deep as basin peats. However, they are very acid with low fertility and have limited agricultural use.

≡ Factors of Soil Formation

Five factors affect the formation of soil: parent material, climate, living organisms, topography and time.

Parent material

Soils are influenced hugely by parent material. Forty-five per cent of soil consists of mineral matter (see Chapter 20), so the characteristics of parent material, particularly its acidity and its texture, are going to influence the acidity and texture of the soil formed from them. Soil formed from granite contains quartz, which is weathered to sand particles and is acidic in nature. The mica particles in the rock are weathered into clay particles.

Limestone is alkaline in nature and the calcium and magnesium present in limestone raise the pH of the soil formed from it.

Broadleaf trees are best suited to growing on soils that are derived from limestone. Such species contribute to the alkalinity of these soils through the organic matter that they produce.

Climate

The climatic conditions that have the most effect on soil formation are temperature and precipitation. Water contributes to the physical and chemical weathering of rock through freezing, solution, hydrolysis and hydration. Temperature plays a role in the heating and cooling of rock. Low temperatures lead to low evaporation levels. This means that more water is available for chemical weathering.

Characteristic	Basin peat/Fen	Raised bog	Blanket peat
Depth	2 m	8–12 m	2.6 m
Shape	Flat	Dome-shaped	Sloped or flat depending on landscape
pH	6.0	4.0–6.0	5.0
Location	Valleys, lakes	Lakes	Mountains and lowland on the west coast

Table 19.3 Summary of basin peats (fens), raised bogs and blanket peat characteristics

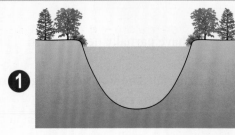

❶ Basin peats develop in depressions in the land such as lakes and valleys.

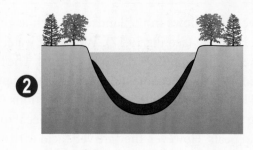

❷ Vegetation growing around the lake dies and accumulates at the bottom of the lake. It does not decompose in the water.

❸ This organic matter continues to build up and fill in the lake. As the lake reduces in size, vegetation grows around the new lake edge. This is called encroachment.

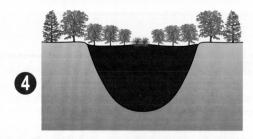

❹ Eventually the lake is completely filled in. Vegetation grows on top of the new land. This is called a fen.

❺ Continued deposition of organic material leads to a raised bog as the peat is above the level of the land.

Fig 19.17 Basin peat formation

Living organisms

Plant and animal species contribute to soil formation. Both contribute humus when they die and micro-organisms help to decompose the organic matter in soil. If soils are lacking in vegetation, they will also lack organic matter. Organic matter contributes to the structure and fertility of a soil.

Soils that develop under grassland benefit from the fibrous root system of grass. The grass roots bind the soil together, preventing erosion, but also contribute large amounts of humus as they die and decompose. Grasses contain higher levels of alkaline compounds, which reduce acidity levels in soil and make them more suitable for cultivation.

Soils that develop under forests can suffer from acidification, particularly if the trees are conifers. The needles from conifers are acidic and, as these accumulate in the soil, they have an acidifying effect on the soil. Deciduous, broadleaf species do not have as severe an effect on soil acidity. The roots of trees are large and do not contribute the same levels of humus to the soil as the fibrous roots of grasses.

Topography

Topography refers to the slope of the landscape; whether is it level or hilly. On steep slopes, erosion will carry soil from the top of the hillsides to the valleys below. This leads to thin soils on hillsides and deep fertile soils in valleys. Water also contributes to soil erosion on hillsides. Water is evaporated rapidly from the hillsides in comparison to the fertile soils in the valleys. The moisture content that remains in these lowland soils makes them particularly suitable for cultivation.

Time

The length of time that the other four factors have had to influence soil formation is important. In soils that are considered old much of the material available for soil formation through weathering has already been eroded or decomposed. Fertility often comes from organic materials in old soils. Irish soils are young soils, as they were formed from glacial deposits left from the last Ice Age. Therefore, there is a high level of parent rock material available for weathering and soil formation, contributing to the overall fertility of the soil.

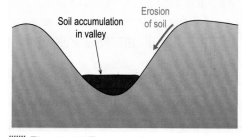

|||| Fig 19.18 Topography

☰ Soil Profiles

The materials provided by parent rock and organic matter for soil formation form layers in the soil known as horizons. Soils have a number of horizons, each with their own characteristics. Excavation of a soil will show these horizons in a vertical section from the uppermost layer at ground level to the bedrock. This vertical section showing all of the soil horizons is known as a soil profile. A typical soil profile is shown in Fig 19.19.

- **O horizon**: This is not always present due to the absence of vegetation. It consists of organic material.

- **A horizon**: This is commonly known as topsoil. It contains minerals that may have organic matter mixed through it, but can experience the effects of leaching, so it may be lacking in minerals in certain conditions.

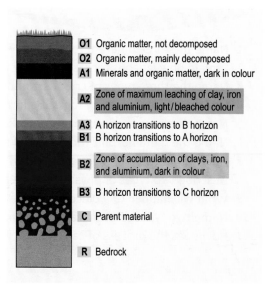

|||| Fig 19.19 Soil profile

- **B horizon**: This is known as subsoil. It is normally a lighter colour than topsoil, except where minerals have been leached and have accumulated in this horizon.
- **C horizon**: This contains parent material and is rocky in nature. It is generally light coloured.
- **R horizon**: This is bedrock and is solid.

Summary

- There are three groups of rocks: igneous (basalt, granite), sedimentary (limestone, sandstone and shale) and metamorphic (marble, quartzite).
- Rocks undergo a number of types of physical weathering processes including heating and cooling, freezing, activity of animals, activity of roots and grinding action.
- Rocks undergo chemical weathering processes such as hydrolysis, oxidation and reduction, hydration, solution and carbonation.
- Organic parent materials consist of the remains of plants that have partially decomposed.
- There are three types of bog in Ireland: basin peats/fens, raised bogs and blanket bogs.
- Basin peats (fens) are flat bogs that have developed in hollows in the landscape where there is a mineral-rich, water supply. A raised bog is formed when material accumulates on top of the basin peat.
- Blanket bogs develop in areas of high rainfall and low evaporation in anaerobic conditions. They are found in mountainous areas all along the west coast of Ireland.
- Five factors affect the formation of soil: parent material, climate, living organisms, topography and time.
- A soil profile is a vertical section from the uppermost layer of soil at ground level to the bedrock. Each layer is known as a horizon.
- The O horizon consists of organic material, the A horizon is topsoil, the B horizon is subsoil, the C horizon is parent rock material and the R horizon is bedrock.

QUESTIONS

1. Name the three different rock types.
2. Explain how igneous rock is formed.
3. Name the three types of crystals found in igneous rock.
4. Explain how sedimentary rocks are formed.
5. Name three types of sedimentary rock.
6. Name the metamorphic rocks formed from (a) granite and (b) limestone.
7. How are metamorphic rocks formed?
8. Describe two types of physical weathering.
9. What will happen to a piece of granite if it is heated in a Bunsen flame and then dipped in water?
10. Name two types of chemical weathering.
11. How does the process of carbonation weather rock?

QUESTIONS

12 What role do micro-organisms play in the decomposition of rock?

13 What are organic parent materials and where are they found?

14 Name two types of peat.

15 Where are blanket peats found and how are they formed?

16 Where are basin peats found and how are they formed?

17 Compare basin and blanket peats under the following headings: (a) pH, (b) depth and (c) shape.

18 How does parent material influence soil formation?

19 What two climatic factors have the most influence on soil formation?

20 How does topography influence soil formation?

21 What is a soil profile?

22 What is found in the O horizon?

23 What is the A horizon more commonly known as?

24 What process is seen in the A2 horizon?

25 What is the B horizon known as?

26 What process is seen in the B2 horizon?

EXAM QUESTIONS

*There is a full question on soil on the Higher Level paper every year.

1 List four factors that are responsible for the development of soil structure. (LC, HL, 2010)

2 Outline the formation of peat bogs in Ireland. (LC, HL, 2010)

3 Name three minerals present in igneous rocks. (LC, HL, 2009)

4 Explain how the weathering of rocks contributes to soil formation. (LC, HL, 2008)

5 Explain why most soils in Ireland are regarded as 'young' soils in geological terms. (LC, HL, 2006)

6 (a) Name the type of sedimentary rock that is prevalent in the Burren, County Clare.

    (b) Describe a chemical process that aids in weathering this rock.

    (c) Name one feature of a soil formed from this type of rock. (LC, HL, 2005)

7 Explain how soils are influenced during their formation by the following factors:

    (a) Parent material

    (b) Climate

    (c) Topography

    (d) Living organisms. (LC, HL, 2004)

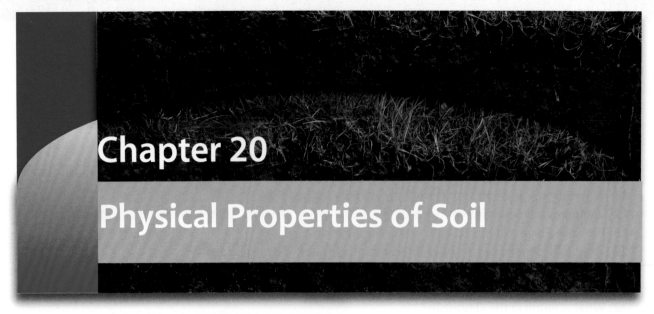

Chapter 20

Physical Properties of Soil

Soil consists of solid, liquid and gas components. Each is necessary for the growth and development of plants. The solid components of soil include mineral matter which is derived from parent rock material, and organic matter which is derived from the remains of plant material. Together mineral and organic matter occupy 50 per cent of soil volume. They are responsible for providing nutrients for the plant and providing the medium to anchor the plant in the ground.

The other half of the soil's components consists of soil pores, which are spaces in the soil. These pores are filled with air and water. Typically, half the soil pores are filled with air and the other half with water. However, these proportions can change under different conditions. During a period of heavy rainfall, the level of water in the soil rises and subsequently the level of air drops. This is common in winter when rainfall levels are high.

In periods of drought and low rainfall, the water level in the soil falls and the amount of air increases. This is more common in summer.

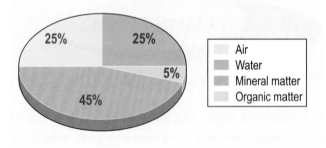

|||||| Fig 20.1 Composition of soil

Soil Composition

Mineral matter

Parent rock material is broken down into mineral particles. The mineral particles are classified by size. The Irish Soil Survey categorises the particles into five different sizes, each smaller than the previous. The five types of particle are: gravel, course sand, fine sand, silt and clay (see Fig 20.2). The particles also have a number of properties associated with them that contribute to the overall characteristics of a soil.

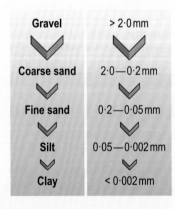

|||||| Fig 20.2 Mineral matter categorised by particle type and size

Table 20.1 Soil mineral particles and their properties

Particle type	Gravel and sand (course and fine)	Silt and clay
Particle size	Large soil particles	Small soil particles
Pore space between particles	Large pore spaces between particles	Small pore spaces between particles
Drainage	Free draining due to large pore spaces	Poor drainage due to small pore spaces
Aeration	Well aerated due to large pore spaces	Poor aeration due to small pore spaces
Waterlogging/Drought	Prone to drought in prolonged periods of dry weather	Do not suffer from drought; retain water in dry weather but can become waterlogged after prolonged rainfall
Fertility/Ion exchange	No contribution to fertility or ion exchange	Clay is a source of K, P, Ca, Mg ions. Its large surface area allows for ion exchange to take place

Ion exchange: This process takes place in soil where ions are attracted to soil particles (clay) and are held on the surface of these particles. This is known as **adsorption**. The clay particles also contain ions of their own and they release these particles in the exchange. The smaller the particle, the more ion exchange that takes place. Colloidal clay particles are the smallest type of clay particles; they are less than 0.001mm in size, but they have the greatest capacity for ion exchange. (Ion exchange is discussed in detail in Chapter 21.)

Organic matter

Organic matter consists of the remains of plants and animals. The type of organic matter found in soil varies in terms of its source and the size of the particles. Some of it is clearly visible, e.g. twigs, leaves and dead insects, and it is not decomposed. The organic matter that has decomposed is called humus. Humus particles are small.

Similar to mineral matter, the size of the particles of organic matter has an effect on their contribution to the soil's properties.

Humus: The dark-coloured, decomposed plant and animal matter found in soil. It is rich in nutrients and contributes to soil structure.

Table 20.2 Effect of organic matter particle size on soil properties

Large particles of organic matter	Small particles of organic matter
Large pore spaces between particles: • Improve drainage • Do not contribute to ion exchange	Small pore spaces between particles: • Provide a source of nutrients for plant growth • Important in ion exchange • Colloidal humus has a higher rate of ion exchange than colloidal clay

Experiment 20.1

To determine the organic matter content of a soil

Note: All organic matter contains carbon, which is combustible (it can be burned). In this experiment the organic matter will be removed from the soil by burning it off.

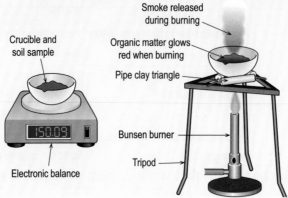

Smoke released during burning

Crucible and soil sample

Organic matter glows red when burning

Pipe clay triangle

Bunsen burner

Tripod

150.09

Electronic balance

|||||| Fig 20.3 Organic matter experiment

Materials
Soil sample, electronic balance/weighing scales, tripod stand, Bunsen burner, crucible, pipe clay triangle, tongs

Method
1   Weigh an empty crucible and record its mass in the table below. (A)

2   Add a sample of soil to the crucible and record its mass. (B)

3   Subtract the mass of the crucible from the combined mass of the crucible and soil sample to calculate the mass of the soil. (C)

4   Put the crucible on the pipe clay triangle on the tripod stand.

5   Heat the soil in the crucible with the Bunsen burner. The humus (organic matter) should glow red as it burns and smoke will be produced. Continue to burn off the humus until there is no more smoke and it does not glow.

6   Remove the crucible from the tripod with tongs and reweigh, noting its mass. (D)

7   Calculate the loss of mass in the soil by subtracting the mass of the crucible and burned soil (D) from the mass of the crucible and soil before burning. (B)

Table 20.3 Results	
Mass of crucible (A)	= g
Mass of crucible + soil sample (B)	= g
Mass of soil = B−A (C)	= g
Mass of crucible + burned soil sample (D)	= g
Soil mass after burning = D−A	= g
Mass of organic matter = C−E	
Calculation of percentage of organic matter in soil:	

$$\frac{\text{Mass of organic matter}}{\text{Mass of original soil sample}} \times \frac{100}{1} = \text{percentage organic matter}$$

☰ Physical Properties of Soil

The physical properties of soil play a large role in determining its suitability for crop growth. The physical properties of soil are as follows:

- Soil texture
- Soil structure
- Soil porosity and density
- Soil colour
- Soil temperature.

> **Soil texture**: A measure of the proportion of different size mineral particles (sand, silt, clay) that are found in a sample of soil.

Soil texture

Soil texture has a huge influence on a soil's characteristics. It is a permanent property of the soil that cannot be changed. Sand, silt and clay particles all have different properties that affect drainage, aeration and fertility. Therefore, the proportions of these mineral particles in the soil influence the water and nutrients available to crops, the aeration of the soil, the drainage of the soil, and how easy it is to cultivate.

The proportions of sand, silt and clay in a soil determine the soil texture. An ideal soil for cultivation contains 40 per cent sand, 40 per cent silt and 20 per cent clay. A loam soil contains equal amounts of all three soil particles.

> **Loam**: A soil that contains equal amounts of sand, silt and clay.

There are a number of ways of determining the texture of a soil. Three of these methods are outlined in the following experiments.

Experiment 20.2

To determine the soil texture of a soil sample by how it feels

Materials
Soil samples, water

Method

1 Take a dry sample of soil and rub it between your thumb and fingers. Take note of its grittiness or smoothness.

2 Wet the soil sample with some water and rub it between your finger and thumb, again noting its grittiness or smoothness. Also, note the plasticity (ability to be moulded) of the sample; check if the wet sample is sticky or not. Use the flow chart (see Fig 20.5 overleaf) to identify the texture of the soil sample.

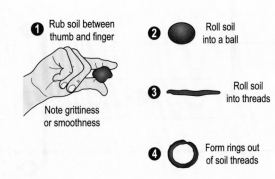

▦ Fig 20.4 Soil testing by feel method

Experiment 20.2

3 Roll the sample into a ball. Record if this is possible or not.

4 Roll the sample into threads on a flat surface. Record if this is possible or not. If the soil can be rolled into threads, attempt to make a ring out of the thread. Record your observations.

5 Compare your results with the flow chart below.

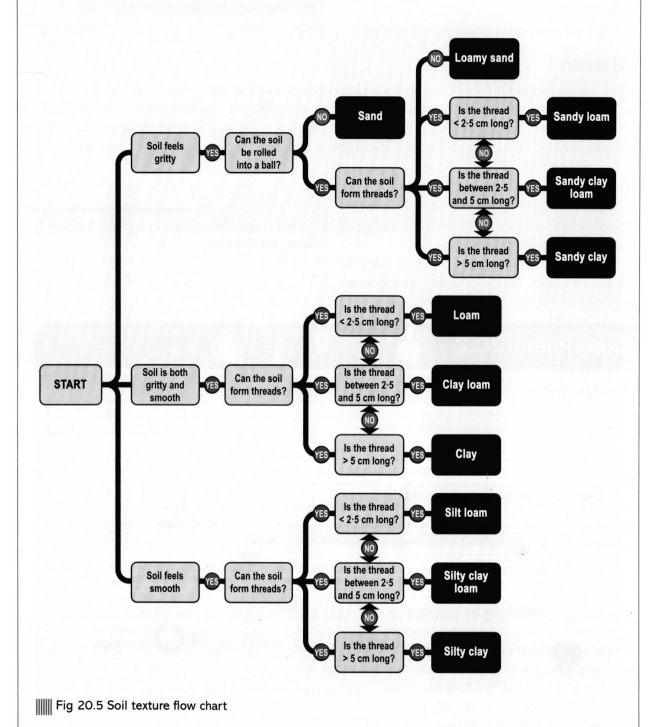

|||| Fig 20.5 Soil texture flow chart

Experiment 20.3

To determine the soil texture of a soil sample by sedimentation

Note: Sedimentation is the process that occurs when particles of a material (in this case soil) settle at the bottom of a container of liquid. The largest particles settle at the bottom, with the smaller particles forming layers above them.

Materials
Soil sample, graduated cylinder, water, stopper, beaker, stirring rod

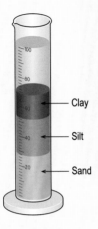

||||| Fig 20.6 Soil texture sedimentation experiment

Method

1 Add a sample of soil to a beaker of water and stir it with the stirring rod to break up any large lumps of soil.

2 Pour the mixture of soil and water into the graduated cylinder, rinsing all soil from the beaker into the cylinder. Add enough water to cover the soil completely.

3 Place a stopper on the cylinder and shake it to mix the soil and water thoroughly.

4 Leave to settle for a few hours or overnight.

5 Observe the layers that have settled in the graduated cylinder. Sand settles at the bottom, silt above the sand layer and clay on top of the silt.

6 Using the graduation marks on the cylinder, record the amount of sand, silt and clay in the soil sample as a percentage of the total soil solids.

Table 20.4 The percentages of sand, silt and clay in a soil sample		
Sand %	Silt %	Clay %

Use the soil triangle (see Fig 20.8, page 167) to help you to classify your soil sample.

Experiment 20.4

To determine the soil texture of a soil sample using a soil sieve

Materials

Soil sample, oven, pestle and mortar, electronic balance, weighing boats

||||| Fig20.7 Soil sieve

Method

1 Place the soil sample in an oven to dry it out completely.

2 When the soil is dry, crush it with a pestle and mortar.

3 Weigh an empty weighing boat; place the crushed sample into the boat and re-weigh. Subtract the mass of the empty boat to calculate the mass of the soil.

4 Place the crushed soil sample in the largest soil sieve. Place the cover on the sieve and shake.

5 Remove the cover from the sieve and separate out each sieve.

6 Weigh the empty weighing boats.

7 Pour the contents of each sieve into separate pre-weighed boats.

8 Weigh each sample in turn.

9 Calculate each separate sample of sand, silt and clay as a percentage of the total soil mass.

10 Use the soil triangle (see Fig 20.8, page 167) to classify your soil sample.

Determination of soil textural class

The soil textural triangle in Fig 20.8 is used to classify a soil sample by the proportions of sand, silt and clay it contains. The percentages of sand, silt and clay are marked out on each side of the triangle. Coarse sand and fine sand are grouped together under sand for classification purposes.

How to use the soil triangle

▨ Taking the three percentage values of sand, silt and clay determined by sedimentation or by using a soil sieve, mark the percentage clay on the left-hand side of the triangle along the scale for clay.

▨ Draw a line from this mark across the triangle, parallel to the side marked 'Percentage sand'.

▨ Mark the percentage silt on the scale for silt on the right-hand side of the triangle. Draw a line from this mark, parallel to the 'Percentage clay' side.

▨ The two lines drawn should intersect in the triangle. The area in which they intersect gives the name of the soil texture of the sample.

▨ To confirm the soil texture of the sample, mark the percentage sand on the bottom of the soil triangle and draw a line parallel to the 'Percentage silt' side of the triangle. The three lines should meet, confirming the soil texture of the sample.

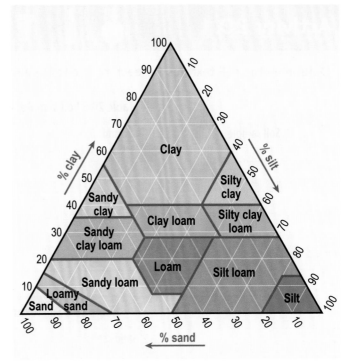

▥ Fig 20.8 Soil triangle

Activity 20.1

Example

A soil sieve was used to determine the percentage sand, silt and clay in a soil sample. The percentages were determined to be: sand 50%, silt 20%, and clay 30%. Use the soil textural triangle to determine the soil texture of the sample.

1 Place a mark at 30 on the clay scale and draw a line across the triangle parallel to the percentage sand scale.

2 Place a mark at 20 in the silt scale and draw a line across the triangle parallel to the percentage clay scale.

3 The two lines intersect in the sandy clay loam section of the triangle. This shows that the sample is a sandy clay loam.

4 To confirm this classification, place a mark at 50 on the sand scale and draw a line parallel to the percentage silt scale. This line will intersect with the other two lines in the sandy clay loam section of the triangle.

Activity 20.1

Determine the soil textures for each of the following soil samples:

Table 20.5 Soil samples for classification			
Soil sample	Sand %	Silt %	Clay %
A	22	24	54
B	41	4	16
C	31	57	12
D	27	43	30
E	48	10	42

Table 20.6 Soil textural properties			
	Sandy soils[1]	Loam soils[2]	Clay soils[3]
Drainage	Well-drained, free draining	Good drainage	Poor drainage
Aeration	Well aerated	Good aeration	Poor aeration
Fertility	Low fertility	Good fertility	Fertile, retain nutrients
Tillage capabilities	Easily tilled	Easily tilled	Not suited to tillage due to plasticity
Temperature	Warm up quickly in spring	Will warm up in spring	Do not warm up due to lack of aeration. Cold soils
Drought/Waterlogging	Prone to drought, do not get waterlogged	Will retain water but will not become waterlogged or be prone to drought	Retain water during drought but are prone to waterlogging and poaching by animals

1   **Sandy soils**: sand, loamy sand.
2   **Loam soils**: loam, sandy loam, silt loam, clay loam.
3   **Clay soils**: clay, silty clay, silty clay loam.

☰ Soil Structure

Soil structure describes the arrangement of soil particles within a soil. Sand, silt and clay particles are the primary particles from which soil is composed. They form clusters in the soil known as aggregates or peds. It is the coming together of these aggregates that determine the soil pore space. As pore space determines how much water and air is in the soil, this is an important characteristic of soil. A good soil structure has a large volume of pores: 50 per cent of the total soil volume and approximately half the pores are filled with air and the other half with water.

Good soil structure is necessary for the following:

- Drainage of excess water.
- Retention of water for plant growth.
- Air movement within the soil.
- Root penetration.
- Emergence of seedlings.

As the primary soil particles aggregate, pores are formed between the particles within the aggregates. These are called micropores. As the aggregates cluster together more pores are formed between the aggregate units. These are called macropores. Both micropores and macropores are necessary for good soil structure. A well-structured soil containing approximately 50 per cent pore space contains both micropores and macropores.

A poorly structured soil typically does not form aggregates. As a result, the only pore space within this soil is between the primary soil particles, and may be as low as 20 per cent.

Aggregate formation

An aggregate is formed when sand, silt and clay particles cluster together. They are held together by the clay particles and other polymers. These particles are colloidal clay and colloidal organic matter particles. The process by which the particles join together is known as flocculation.

> **Flocculation:** The clustering together of soil particles to create larger structures called floccules.

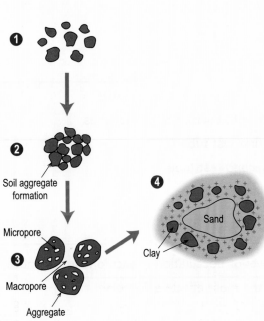

Soil aggregate formation

Micropore

Macropore

Aggregate

Sand

Clay

How flocculation occurs

1   Chemical reactions in the soil cause the formation of negative charges on the soil colloids.

2   Cations (ions with positive charges) are attracted to these charges and are adsorbed onto the surface of the soil colloids. Water between the soil colloids becomes charged (polarised) and acts as a link between the colloids. The colloids are linked together by the polarised water and this is known as a floccule. The floccule is essentially a chain of colloidal particles held together by water and the force of attraction between the water and the cations.

3   The floccules then trap larger particles such as sand and silt, forming aggregates.

Fig 20.9 Soil structure flocculation

Cations that promote flocculation: → Al^{3+}, Fe^{3+}, Ca^{2+}, Mg^{2+}, H^+, K^+, Na^+

Experiment 20.5

To show flocculation in a soil

Materials

Clay soil, deionised water, test tubes, test-tube rack, stoppers, droppers, 0.1M hydrochloric acid (HCl), 0.1M sodium chloride (NaCl), 0.05M calcium chloride ($CaCl_2$), 0.02M aluminium chloride ($AlCl_3$)

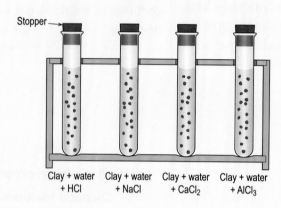

Stopper

Clay + water + HCl   Clay + water + NaCl   Clay + water + $CaCl_2$ Clay + water + $AlCl_3$

Fig 20.10 Flocculation experiment

Method

1 Add 1 g of clay to 100 cm³ of deionised water and mix thoroughly.
2 Pour 10 cm³ of the clay-water suspension into each of four test tubes.
3 Add 1.0 cm³ of hydrochloric acid to the first test tube.
4 Add 1.0 cm³ of sodium chloride to the second test tube.
5 Add 1.0 cm³ of calcium chloride to the third test tube.
6 Add 1.0 cm³ of aluminium chloride to the fourth test tube.
7 Place a stopper on each test tube and shake to mix.
8 Observe the test tubes and record the level of flocculation in each one at 5-minute intervals.
9 Determine which reagent (chemical) was the most effective flocculant.

Structural development of a soil

All soils are structureless to begin with. Soil particles join together to form aggregates and over time a soil develops and becomes structured. Other activities can also influence the development of soil structure. Some of these activities are climatic, some are biological or chemical and some are human influenced. All of the activities that influence soil structure can be classified either as cementation or separation processes.

Cementation: The binding together of soil particles, e.g. when silt and sand particles are cemented together in aggregates during flocculation by clay particles.

Separation: Soil aggregates are broken up within the soil. Large cracks may develop in the soil and this damages its overall structure.

Factors affecting structural development

▦ **Freezing and thawing**: Water in the soil expands and contracts, causing a change in the soil volume. This leads to aggregation of soil.

▦ **Wetting and drying**: Causes the soil volume to change as it expands and shrinks. As the soil dries out, the particles are cemented together. When the soil is wet again, the soil breaks up and cracks may form.

▦ **Soil organic matter**: Provides a substrate for building aggregates. The presence of organic matter in the soil will lead to aggregation of the soil, particularly in the upper horizons.

▦ **Plant root activity**: Small roots compact the soil and bind it together. The roots of larger plants and trees can break up the soil, forming cracks in the structure.

▦ **Animal activity**: Small burrowing animals, in particular earthworms, contribute to soil compaction, forming aggregates. Earthworms also contribute to the organic matter in the soil through the ingestion and egestion of soil.

▦ **Cultivation and tillage**: Agricultural activities such as ploughing and harrowing break up soil and encourage aggregation.

Soil porosity

Porosity refers to the total volume of the soil occupied by soil pores. A soil with good structure should have 50 per cent of its volume occupied by soil pores. These pores are filled with air and water. Approximately half of the pores are air filled and the other half occupied by water. The levels of water and air in the soil can fluctuate with heavy rainfall or drought conditions.

The number of pores present in a soil and the size of the pores are also important factors in determining the characteristics of a soil.

Soil air

Air is necessary in the soil for plant root respiration. Soil air has almost the same composition as atmospheric air; the main difference is the higher level of carbon dioxide in soil air than in atmospheric air, and there is a lower level of oxygen in soil air than in the atmosphere. The main reason is that the plant roots take in oxygen when they are respiring and release carbon dioxide. This leads to a depletion of oxygen in the soil and a build up of carbon dioxide.

A continual depletion of oxygen and subsequent build up of carbon dioxide will negatively affect crop growth and development. The plant will be starved due to a lack of oxygen, but will be affected also by carbon dioxide toxicity.

It is important for crop growth that the carbon dioxide can be continually removed from the soil to the atmosphere and that oxygen will be replaced. This process is known as diffusion.

Carbon dioxide will diffuse from the soil into the atmosphere and oxygen will diffuse from the atmosphere into the soil. Diffusion of carbon dioxide and oxygen is dependent on there being

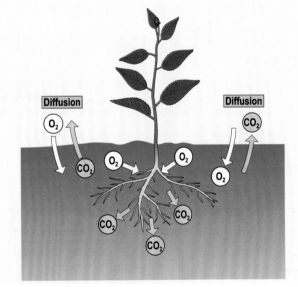

||||| Fig 20.11 Soil air root respiration

sufficiently large pores in the soil for this process to take place. Soils with a good soil structure have sufficient pore spaces for diffusion to take place. A soil with poor structure has a lesser number of air-filled pores. Crops can fail if the level of air-filled pores drops drastically.

Soil aeration can be improved by mechanical means. Compacted soil can be broken up using a subsoiler. A subsoiler is also used to break up compacted soil that has been repeatedly ploughed at the same depth. This layer of compaction is known as the plough pan.

Experiment 20.6

To compare the total pore space in a structured soil and a structureless soil (to calculate the total pore space of a soil sample)

Materials
Soil sample, pestle and mortar, two graduated cylinders, water

Method
1 Take a dry sample of soil, and add 50 g of the sample to a graduated cylinder.

2 Tap the cylinder to remove any large air pockets in the soil.

3 Record the volume of soil in the cylinder.

4 Take another 50 g sample of the same soil and crush it with a pestle and mortar. Add this soil to a second graduated cylinder.

5 Measure out 50 cm³ of water and add it to the first cylinder. Repeat for the second cylinder.

6 Allow the cylinders to stand for an hour. Record the total volume of soil and water in each cylinder.

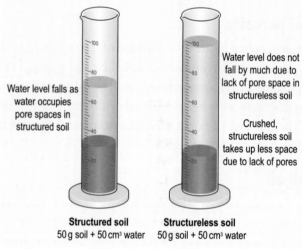

Water level falls as water occupies pore spaces in structured soil

Water level does not fall by much due to lack of pore space in structureless soil

Crushed, structureless soil takes up less space due to lack of pores

Structured soil
50 g soil + 50 cm³ water

Structureless soil
50 g soil + 50 cm³ water

▌▌▌ Fig 20.12 Effect of soil structure on pore space

Results

Table 20.7 Results	Structured soil	Structureless soil
Initial volume of soil (A)	____ ml	____ ml
Total volume of soil and water (B)	____ ml	____ ml
Total volume when soil and water combine (C)	____ ml	____ ml
Volume of water occupying pore spaces (B–C)	____ ml	____ ml
Percentage of soil that is pore space: $\dfrac{\text{Pore space (B–C)}}{\text{Volume of soil (A)}} \times \dfrac{100}{1}$		

Compare the percentage pore space for the structured soil and the structureless soil.

Soil Water

The size of pores is important in determining water levels in soil. Large soil pores are needed for adequate drainage, while small soil pores are needed for water retention for plant uptake.

Sandy soils, because of their larger particles, tend to have large pores, which lead to good drainage in the soil, but can also contribute to drought in a prolonged period of dry weather, as the soil is unable to retain water.

Clay soils, which contain the smallest particles, also contain the smallest pores. These pores are better at retaining water, but a soil with high clay content may also become waterlogged.

An ideal soil, such as a loam soil, contains sand, silt and clay in equal amounts and, as a result, contains an equal proportion of large and small pores that provides good drainage, while retaining enough water for plant uptake.

Water is held in soil by adsorption and capillary action. Adsorbed water is held on the surface of the soil particles as it is polarised (positively charged) and is attracted to negative charges on the soil particles. The water forms a thin film around the surface of the soil particles. This water is unavailable to plants and cannot be removed from the soil by their roots. Adsorbed water is also known as hygroscopic water.

> **Hygroscopic water** (adsorbed water): Water forms a thin film around a soil particle and is held on the surface of the particle by force of attraction. It cannot be removed from the soil and is unavailable to plants.

Capillary action occurs when water is drawn into pores in the soil and is drawn upwards through the soil against the force of gravity. The water molecules are attracted to the soil particles and held in the soil by adsorption. The water molecules are also attracted to other water molecules in the soil. The smaller the pores in the soil, the more water will be held in the pores and the further it will travel upwards through the soil. Therefore, water is drained from large cracks in the soil but is retained in the smaller pores. The following experiment demonstrates capillary action in a sandy soil and a clay soil.

Experiment 20.7

To demonstrate capillary action in a sandy soil and a clay soil

Materials
Sample of sandy soil, sample of clay soil, two open-ended glass tubes of equal size, water trough, cotton wool or muslin cloth, rubber bands, water, cress seeds (optional), ruler

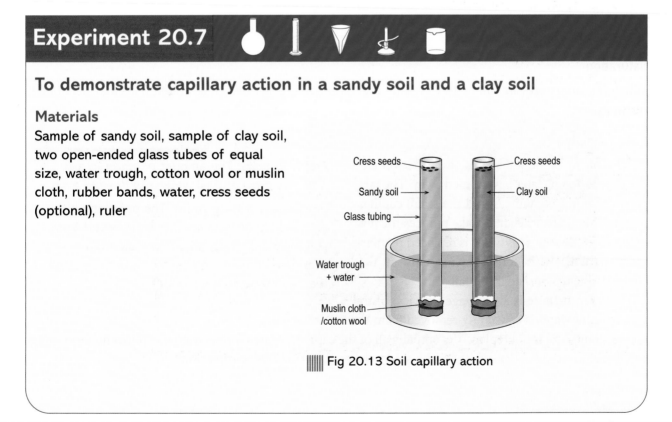

||||| Fig 20.13 Soil capillary action

Experiment 20.7

Method

1. Plug the ends of both tubes with cotton wool or cover the ends of each tube with muslin cloth and hold in place with rubber bands.
2. Fill the first tube with sandy soil. Fill the second tube with an equal amount of clay soil.
3. Stand both tubes in a water trough as shown in Fig 20.13.
4. Leave the tubes in the water trough for a few hours.
5. Observe the tubes and note any rise in water level in each tube. Use a ruler to measure the level to which the water has risen. Compare the level in the sandy soil with the clay soil to determine which soil had the greatest capillary action.

Option: Add an equal number of cress seeds to the surface of the soil in each tube. The cress seeds will germinate if the water rises to a sufficient level so that it is available to the seeds for germination.

Capillary water

Capillary water is held in the pores within the soil aggregates and in the pores between the soil aggregates. Capillary water that is held within small pores within the soil aggregates is unavailable to plants. Capillary water that is held in large pores between the soil aggregates is available for plant uptake.

Gravitational water

Gravitational water is moved through the soil by gravity. It is found in cracks in the soil and large soil pores. It is normally only available on a temporary basis to plants (e.g. after heavy rainfall) as it drains away quickly. Air fills the pores when the gravitational water has drained away.

Water availability in the soil

Saturation

When the large pores are full of gravitational water, the soil is described as saturated. This may occur after heavy rainfall.

Field capacity

Field capacity is the water present in the soil after the gravitational water has drained away. The large capillary pores contain air and the small capillary pores contain water. Plant uptake reduces the level of water in the soil. This water is replaced regularly from rainfall. Irish soils are normally at field capacity due to consistent rainfall.

However, if there is a prolonged period of dry weather and water is constantly removed from the soil by plants and is not replaced, eventually all of the capillary water will be used up. When no more water can be removed from the soil, the soil is said to be at its permanent wilting point.

Field capacity: The amount of water in a soil after the gravitational water has drained away.

Permanent wilting point: The point at which no more capillary water can be removed from a soil (by plant roots). Plants will die from drought if the soil in which they are growing reaches its permanent wilting point.

Available water capacity

Soils that retain a high volume of water such as clay soils do not necessarily have a high available water capacity. This is because much of the water retained in clay soils is found in capillary pores and is hygroscopic water, which is unavailable to plants.

> **Available water capacity**: The amount of water between the field capacity and permanent wilting point that is available for absorption by plant roots.
> Available water capacity =
> field capacity – permanent wilting point.

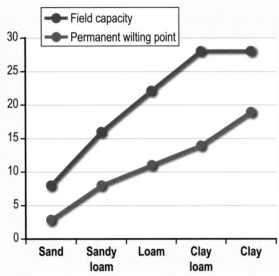

Fig 20.14 Field capacity and permanent wilting point for a range of soil textures

As can be seen from the graph, clay soils have a high field capacity. However, they also have a high permanent wilting point, which means the available water capacity of these soils is quite small. This is due to the high number of small capillary pores found in clay soils. The water in these pores is unavailable to plants. The water in these pores is also hygroscopic in nature and cannot be removed from the soil.

In contrast, loam and clay loam soils have a much lower permanent wilting point, giving a higher available water capacity. This means that there is a greater volume of water available for plant uptake in these soils.

Experiment 20.8

To compare the infiltration rate (drainage) in a sandy soil and a clay soil

Materials
Sample of sandy soil, sample of clay soil, retort stands, water, beakers, filter paper, filter funnels, graduated cylinders, stopwatch

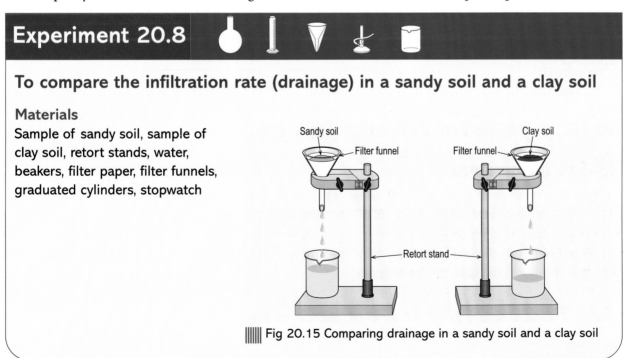

Fig 20.15 Comparing drainage in a sandy soil and a clay soil

Experiment 20.8

Method

1   Set up apparatus as show in Fig 20.15. Line a filter funnel with filter paper and fill it with sandy soil. Repeat with the second funnel but fill it with an equal amount of clay soil.

2   Using a graduated cylinder measure out 20 cm³ of water and pour it into a beaker. Repeat with a second beaker.

3   Pour each beaker of water into one of the soil samples at the same time.

4   Drainage and infiltration rates can be measured in two ways:

   (a) Use a stopwatch to time how long it takes for the first drop of water to pass through the soil and be collected in the beaker below the funnel for each sample.
   Or

   (b) Use a stopwatch for a set time, e.g. five minutes, 10 minutes, to measure the volume of water that passes through each soil sample in the time allowed. Compare the results of both samples.

Result

The soil with the best drainage/infiltration rate will have the higher volume of water pass through it in the time allowed. The time taken for a drop of water to pass through this soil will also be the shorter of the two.

Soil Colour

In terms of physical properties, the colour of a soil indicates its humus and mineral content. A soil that is a dark, brown-black colour is usually rich in humus. These types of soils have high fertility and nutrient content. The high humus content leads to good soil structure. Dark-coloured soils also absorb more sunlight and so are warm soils.

As humus tends to be found in the top layer of soil, it may be necessary to examine the subsoil and lower horizons to assess the soil colour. Soils that are light-coloured or grey tend to be low in fertility, low in nutrients and lacking in humus. This is particularly true of the soil horizons nearest the surface. These soils can suffer from leaching, where the minerals are washed out of the soil or accumulate in a lower horizon in the subsoil.

Red colouring in soil indicates the presence of iron. Often iron is leached from the upper layers of the soil and accumulates in the lower horizons where it forms an iron pan, which may be impermeable to water and roots. This will be characterised by a thin, red layer in the subsoil.

Soil Temperature

Air that is found in pores in the soil is more easily heated than water. Therefore, it is more advantageous to have a well-drained sandy soil or a loam soil for crop growth, as this soil will warm up quicker in springtime. Soil temperature is an important factor in crop growth as cold temperatures will slow or stunt the growth of a crop. The rate of chemical reactions doubles with every 10°C rise in temperature (Van't Hoff's Law) so the warmer the soil, the faster the growth rate.

Summary

- Soil consists of mineral matter (45%), air (25%), water (25%) and organic matter (5%).

- The five types of mineral particle found in soil are: gravel, course sand, fine sand, silt and clay.

- Gravel and sand lead to good drainage and aeration. Silt and clay are good for water retention and clay has high fertility levels.

- Ion exchange takes place in soil where ions are attracted to soil particles (clay) and are held on the surface of these particles.

- Organic matter consists of the remains of plants and animals.

- Humus is the dark-coloured, decomposed plant and animal matter found in soil. It is rich in nutrients and contributes to soil structure.

- The physical properties of soil are texture, structure, porosity and density, colour and temperature.

- Soil texture is a measure of the proportion of different size mineral particles (sand, silt, clay) that are found in a sample of soil.

- Loam soil contains equal amounts of sand, silt and clay.

- Soil structure describes the arrangement of soil particles within a soil. A good soil structure has a large volume of pores – 50 per cent of the total soil volume and approximately half the pores are filled with air and the other half with water.

- Flocculation is the clustering together of soil particles to create larger structures called floccules.

- Cementation: The binding together of soil particles.

- Separation: Soil aggregates are separated within the soil.

- Structural development is affected by freezing and thawing, wetting and drying, soil organic matter, plant root activity, animal activity, cultivation, and tillage.

- Porosity refers to the total volume of the soil occupied by soil pores.

- Hygroscopic water (adsorbed water) forms a thin film around a soil particle and is held on the surface of the particle by the force of attraction. It cannot be removed from the soil and is unavailable to plants.

- Capillary water is held in the pores **within** the soil aggregates and in the pores **between** the soil aggregates.

- Gravitational water is moved through the soil by gravity.

- Field capacity is the amount of water in a soil after the gravitational water has drained away.

- Permanent wilting point: The point at which no more capillary water can be removed from a soil (by plant roots).

- Available water capacity is the amount of water between the field capacity and permanent wilting point that is available for absorption by plant roots.

- The colour of a soil can indicate the humus and mineral content of a soil.

- The rate of chemical reactions doubles with every 10°C rise in temperature (Van't Hoff's Law) so the warmer the soil, the faster the growth rate.

QUESTIONS

1 What is the ideal composition of soil? Draw a diagram to demonstrate this.
2 Why is the air and water content of soil so variable?
3 Soil is made up of particles of varying size. Starting with the largest, name the five types of particle that make up soil.
4 Describe the properties of soils that contain sand and gravel under the following headings: pore space, drainage, aeration, and fertility.
5 Describe the properties of soils that contain silt and clay under the following headings: particles size, aeration, fertility, and water logging.
6 What is ion exchange?
7 What are colloidal clay particles?
8 What types of material does organic matter consist of?
9 What is humus?
10 List four advantages of the presence of organic matter in the soil.
11 List five physical properties of soil.
12 What is a loam soil?
13 A student tested a soil by the feel method to determine its texture. She found on testing that the soil was smooth and could form threads between 2.5 and 5 cm long. Use the flow chart of soil textures to determine the soil texture of the soil sample.
14 A student tested a soil using a soil sieve. He found that in a 100 g soil sample 30 g was sand, 60 g was silt and 10 g was clay. Identify the soil texture of the soil using the soil triangle.
15 What are the advantages and disadvantages (two of each) of (a) sandy soils, (b) clay soils?
16 Why are loam soils considered to have the best soil texture?
17 What is meant by the term *soil structure*?
18 List three reasons why a good soil structure is necessary.
19 What is an aggregate or ped?
20 What is meant by the term *flocculation*? How does flocculation occur?
21 List two cations that promote flocculation.
22 List three factors that affect the structural development of a field.
23 What is meant by the term *soil porosity*?
24 What factor contributes to the difference between atmospheric air and soil air? Explain how it contributes to this difference.
25 What is diffusion?
26 How can a crop be affected if the air in the soil is less than 25 per cent?
27 How can poor aeration occur? How can this be rectified?
28 With regard to water, what is the role of the large soil pores?
29 What is hygroscopic water?
30 Explain capillary action.
31 What is gravitational water?
32 Explain what is meant when a soil is described as saturated.
33 When is soil at field capacity?
34 When is a soil at permanent wilting point?
35 What is the available water capacity of a soil?
36 Why does a clay soil have a lower available water capacity than a clay loam or a loam soil?
37 What information can be determined about a soil sample if it is (a) dark brown, (b) red and (c) grey?
38 Why is air temperature in the soil considered an important factor when growing crops?

EXAM QUESTIONS

1 (a) List four factors that are responsible for the development of soil structure.
   (b) Describe an experiment to estimate the percentage organic matter in a soil sample.
       (LC, HL, 2010)
2 Describe a laboratory or field method to determine the texture of a sample of wet soil. (LC, HL, 2010)
3 Explain the following terms as used in the context of plant growth in soil:
   (a) Field capacity
   (b) Permanent wilting point
   (c) Available water. (LC, HL, 2008)
4 The following table shows the water content of three soil samples.

Table 20.8		
Soil sample	% Water at field capacity	% Water at wilting point
A	6	2
B	24	12
C	30	22

   (a) What is the percentage of available water in sample A?
   (b) Which sample would be the most suitable for a crop suffering a drought during the growing season?
   (c) Which sample would be the most suitable for a crop growing during a wet spring?
   (d) Describe an experiment to compare the capillarity of two contrasting soils. (LC, HL, 2007)
5 (a) State two differences in composition between soil air and atmospheric air.
   (b) Explain how any one of the differences you have mentioned occurs.
   (c) Describe an experiment that compares the movement of water by capillarity within two contrasting soils.
   (d) Describe a laboratory or field experiment to show the effect of structure formation on total pore space in soils. (LC, HL, 2007)
6 State three reasons why texture is an important soil property. (LC, HL, 2006)

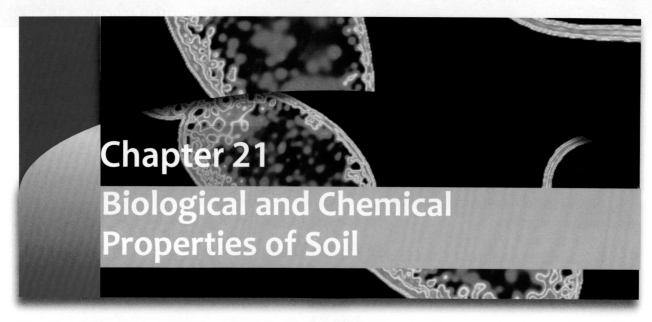

Chapter 21
Biological and Chemical Properties of Soil

The chemically active particles in soil are the clay and humus particles. These are also the smallest particles found in a soil. Clay and humus both have positive and negative charges on their surfaces. These charges attract ions of the opposite charge. These ions are necessary for plant nutrition and also influence the acidity or alkalinity of the soil.

≣ Chemical Properties of Soil

Two chemical properties are important in determining the characteristics of a soil:
1 Cation exchange capacity (CEC)
2 pH.

Cation exchange capacity

Cations are positively charged ions such as H^+, K^+, Ca^{2+}. Positively charged cations are attracted to negatively charged humus and clay particles. They are held on the surface (adsorbed) as the opposite charges of the particles attract each other. Clay and humus particles can release cations that are adsorbed onto their surfaces and replace them with other cations. The ability of soil particles to attract, retain and release cations is called cation exchange.

Soil colloids are the smallest particles that exist in the soil. They are also the most chemically active. Colloidal clay and colloidal humus have the highest rates of cation exchange in the soil. The amount or volume of cation exchange that can take place on a soil particle is known as its cation exchange capacity (CEC).

The cations are released into the soil through weathering. Cations are present in the water in the soil, known as soil solution. A cation with two positive charges (e.g. Ca^{2+}) can displace (take the place of) two separate cations each with one positive charge (K^+).

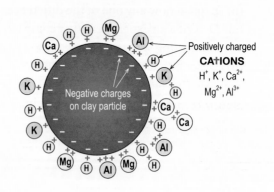

|||| Fig 21.1 Soil cations

Cation exchange capacity (CEC): The quantity of cations that a soil absorbs. It can also be described as the capacity of a soil to exchange cations between the soil surfaces and the soil solution (water).

Cation exchange is constantly taking place. Cations are removed from the soil solution by plant roots and replaced through cation exchange between the soil solution and the soil particles.

> **Cation exchange**: The ability of soil particles (clay and humus) to attract, retain and release cations.

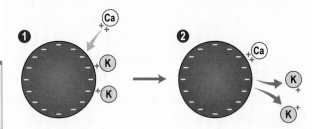

Fig 21.2 Cation exchange soil colloid

Experiment 21.1

To demonstrate cation exchange capacity in a soil

Materials
Dry soil sample with high pH, filter paper, funnel, dropper, beaker, potassium chloride, ammonium oxalate

Method
1   Add 5 g of dry, sieved soil to the filter funnel.

2   Use a dropper to add potassium chloride solution to the soil, drop by drop. Collect the water that filters from the soil in a beaker. This is known as the leachate.

3   Test the leachate for calcium by adding ten drops of ammonium oxalate to the leachate. If a white precipitate is formed calcium is present.

4   Discard the leachate and repeat the experiment by adding more KCl to the soil and testing the leachate for calcium.

5   Repeat until the leachate does not test positive for calcium.

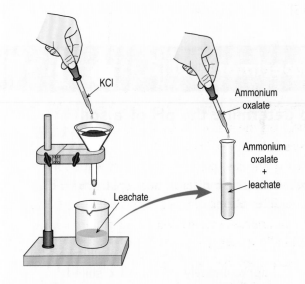

Fig 21.3 Potassium-calcium ion exchange

Result
The soil that initially contained calcium ions has undergone cation exchange and the potassium ions have replaced the calcium ions.

pH

The term pH refers to the concentration of hydrogen ions in a solution and their activity. The solution in this case is the soil solution.

The pH scale extends from 0 to 14 where 7 is neutral. Values below 7 are described as acidic and values above 7 are described as alkaline (basic).

pH: A measure of the concentration of the hydrogen ions in a solution. It can also be expressed as the negative log of the hydrogen ion concentration: $-log_{10}[H^+]$.

For each unit decrease on the pH scale the H^+ ion concentration increases by a factor of 10. This means that a pH of 5 is ten times more concentrated than a pH of 6.

The concentration of acidic ions adsorbed on the surface of the soil colloids determines the acidity of the soil. Hydrogen and aluminium ions (H^+ and Al^{3+}) are acidic ions and the soils that they dominate are also acidic. Calcium and magnesium (Ca^{2+} and Mg^{2+}) are alkaline ions and the soils that they dominate are alkaline. Hydrogen ions are derived from carbonic acids and aluminium ions from granite or sandstone. Calcium and magnesium are derived from limestone or from the application of lime to the land.

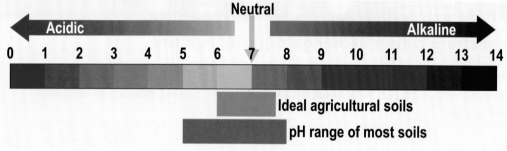

|||||| Fig 21.4 Soil pH scale

Experiment 21.2

To determine the pH of a soil

Materials
Dry soil sample, pH meter, distilled water, pH paper/universal indicator, beaker, stirring rod, funnel filter paper

Method
1 Add 20 g of the soil sample to a beaker. Add approximately 25 cm³ of distilled water to the soil and stir for 5 minutes.

2 Turn on the pH meter and insert the electrode in a beaker of distilled water (pH 7) to ensure that the probe is clean and reading the pH accurately.

3 Insert the electrode into the soil and water mixture. Note the pH reading on the meter. Clean the electrode with distilled water after use.

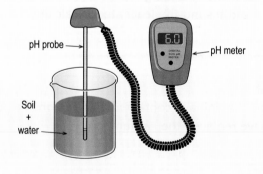

|||||| Fig 21.5 Measuring the pH of soil

Experiment 21.2

Alternative methods for determining pH

(a) If a pH meter is not available, dip a strip of pH paper into the soil and water mixture. Observe the colour change (if any) of the pH paper. Compare the colour of the pH paper with the colour chart supplied to determine the pH of the soil.

(b) If using universal indicator, set up a funnel and place the filter paper in the funnel. Pour the soil and water mixture into the funnel and collect the water that is filtered from the soil in a clean, dry beaker. Add a couple of drops of universal indicator to the water and note the colour. Compare the colour of the indicator with the colour chart supplied to determine the pH of the soil.

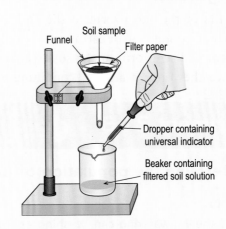

||||| Fig 21.6 Soil pH universal indicator

Importance of pH on soil activity

Most crops will grow in a pH range from 5.5 to 8.5. Some crops will grow at pH levels slightly above or below this range. The optimum pH level for crop growth is between 6.5 and 7.5. Outside these ranges, a very low or very high pH can reduce the availability of nutrients to plants, and certain ions may become abundant in the soil, to the point where they are at toxic levels. The activity of some micro-organisms may decrease because of unsuitable environmental conditions.

☰ Biological Properties of Soil

Soil provides a habitat for a variety of living organisms. The list of organisms is extensive and includes insects, worms, small mammals, fungi and bacteria. These living organisms help to improve the soil through physical activity. Their activities improve the growing conditions available to crops.

Most plants need soil as a medium for growth. They extract water and nutrients from the soil and use it to anchor themselves. Plants also contribute large amounts of organic matter to the soil when they lose their leaves and when they die and their remains decompose. All of these plants and animals are collectively known as soil biomass.

> **Soil biomass:** The total mass of living material in a habitat.
> **Humification:** The process by which soil organic matter is converted to humus.

The plant and animal material that has decomposed is called humus. Humification is the name given to the process of converting organic matter to humus.

Soil organisms

Most humus-forming organisms are microscopic. They feed on plant and animal remains, producing humus. This releases nutrients into the soil, which are then available for plant uptake. This allows nutrients to be recycled continuously. Nutrient recycling is examined in more detail in the carbon cycle and nitrogen cycle (see pages 186, 187). Organisms that the naked eye can see are described as macro-organisms. The earthworm is the most important macro-organism in soil and to the farmer.

Macro-organisms: the earthworm

The benefits of the earthworm to the soil have already been outlined in Chapter 7. The optimum environmental conditions for earthworm populations are in moist soils, rich in organic matter, with a pH close to neutral. Earthworms prefer soils with a pH range of 6 to 8. Earthworm populations are affected by temperature; they prefer warm soil conditions above 12°C.

Experiment 21.3

To determine the population of earthworms in a field or pasture

Materials
Quadrat, shears, watering can, washing up liquid and water solution, bucket, trundle wheel

Method

1   Mark out an area of a field or pasture with a quadrat (1 m², 0.25 m²).

2   Remove all vegetation and ground cover within the quadrat, using shears or scissors.

3   Make up a solution of warm water and washing up liquid.

4   Apply the solution to the area inside the quadrat with a watering can.

5   Wait for a few minutes for the earthworms to come to the surface.

6   Count each worm that comes to the surface and place the worm in a bucket or suitable container so that it will not be counted a second time. Do not count worms that surface outside the quadrat.

7   Record the number of worms that were observed.

||||| Fig 21.7 Water and washing up liquid solution poured inside a quadrat

8   Repeat the experiment in other areas of the field.

9   Calculate an average number of earthworms per quadrat.

Experiment 21.3

Results

Calculate the area of a field by measuring its length and width with a trundle wheel.

- If the quadrat was 1 m², multiply the average number of earthworms by the area of the field in metres squared to calculate the average population for the field.
- If the quadrat was 0.25 m², multiply the earthworm number by four to calculate the number of worms per metre squared and then multiply by the area of the field.

Worked example

A group of students carried out the above experiment to determine the earthworm population of their school football pitch. The pitch was measured with a trundle wheel and was found to be 80 m wide and 130 m long. The students sampled the earthworm population in five areas of the pitch using a 0.25 m² quadrat. The number of earthworms found in each quadrat is shown in Table 21.1.

Table 21.1				
Site 1	Site 2	Site 3	Site 4	Site 5
18	23	20	22	17

Use the above figures to calculate the earthworm population of the pitch.

Area of pitch = 130 m × 80 m = 10 400 m²

Average number of earthworms per 0.25 m² quadrat = $\frac{(18 + 23 + 20 + 22 + 17)}{5}$ = 20

Average number of earthworms per 1 m² = 20 × 4 = 80

Area of pitch x Number of earthworms/m² = 10 400 × 80 = 832 000 worms in the pitch

Types of micro-organisms

- **Bacteria**: Single-celled organisms responsible for converting soil organic matter into humus. They also convert nitrogen into usable forms (nitrogen fixation and nitrification) and convert usable nitrogen into atmospheric nitrogen, which is unavailable for plant use (denitrification) (see The nitrogen cycle, page 187).

- **Actinomycetes**: Mycelial bacteria that have thread-like extensions radiating from their single cell structure. They are responsible for the humification of soil organic matter.

- **Fungi**: Fungi range from microscopic in size to large mushrooms. They are responsible for the humification of soil organic matter. Some species form symbiotic relationships with other living organisms in the habitat. Some fungi are parasitic and can have a detrimental effect on a crop when they attack it.

> **Parasite**: An organism that lives on another host organism. The parasite usually benefits at the expense of the host and may cause damage to the host.

Nutrient recycling: the carbon cycle and the nitrogen cycle

The carbon cycle

All organic matter contains carbon. Most living organisms derive their energy from material that contains carbon. Plants take carbon dioxide from the atmosphere during photosynthesis. Other living organisms produce carbon dioxide when they respire. Many of the microscopic organisms in the soil convert carbon from one form to another in what is known as the carbon cycle.

▦ Plants take in CO_2 from the atmosphere during photosynthesis and convert it to carbohydrate. Plant roots respire, producing carbon dioxide.

▦ Animals eat plants. Animals respire to produce carbon dioxide and animal manure. Plants also produce manure, known as green manure, when they die.

▦ Micro-organisms in the soil break down plant and animal manures. They respire, producing carbon dioxide.

▦ The CO_2 produced by plant roots and soil micro-organisms is converted to carbonate ions in the soil. These can be taken up by plant roots, but can also be lost due to leaching.

▦ Some of the carbon dioxide produced in the soil diffuses back into the atmosphere, where it is used by plants during photosynthesis.

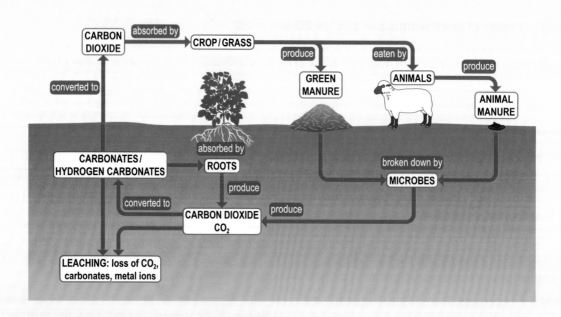

||||| Fig 21.8 The carbon cycle

The nitrogen cycle

Nitrogen, unlike other nutrients, is derived mainly from the atmosphere. It can also be added to the soil through the application of manures and artificial fertilisers. Like carbon, it is converted into usable forms in the soil, which can then be absorbed by plant roots. Nitrogen is converted into a number of different forms in the nitrogen cycle. Bacteria have a fundamental role in the conversion of nitrogen to usable forms.

▓ Nitrogen is applied to the land in the form of artificial fertiliser. N-fertiliser contains compounds such as nitrates, urea and ammonia. The nitrates (NO_3^-) are available immediately for plant uptake. Urea and ammonia must be converted to nitrates by the process of nitrification.

▓ Atmospheric nitrogen diffuses into the soil where it undergoes nitrogen fixation. Nitrogen fixation is the process by which nitrogen gas is converted into nitrates, which can be used by plants. Rhizobium bacteria are an important part of this process. Rhizobium are found in nodules on the roots of leguminous plants such as clover. They form a symbiotic relationship with clover as they fix nitrogen, while at the same time receiving nutrition from the plant tissues. Planting clover in a pasture reduces the need to apply artificial nitrogen fertiliser to the land.

▓ Animals eat plants. Plant and animal manures are added to the soil. This organic matter undergoes mineralisation in the soil, producing ammonium ions (NH_4^+).

▓ The ammonium ions produced from organic matter and the application of fertilisers undergoes nitrification. *Nitrosomonas* bacteria convert ammonium ions to nitrite ions and *Nitrobacter* bacteria convert nitrite ions to usable nitrate ions. Nitrate ions are then available for plant uptake.

▓ Some nitrates are used to provide proteins to soil micro-organisms. They are not available again until the micro-organism dies. This is known as immobilisation.

▓ Some of the nitrates are leached from the soil, while some nitrates undergo denitrification where nitrates are converted to nitrogen gas and nitrogen oxide. These gases are not available to plants and diffuse back into the atmosphere.

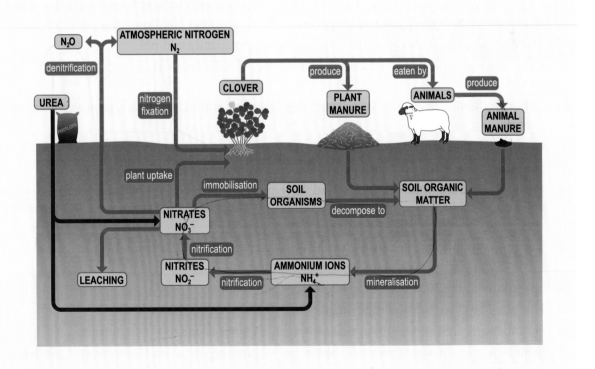

||||| Fig 21.9 The nitrogen cycle

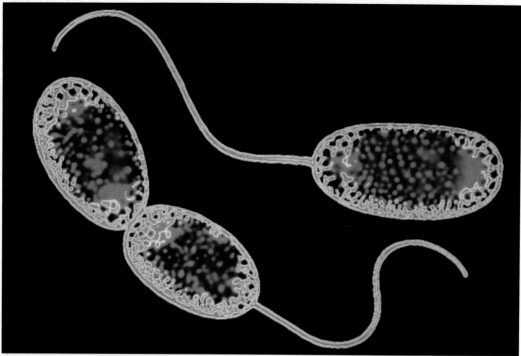

|||||| Fig 21.10 Nitrobacter bacteria

Summary

▨ The smallest and most chemically active particles in soil are clay and humus particles. They attract ions due to the charges on their surfaces, which affect plant nutrition and soil pH.

▨ The chemical properties of soil are: cation exchange capacity and pH.

▨ Cations are positively charged ions that are attracted and adsorbed onto the surface of soil particles.

▨ Cation exchange: The ability of soil particles (clay and humus) to attract, retain and release cations.

▨ Cation exchange capacity (CEC): The quantity of cations that can be adsorbed by a soil.

▨ pH: A measure of the concentration of the hydrogen ions in a solution.

▨ Hydrogen and aluminium ions (H^+ and Al^{3+}) are acidic ions and the soils in which they dominate will also be acidic. Calcium and magnesium (Ca^{2+} and Mg^{2+}) are alkaline ions and the soils in which they dominate will be alkaline.

▨ The optimum pH level for crop growth is between 6.5 and 7.5. Outside these ranges, a very low or very high pH can reduce the availability of nutrients to plants.

▨ Soil biomass: The total mass of living material in a habitat.

▨ Humus: The dead and decomposing remains of plants and animals.

▨ Humification: The process by which soil organic matter is converted to humus.

▨ Symbiotic relationship: A mutually beneficial relationship between two unrelated species.

Summary

- Parasite: An organism that lives on another host organism. The parasite usually benefits at the expense of the host and may cause damage to the host.

- The carbon cycle is the way carbon is used, reused and recycled in nature by living organisms converting it from carbon dioxide (photosynthesis) to carbohydrate and in the soil to carbonate ions.

- The nitrogen cycle is the way in which nitrogen is recycled in nature, being converted from atmospheric nitrogen to ammonia and then to nitrates and nitrites before being converted back into nitrogen gas.

- Nitrification: The conversion of urea and ammonia into nitrates.

- Denitrification: The conversion of nitrates and nitrogen gas.

- Rhizobium bacteria found in the nodules on clover roots have the ability to convert nitrogen gas into nitrates in a process known as nitrogen fixation.

QUESTIONS

1 What is meant by the term *cation exchange*?
2 What is meant by the term *pH*?
3 Name one acidic and one alkaline ion found in the soil.
4 What is the normal pH range for agricultural land in Ireland?
5 When measuring the pH of a soil, the concentration of what solution is actually being measured?
6 How can the pH of a soil be raised?
7 What is soil biomass?
8 What is meant by the term *humification*?
9 Which earthworm activities are of importance to the soil?
10 Earthworm numbers and activities are dependent on a number of environmental factors. List two of these conditions.
11 A group of students carried out a survey of the earthworm population on 1 hectare of land. They sampled the population in five parts of the land using a 1 m² quadrat. The population of worms in each of the five areas was found to be 77, 79, 81, 70, and 73. Calculate the earthworm population per hectare.
12 What bacterial activities are of importance to the soil?
13 What is meant by a symbiotic relationship?
14 What is a parasite?
15 Describe with the aid of a suitable diagram, how the carbon cycle works.
16 What is nitrogen fixation?
17 Which bacteria are needed for nitrogen fixation?
18 With which plants do the bacteria have a symbiotic relationship?
19 What is nitrification? Name the two bacteria involved in the nitrification process.
20 What is denitrification?

EXAM QUESTIONS

1 Describe a laboratory or field method to determine the number of earthworms in a pasture. (LC, HL, 2010)

2 (a) Explain the term *cation exchange capacity* (CEC).
   (b) Mention a soil type where CEC is very low.
   (c) Describe a method by which CEC may be increased in a soil. (LC, HL, 2009)

3 Give three reasons for low earthworm populations in certain soil conditions. (LC, HL, 2009)

4 (a) With the aid of a labelled diagram briefly describe the carbon cycle.
   (b) Suggest one practice farmers could adopt to reduce the carbon footprint of Irish agriculture. (LC, HL, 2009)

5 Describe a laboratory experiment that would demonstrate the phenomenon of cation exchange in a soil. (LC, HL, 2005)

6 Describe in detail any two steps in the nitrogen cycle. (LC, HL, 2006)

Chapter 22

Soil Classification

It is important for farmers to know which types of soil exist on their land. Soil fertility can be improved through fertilisation and liming. Soil structure can be maintained and improved by the addition of organic manures and by crop rotation. However, the overall soil type found on a farm remains largely the same and this must be taken into account when deciding how to use the land. Knowing the type of soil determines what steps can be taken to improve the land.

A general soil profile was outlined in Chapter 19. This chapter examines the profile of specific soil types in greater detail and outlines their agricultural uses and limitations.

The System of Soil Classification

The soils of Ireland are classified using a system that is adapted from an American soil classification system. Under this system, the soils found in Ireland are categorised into ten different groups listed below. The soil profiles of a number of these soils will be studied in greater detail.

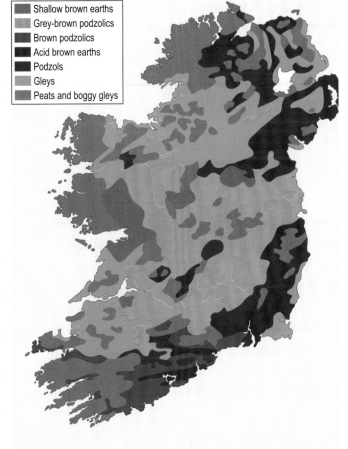

- Shallow brown earths
- Grey-brown podzolics
- Brown podzolics
- Acid brown earths
- Podzols
- Gleys
- Peats and boggy gleys

||||| Fig 22.1 Soil map of Ireland

Soils of Ireland

1 **Podzols**: Acidic, highly leached, waterlogged soils.

2 **Brown podzolics**: Exhibit some leaching, but are suitable for crop production.

3 **Brown earths**: Well-drained, fertile soils with a wide range of agricultural uses.

4 **Grey-brown podzolics**: Good agricultural soils with little leaching.

5 **Gleys**: Poorly structured, waterlogged soils with limited agricultural use.

6 **Blanket peat**: Poorly drained, acidic soils rich in organic material.

7 **Basin peat**: Deep, waterlogged soils, rich in organic matter.

8 **Rendzinas**: Shallow, lime-rich soils overlying limestone. Restricted to grazing.

9 **Regosols:** Lack horizon development, derived from alluvial deposits.

10 **Lithosols:** Shallow, stony soils restricted to rough mountain grazing.

Podzols

Podzols are found overlying acid parent material such as sandstone. They occur in mountainous and hillside areas. They are mainly used for forestry or rough grazing because of their acidic nature. They are prone to leaching of minerals. Acid leaching of minerals causes the leaching of iron and aluminium from the A horizon. This causes bleaching of the A horizon. The minerals accumulate in the B horizon and form an iron-pan. The iron-pan is impermeable to water. This can cause waterlogging above the iron-pan and prevents roots from penetrating deeper into the soil. The iron-pan can be broken up with a subsoiler.

Liming may also be carried out to raise the pH of the soil.

> **Leaching:** Soluble matter, such as minerals, dissolves in water filtering through soil and is carried downward. The leached minerals may accumulate at a lower horizon.
>
> **Podzolisation:** Occurs in acidic pH conditions where minerals such as iron and aluminium are leached from the A horizon, leaving it bleached in colour. They accumulate in the B horizon, forming an iron-pan that is impermeable to water.

- **O horizon:** Organic matter has not decomposed due to the acidic conditions.
- **A horizon:** Thin A1 horizon and thick A2 horizon, bleached in colour due to the leaching of minerals.
- **B horizon:** Red-brown colour due to the accumulation of minerals. Iron-pan is formed at the B2 horizon.

Brown podzolic soils

Brown podzolic soils are found in lowland areas. They are suitable for forestry but can also be used for crops and grazing. Liming and fertilisation contribute to the improvement of these soils. They are similar to podzols in that they are found overlying acid parent materials such as shale, sandstone and granite. However, they are not as severely leached.

- **A horizon:** Large quantity of organic matter in the A1 horizon; the A2 horizon is thin and shows little development.
- **B horizon:** Red-brown in colour due to the accumulation of minerals, particularly iron.

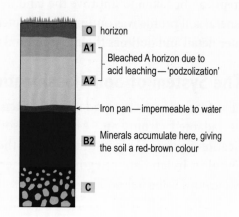

O horizon

A1 — Bleached A horizon due to acid leaching—'podzolization'

A2

Iron pan—impermeable to water

B2 — Minerals accumulate here, giving the soil a red-brown colour

C

Fig 22.2 Podzol

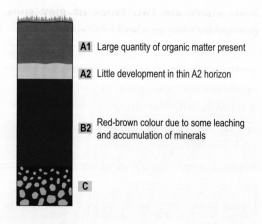

A1 — Large quantity of organic matter present

A2 — Little development in thin A2 horizon

B2 — Red-brown colour due to some leaching and accumulation of minerals

C

Fig 22.3 Brown podzolic soil

Brown earth soils

Brown earths are found in lowland areas. They are very suitable for crop production. They are found overlying limestone or lime-rich parent materials and have a high pH. They require little lime or fertiliser and have good drainage. Very little leaching takes place in these soils. They are dark brown in colour and do not appear to have distinct horizons.

- High levels of organic matter give the soil a dark appearance at the surface (topsoil).
- Uniform brown colour throughout, showing little leaching of minerals.
- Very fertile soils.

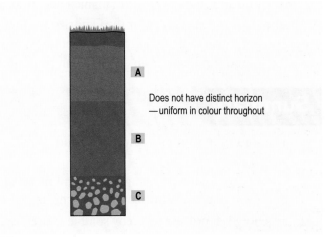

Does not have distinct horizon —uniform in colour throughout

|||||| Fig 22.4 Brown earth soil

Grey-brown podzolic soils

Grey-brown podzolic soils are found in lowlands. They are suitable for crop production, grassland and forestry (broadleaf and conifer). They are well-drained, fertile soils overlying limestone parent material. As a result, they are not prone to acid leaching. Like brown earths, they do not appear to have horizons. They do not require liming due to their high pH level.

- **A horizon**: Clay particles are leached from this horizon.
- **B horizon**: Clay particles accumulate in the B2 horizon.

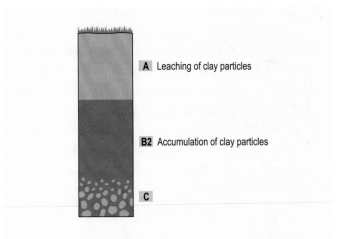

A   Leaching of clay particles

B2   Accumulation of clay particles

C

|||||| Fig 22.5 Grey-brown podzolic soil

Gley soils

Gleys are poorly-drained soils that form in waterlogged conditions. They have poor structure. They can be improved by drainage but their use is limited. Gley soils are confined to grazing and the planting of some broadleaf tree species. Gleys are not leached. There are two types of gley soils, categorised by their method of formation.

Groundwater gleys form in depressions in the landscape. Surface-water gleys form in overlying land impervious to water.

- **A horizon**: There is no definition in the A horizon, and the A1 and A2 horizons are not identified. Grassland provides a limited soil structure to the A layer.
- **B horizon**: There is no defined horizon within the B horizon. Oxidation and the reduction of minerals give it a mottled appearance.

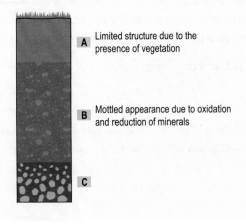

A   Limited structure due to the presence of vegetation

B   Mottled appearance due to oxidation and reduction of minerals

C

|||||| Fig 22.6 Gley soil

Blanket and basin peats

The formation and characteristics of blanket and basin peats were discussed in Chapter 19. Both peats show an absence of horizons except for the O horizon, which is dark, brown-black in appearance. Both peats are widely used for providing fuel in the form of turf. Basin peats are mainly restricted to forestry due to their low pH and poor drainage. Blanket peats can be used in a limited capacity for grazing.

Summary

- The soils of most importance in Ireland include podzols, brown podzolics, brown earths, grey-brown podzolics and gleys.
- Podzols are found overlying acid parent material such as sandstone. They are prone to leaching of minerals from the A horizon to the B horizon.
- Leaching is a process whereby soluble matter, e.g. mineral matter, dissolves in water filtering through soil and is carried downward.
- Podzolisation occurs in acidic pH conditions where minerals such as iron and aluminium are leached from the A horizon, leaving it bleached in colour. They accumulate in the B horizon, forming an impermeable iron-pan.
- Brown podzolic soils are found in lowland areas overlying acid parent materials. They are suitable for forestry but can also be used for crops and grazing.
- Brown earths are found in lowland areas overlying limestone or lime-rich parent materials. They are suitable for crop production as they require little lime or fertiliser and have good drainage.
- Grey-brown podzolics are found in lowlands and are well-drained, fertile soils overlying limestone parent material. They are suitable for crop production, grassland and forestry.
- Gleys are poorly-drained soils that form in waterlogged conditions. There are two types of gley: groundwater gleys form in depressions in the landscape; surface-water gleys form in overlying land impervious to water.

QUESTIONS

1 What parent material is typically associated with podzols?
2 What is acid leaching?
3 What causes the light colour of the leached horizons in the soil?
4 Which minerals are leached from a podzol?
5 Where do the minerals accumulate?
6 What is podzolisation?
7 What is an iron-pan?
8 What negative effects does an iron-pan have on a soil?
9 How can an iron-pan be removed?
10 What parent materials are associated with brown podzolics?
11 Suggest an agricultural use for a brown podzolic.
12 Why are brown earths considered good agricultural soils?
13 Grey-brown podzolics are prone to a specific form of leaching. Describe the type of leaching that takes place in these soils.

QUESTIONS

14 Name the two types of gley soils found in Ireland.
15 Why are gleys limited in their suitability for agriculture?
16 What form of chemical weathering gives gleys a mottled appearance?
17 Give one common use for blanket and basin peats.
18 Why do peats only have one horizon?

EXAM QUESTIONS

1   Draw a labelled diagram to show the main features of a podzol soil. (LC, HL, 2008)
2   List the main steps in the podzolisation of a soil. (LC, HL, 2006)
3   Using a labelled diagram, describe any named soil profile. (LC, HL, 2004)

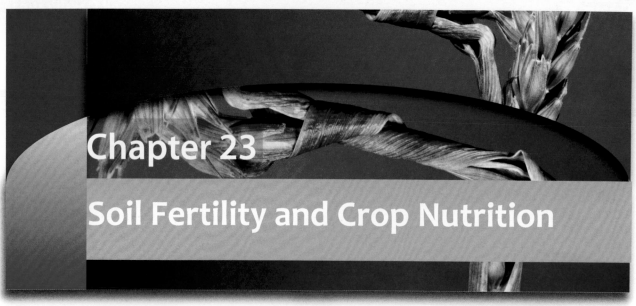

Chapter 23
Soil Fertility and Crop Nutrition

Essential Elements

Seventeen elements are essential for plant growth. The first three of those elements are carbon, hydrogen and oxygen. Together they form the carbohydrate $C_6H_{12}O_6$, which is produced during photosynthesis. Carbon and oxygen come from carbon dioxide that comes from the atmosphere. Hydrogen comes from water that plants extract from the soil.

The remaining fourteen elements are classified as macronutrients or micronutrients. Macronutrients are used in large quantities by plants. Micronutrients are used in small quantities.

- **Macronutrients**: Nitrogen, phosphorus, potassium, calcium, magnesium and sulfur.
- **Micronutrients**: Iron, zinc, manganese, copper, boron, molybdenum, chlorine and nickel.

All of the above are **essential elements** because plants would not be able to grow or complete their life cycles without them.

There are also a number of elements classified as **beneficial elements**. They promote plant growth but are not absolutely essential in the life cycle of the plant.

- **Beneficial elements**: Sodium, cobalt, silicon and selenium.

All of the elements listed above, except for carbon, hydrogen and oxygen, are extracted from the soil by plants. They are normally found in ionic form and are derived from rock or organic parent materials.

Macronutrients

The three elements of most importance are the macronutrients nitrogen (N), phosphorus (P) and potassium (K).

Nitrogen

Nitrogen is the most important of the macronutrients. Without it plant and animal life would not exist. The many ways in which nitrogen is used and recycled have already been outlined in Chapter 21 in 'The nitrogen cycle', page 187. Nitrogen has many essential functions in both plants and animals:

- Component of chlorophyll, which is needed for photosynthesis.
- Component of amino acids, which are needed to create protein.
- Component of DNA, which is responsible for growth and reproduction in plants.
- Component of ATP, a compound responsible for the control of metabolic energy in the plant.

Table 23.1 Nitrogen	
Sufficient nitrogen	**Nitrogen deficiency**
Rapid plant growth	Slow growth, small plants
Dark-green vegetation	Pale green or yellow due to a lack of chlorophyll
High protein content in seeds	Necrosis (death) in older leaves as N is used in younger leaves

Phosphorus

Phosphorus is the second most important macronutrient. Phosphorus, like many mineral elements, is found in ionic compounds in the soil. It is soluble in water and is taken up by plants in this soluble form. However, phosphorus uptake is largely dependent on the pH of the soil. At pH levels below 5 and above 7.5, phosphorus forms compounds that are insoluble in water and unavailable to plants. This is known as the immobilisation of phosphorus. Like nitrogen, phosphorus has many essential roles in the plant:

▨ Required for optimum growth and reproduction.

▨ Involved in energy transfer in the plant.

▨ Production and development of new cells.

▨ Transfer of DNA to new cells.

▨ Seed formation and development.

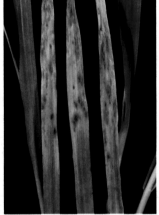

Fig 23.1 Phosphorus deficiency in barley leaves

Table 23.2 Phosphorous	
Sufficient phosphorus	**Phosphorus deficiency**
Vigorous growth	Stunted growth
Early maturing	Lack of fruit or flowers
Increased resistance to plant disease	Wilting
Improved flower formation	Discoloured, blue-purple leaves
Increased stalk/stem strength	Delayed maturity

Potassium

Potassium carries out a number of important functions in the plant including:

▨ Protein synthesis.

▨ Translocation of carbohydrates.

▨ Regulation of plant stomata and water use.

▨ Promotion of disease resistance.

▨ Activation of plant enzymes.

Fig 23.2 Scorched leaves showing potassium deficiency in potato leaves

Table 23.3 Potassium	
Sufficient potassium	**Potassium deficiency**
Increased crop yields	Reduced crop yield
Increased root growth	Scorching of leaves (chlorosis) along leaf margins Slow growth Poorly-developed root system Weak stalks, leading to lodging in cereals Low sugar content in fruit

Calcium, magnesium and sulfur

Soils do not suffer from the same level of depletion of calcium, magnesium and sulfur as they do other nutrients. Of the three, sulfur is the mineral most likely to be deficient in a soil. Sulfur is now added to many of the compound fertilisers (see Chapter 24) available to farmers to rectify this problem.

Calcium and magnesium deficiencies are less common as both elements are present in lime, which is spread on the land to raise pH levels. The three macronutrients play an important role in plant development and without them deficiencies would occur.

Table 23.4 Role of calcium, magnesium and sulfur		
Macronutrient	Role in plant	Deficiency symptom
Calcium (Ca)	Needed for cell wall formation	No development of terminal buds
Magnesium (Mg)	Part of the chlorophyll molecule	Chlorosis of lower plant leaves
Sulfur (S)	Contained in amino acids for protein formation	Chlorosis of upper plant leaves

☰ Micronutrients

Deficiencies in plants (and animals) may be caused due to the absence of a mineral element from the soil. Sandy soils, due to their low fertility status, often lack essential minerals. Minerals may not be available for plant uptake due to an unsuitable pH.

Table 23.5 Deficiencies caused by lack of micronutrients	
Micronutrient	Deficiency disease
Iron (Fe)	Chlorosis leading to reduced yield/poor quality fruit in pears and raspberries. Anaemia in pigs
Zinc (Zn)	Yield reduction in cereals; stunted growth and reduced flowering in legumes
Manganese (Mn)	Grey speck in oats, marsh spot in peas, speckled yellows in sugar beet
Copper (Cu)	Swayback in sheep
Boron (B)	Heart rot/Crown rot in sugar beet
Molybdenum (Mo)	Whiptail (narrow distorted leaves) in cauliflower
Cobalt (Co)	Pine disease in cattle and sheep

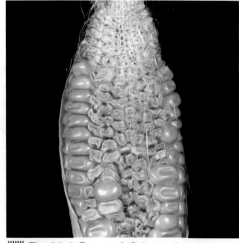

||||| Fig 23.3 Boron deficiency in sweetcorn

||||| Fig 23.4 Copper deficiency in wheat

Experiment 23.1

To test a soil for the presence of macronutrients and micronutrients

These tests are designed to test for the presence of nitrates, phosphates, sulfates, chlorides in a soil sample.

Materials

Soil sample, test tubes, test-tube rack, droppers, filter paper, funnel, deionised water, beaker, iron sulfate ($FeSO_4$), sulfuric acid (H_2SO_4), ammonium molybdate, nitric acid, barium chloride ($BaCl_2$), silver nitrate ($AgNO_3$)

Method

1 Set up the filter funnel. Add soil to the funnel. Pour deionised water through the soil and collect it in a beaker as it filters through.

2 Pour the filtrate into four test tubes.

3 Test for nitrates: Add a solution of iron sulfate ($FeSO_4$) to the test tube of filtrate. Use a dropper to add five drops of concentrated sulfuric acid (H_2SO_4) down the side of the test tube. Observe any change.

4 Test for phosphates: Add a solution of ammonium molybdate to the second test tube. Add a few drops of nitric acid. Observe any change.

5 Test for sulfates and sulfites: Add a solution of barium chloride ($BaCl_2$) to the filtrate in the third test tube. Observe any change.

6 Test for chloride: Add a few drops of silver nitrate solution to the filtrate in the fourth test tube. Observe any change.

Results

● Nitrates: If nitrates are present in the soil filtrate, a brown ring will form in the test tube.

● Phosphates: A yellow precipitate is formed if phosphates are present.

● Sulfates and sulfites: A white precipitate is formed if the test is positive.

● Chloride: A white precipitate is formed.

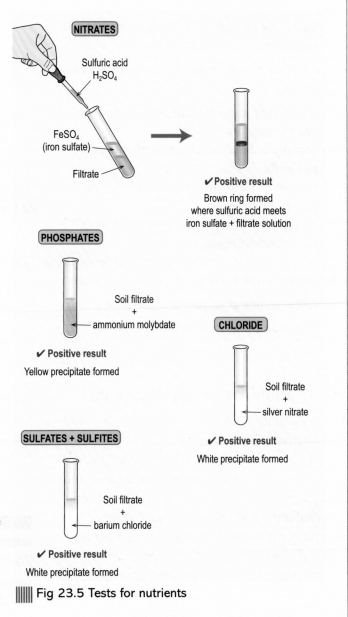

Fig 23.5 Tests for nutrients

Experiment 23.2

To show the importance of nitrogen, potassium and phosphorus on plant growth

Materials
Polystyrene seed trays, seedlings, water culture solutions, water troughs

Method

1 Set up four seed trays as shown in the diagram. Each polystyrene tray has holes in it to hold the seedlings.

2 Each tray should have an equal number of seedlings placed in it.

3 Place each seed tray into a separate water trough.

4 A different mineral solution is added to each trough as follows:

- Trough 1: Solution contains all mineral nutrients.
- Trough 2: Contains all mineral nutrients except nitrogen.
- Trough 3: Contains all mineral nutrients except phosphorus.
- Trough 4: Contains all mineral nutrients except potassium.
- Leave all the trays in sunshine for a week.

5 Observe any change in the seedlings.

6 Continue observations for one month.

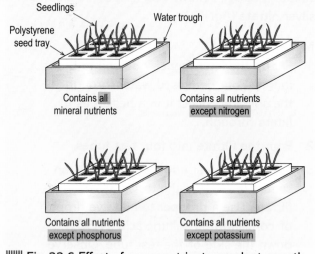

Fig 23.6 Effect of macronutrients on plant growth

Availability of Soil Nutrients

The availability of the macronutrients and micronutrients in the soil is shown in Fig 23.7. As soils become increasingly acidic or alkaline, the availability of particular nutrients is reduced and in some instances is unavailable. Most nutrients are available between pH 6 and 7. This is the optimum pH range for crop growth in a wide range of crops.

In soils that are acidic, availability of nutrients can be increased by raising the pH of the soil. This is normally achieved by liming.

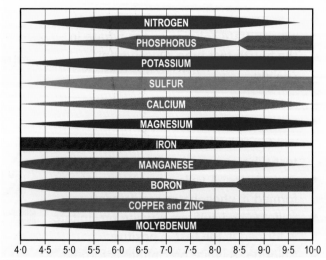

Fig 23.7 Nutrient availability over a range of pH values. Most nutrients are available at a pH of 6

Liming

Liming involves spreading ground limestone on the soil. Ground limestone contains calcium and magnesium, both of which are alkaline. The calcium (Ca^{2+}) and magnesium (Mg^{2+}) ions replace acidic hydrogen and aluminium ions through cation exchange (see Chapter 21). As acidity in the soil is reduced, the pH level increases. This reduces acid leaching and makes soils more suitable for crop growth.

Liming is a medium-term activity as it takes approximately two years for the full effects of lime to be seen on the land. It is unsuitable, therefore, to spread lime on the land as a quick fix solution to a low pH soil.

Ground limestone

▨ Ground limestone for agricultural use should consist of crushed natural limestone containing calcium carbonate or magnesium carbonate.

▨ Moisture content should be no greater than 2.5 per cent.

▨ Total neutralising value should be no less than 90 per cent.

▨ All ground limestone should pass through a 3.35 mm sieve and not less than 35 per cent of it should pass through a 0.15 mm sieve.

☰ Soil Testing

Soil testing allows farmers to discover the nutrients available on their land and to determine how suitable an area is for crop growth. Soils can be tested for a variety of nutrients, lime requirement and pH. A soil test is valid for five years.

However, farmers engaged in intense crop production may test their soils more often to optimise crop production. Soils tested are ranked on the soil index from 1–4, where 1 is the poorest soil and 4 is the best. A soil given a rank of 1 for the availability of a particular nutrient will need a high level of fertiliser applied, whereas a soil ranked 4 will not need any. (Soil indexing is discussed further in Chapter 24.) Soil tests are essential in order to ensure the correct application of fertiliser to the soil and in the correct quantities. It also helps to determine the suitability of a soil for the production of a particular crop.

▥ Fig 23.8 A soil auger is used to take soil samples

Guidelines for taking a soil sample

▨ Divide the area to be sampled into regions 2–4 ha in size.

▨ Take samples from a wide range of areas accounting for differences, including different soil types, previous cropping history and slopes.

▨ Avoid taking samples from areas that are not typical of the area, e.g. entrances and exits to fields, around drinking troughs, beside ditches and on marshland.

▨ Do not sample for P and K for at least three months after the last P and K application.

▨ Do not sample for lime for at least two years after the last application.

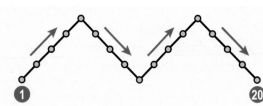

▥ Fig 23.9 Soil sampling pattern

▨ Samples should be taken using a soil auger. At least twenty samples should be taken in a W shape across the field. The samples should be 10 cm in depth.

▨ Samples from the same field should be stored together and sent to Teagasc for analysis.

Summary

- Macronutrients are used in large quantities by plants, and micronutrients are used in small quantities.
- Macronutrients: Nitrogen, phosphorus, potassium, calcium, magnesium and sulfur.
- Micronutrients: Iron, zinc, manganese, copper, boron, molybdenum, chlorine and nickel.
- Nitrogen is needed for photosynthesis, protein production, growth and reproduction in plants. Plants deficient in nitrogen show slow growth, are pale green from a lack of chlorophyll and are necrotic.
- Phosphorus is needed for growth and reproduction, production of new cells and seed formation. Plants deficient in phosphorus have stunted growth, do not produce fruit, and show signs of wilting and leaf discolouration.
- Potassium is needed for protein synthesis and translocation of carbohydrates. A lack of potassium leads to scorching of leaves, reduced crop growth, poor root development and slow growth.
- Most nutrients are available between pH 6 and 7. As soils become increasing acidic or alkaline the availability of particular nutrients is reduced, and in some instances is unavailable.
- Liming is a medium-term activity as it takes approximately two years for the full effects of lime to be seen on the land.
- Ground limestone contains calcium and magnesium, both of which are alkaline. The calcium (Ca^{2+}) and magnesium (Mg^{2+}) ions replace acidic hydrogen and aluminium ions through cation exchange.
- Soil testing allows farmers to discover the nutrients available in their land and to determine how suitable an area is for crop growth.
- When sampling a soil, use a soil auger to take at least twenty samples from a variety of areas in a field.

QUESTIONS

1 What is an essential element?
2 What is a macronutrient? Name two macronutrients.
3 What is a micronutrient? Name two micronutrients.
4 Name two beneficial elements.
5 State two functions of nitrogen in plants.
6 State two signs of sufficient nitrogen in plants.

QUESTIONS

7 State two signs of nitrogen deficiency in plants.

8 Why is phosphorus needed by plants?

9 What are the signs of phosphorus deficiency in plants?

10 Why is the pH of the soil important for the availability of phosphorus to plants?

11 State two functions of potassium in plants.

12 Describe two signs of potassium deficiency in plants.

13 What are the names of the micronutrients with the chemical symbols Fe, Co, Mn?

14 What deficiency disease is associated with (a) boron and (b) copper?

15 What chemical is needed to test for (a) phosphates and (b) chloride?

16 In a test for nitrates using iron sulfate and sulfuric acid, what result would be observed in a positive test?

17 At what pH range are most nutrients available for plant uptake?

18 What is liming?

19 Why is liming carried out?

20 What are the requirements for ground limestone?

21 What instrument is used to take soil samples?

22 What is the recommended number of soil samples that should be taken from a field?

23 Why is soil sampling carried out?

24 List two areas that should not be sampled for soil testing.

25 How often should a soil be sampled?

EXAM QUESTIONS

1 When lime is added to the soil, it provides calcium. Give two other reasons for spreading lime. (LC, OL, 2005)

2 (a) List two minor (trace) elements.
   (b) In the case of one named minor element, state why it is important in agriculture. (LC, OL, 2005)

3 Speckled yellows is a disease of sugar beet caused by a deficiency of a trace element.
   (a) Name the trace element involved.
   (b) Name another disease of sugar beet caused by a deficiency of a named trace element.
       (LC, HL, 2005)

4 Outline the chemical exchanges that would occur in the soil between the lime, soil colloids and soil solution following the application of lime. (LC, HL, 2006)

5 State one function of nitrogen in plants. (LC, HL, 2006)

6 Describe a laboratory or field method to show the presence of a named mineral nutrient in a soil sample. (LC, HL, 2006)

EXAM QUESTIONS

7 Complete the following table, which gives details of the elements needed for plant growth. You must name a different fertiliser in each case. (LC, OL, 2007)

Table 23.6

	Nitrogen	Phosphorus	Potassium
Name of an artificial fertiliser that supplies this element			
Deficiency symptoms in plants			

8 Describe a laboratory experiment to test a soil for the presence of phosphates. (LC, HL, 2009)

9 (a) Describe a laboratory or field experiment to assess the effect of a named major mineral element on plant growth.

   (b) State the role in the plant of the element you have named. (LC, HL, 2007)

10 State the purpose of the following piece of equipment used in agriculture:

- Soil auger

(LC, HL, 2010)

●●●UNIT 6

Fertilisers, Forestry and the Environment

Chapter 24

Fertilisers and Manures

Fertilisers and manures are any naturally or artificially produced materials that can be added to soil to provide one or more of the elements that are essential for plant growth. They exist in solid, liquid and gaseous forms. The quantity of an essential element present in a fertiliser can vary enormously. Farmers need to know how much of a particular element is present when spreading fertiliser or manure on their crops. This is to ensure that the crop is receiving the correct level of nutrients.

It is important not to waste fertiliser, as it increases the farm's costs and can contribute to pollution. Sales of fertiliser and subsequently the application of fertilisers have decreased in Ireland in the last decade. This is partly due to restrictions on the use of fertilisers in agriculture, but also due to the increase in the number of farmers opting to farm organically. Nevertheless, fertilisers are an important aspect of crop production.

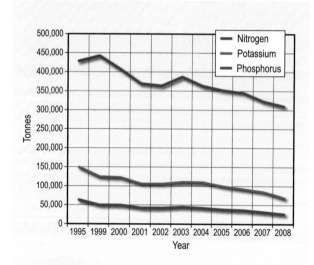

|||||| Fig 24.1 Sales of N, P and K fertilisers 1995–2008

Fertiliser: An inorganic, manufactured material that may contain one or more of the essential elements required for crop growth.

Manure: An organic material that consists of the wastes of plants and animals.

Fertilisers and Essential Elements

The most important elements needed for crop growth are nitrogen (N), phosphorus (P) and potassium (K) (see Chapter 23). The vast majority of fertilisers sold in Ireland contain at least one of these essential elements.

There are many commercially produced fertilisers that farmers can buy to use on their farms. The most common N, P and K straight fertilisers are listed in Table 24.1.

Table 24.1 Fertilisers		
Fertiliser name	Nutrient	Percentage nutrient present
Urea	N	46
Calcium ammonium nitrate (CAN)	N	27.5
Sulfate of ammonia	N	21
Ground rock phosphate	P	12
Superphosphate	P	7
Triple super phosphate	P	16
Muriate of potash	K	50
Sulfate of potash	K	42

Straight nitrogen fertilisers

The most commonly used straight nitrogen fertilisers in Ireland are urea and calcium ammonium nitrate (CAN). Ground rock phosphate is used as a straight fertiliser in forestry. The other straight fertilisers listed in the table are not widely used as straight fertilisers. However, they are used to produce compound fertilisers.

> **Straight (simple) fertiliser**: Contains only one of the essential elements.
> **Compound fertiliser**: Any fertiliser that contains two or more nutrient elements. Compound fertilisers are often produced by the combination of two or more straight fertilisers.

☰ Fertilisers of Importance

Calcium ammonium nitrate (CAN)

Calcium ammonium nitrate (CAN) is the most widely used straight nitrogen fertiliser in Ireland. It contains nitrogen in two forms: ammonium ions and nitrate.

The ammonium ions are acidic and can lower the pH of the soil. A lower soil pH would normally have a negative effect on crop growth, as optimum growth levels in crops are seen in soils with a pH range from 5.5 to 6.5. However, as CAN contains calcium, which is alkaline, this acts as a buffer against the acidic ammonium ions and prevents pH levels becoming too acidic.

One of the main advantages of CAN is that it is a fast acting fertiliser. The nitrate in CAN is immediately available for uptake by crops. The ammonium ions are slower acting as they must first be converted to the nitrate form. This means that nitrogen is available on a long-term basis when CAN is spread on the land.

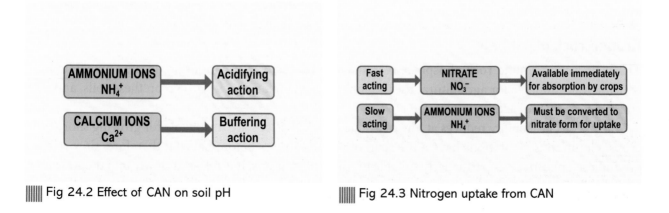

Fig 24.2 Effect of CAN on soil pH   Fig 24.3 Nitrogen uptake from CAN

CAN is hygroscopic and must be stored carefully. Containers of CAN should remain sealed until they are needed and should be used immediately once they are opened. If CAN is not kept in airtight conditions the granules will cake together and cannot be spread on the land. It is sold in granulated form, which allows for uniform spreading.

|||||| Fig 24.4 Urea and CAN are the most common straight nitrogen fertilisers used in Irish agriculture

> **Hygroscopic:** A substance that can absorb moisture from the atmosphere.

Urea

Urea is not as popular as CAN in terms of fertiliser usage. However, it contains a higher concentration of nitrogen, which means less fertiliser is needed for spreading on the land. This can reduce costs and labour. Urea is a slower acting fertiliser than CAN. It must be converted from urea to ammonium form and then into nitrate before it is available for crops. This results in a slower crop response.

Urea is also hygroscopic and needs to be stored in a similar manner to CAN.

One of the other disadvantages of urea as a nitrogen fertiliser is that it undergoes volatilisation.

Volatilisation is wasteful as the ammonia lost to the atmosphere cannot be used by the growing crop. A high level of ammonia gas in the atmosphere, particularly at ground level, causes toxicity in germinating seedlings. It most commonly occurs when the weather is warm and dry. It can be avoided by spreading urea when rain is due and the soil is moist.

Crop losses due to volatilisation may also be reduced by spreading urea on established crops.

Applying a fertiliser to an established crop is known as top-dressing.

|||||| Fig 24.5 Urea conversion

> **Volatilisation:** A process where the ammonium ions produced are converted to ammonia gas, which is then lost to the atmosphere.

Ground rock phosphate

The main use of ground rock phosphate is in the forestry sector. Plantations are located on acidic soils, which are not suitable for agricultural uses. Conifers are the main species grown on these soils, and they contribute to the soil acidity.

Phosphorus availability reduces at low pH values, so acidic soils are unsuitable for growing short-term crops. Coniferous plantations have a life span of about 40 years before harvest; therefore, slow release, ground rock phosphate is particularly suitable for these plantations. It is released slowly into the soil and is available for uptake by the trees over a long period.

Sulfur deficiency

A number of soils can become deficient in sulfur, particularly if they are sandy soils and the land is being used for intensive crop production. To combat this problem, sulfur is added to both straight and compound fertilisers.

Compound fertilisers

As already mentioned, compound fertilisers are produced by combining straight fertilisers. They are also made by mixing N, P and K compounds in their raw state. The main advantage of compound fertilisers is that only one fertiliser may be needed for application to a crop or grassland as it provides all of the nutrients required by the crop. Compound fertilisers may contain the three main minerals, or just two of the minerals. There are many compound fertilisers available, which allows farmers to choose the most suitable fertiliser for their land. A fertiliser may be applied after a soil test has been completed to determine which mineral nutrients are required.

Fig 24.6 10-10-20 is one of the most commonly used compound fertilisers in Ireland

Naming compound fertilisers

All compound fertilisers are labelled with three numbers. These numbers represent the percentages of N, P and K present in the fertiliser mix. Fig 24.6 shows a fertiliser called 10-10-20. This is a commonly used fertiliser in Ireland. It contains 10 per cent N, 10 per cent P, and 20 per cent K. Table 24.2 lists common compound fertilisers and their uses.

Table 24.2 Uses of N-P-K fertiliser	
N-P-K fertiliser	**Common use**
18-6-12	Grassland, cereals
27-2.5-5	Cereal crops, intense grazing
24-2.5-10	Grassland
7-6-17	Root crops

☰ Application of Fertilisers

The soil index system

A soil test should be carried out every two to three years to determine the nutrient requirements of an area of land. This is particularly important if the land is farmed intensively. When a soil test has been completed, it is possible to determine which fertiliser to apply to the land and what quantity of the fertiliser to use.

Teagasc categorises soils in a soil index system (see Table 24.3 on page 210). This ranks a soil by its fertility level and its likely response to fertiliser application. The level of nutrients required to grow a particular crop and the pH of the soil are also taken into account. If the pH is too low, liming may be recommended. The index ranking a soil receives determines which mineral nutrients need to be applied and the level of fertiliser that is required.

When a soil test is completed, the soil sample is given an index value. The levels of mineral nutrients in the soil are included in the results of the analysis and a recommendation is made with regard to fertiliser application.

Table 24.3 Teagasc soil index		
Teagasc soil index	Index description*	Response to fertiliser
1	Very low	Definite
2	Low	Likely
3	Medium	Unlikely/Tenuous
4	Sufficient/Excess	None

The index description refers to the fertility levels in the soil.

Fertiliser application

Fertiliser may be applied in one of three ways:

1 **Placed in soil**: Fertiliser is applied to the land when the seeds are sown. The seed drill sows the seed and applies the fertiliser in a band close to the seed so that nutrients are available to the crop.

2 **Broadcast**: Fertiliser is spread (broadcast) onto the soil using a fertiliser spreader and then harrowed into the soil. This may take place prior to sowing.

3 **Top-dressing**: Fertiliser is spread onto an established crop.

☰ Manures

There are many different types of manure used in agriculture. Manure is a cheap, alternative source of nutrients. It is a cost-effective way of recycling waste on a farm, particularly animal waste. It can also reduce the need to purchase artificial fertilisers. It adds organic matter (humus) to the soil, which improves soil fertility and structure. Organic farmers can also use manures on their farms. The main source of manure on a farm is from animal waste.

|||| Fig 24.7 Fertiliser spreader

Farmyard manure (FYM)

Farmyard manure (FYM) consists of animal dung, animal urine and straw from winter bedding. The manure rots over time and can be applied to the land. As it decomposes it releases nutrients. It also contributes to the organic matter content of the soil, and helps to maintain soil structure.

FYM is particularly useful on organic farms as a source of nutrients because artificial fertilisers are not used.

FYM is considered a bulky fertiliser, as the nutrient level is quite low (see Table 24.4). FYM can be applied to the land with a muck spreader.

|||| Fig 24.8 Spreading manure with a muck spreader

Table 24.4 Nutrient levels and nutrient availability in manures				
Type of manure	N content (%)	P content (%)	N availability (%)	P availability(%)
Cattle manure	0.35	0.09	40	100
Farmyard manure	0.45	0.12	30	100
Mushroom compost	0.80	0.25	45	100

Slurry

Slurry is a liquid manure that contains animal dung and urine. It is collected in a tank underneath the floor in slatted housing. The level of nutrients in animal slurry is similar to that in FYM, but it contains less organic matter due to the absence of straw from winter bedding. Therefore, it does not have as great a benefit to soil structure.

Slurry is spread on the land using a slurry spreader, where it is absorbed quickly because of its liquid composition. As a result, it gives a faster growth response than FYM.

The spread of pests and diseases is a factor to be considered when spreading slurry and as such, it should be confined to grassland applications. It may be used for slurry seeding when reseeding grassland. It can also contribute to weed dispersal, particularly dock leaves.

Fig 24.9 Slurry spreader

Table 24.5 Nutrient content of animal slurry		
Animal	N content (%)	P content (%)
Cattle slurry	0.50	0.08
Sheep slurry	1.00	0.15
Pig slurry	0.42	0.08

Straw/Stubble

Straw is a green manure, as it is a by-product of crop production. The straw or stubble that remains in a field after harvesting cereal crops can be ploughed back into the field, providing organic matter which improves soil structure. As straw decomposes, it releases a small amount of nutrients.

Summary

- Fertiliser: An inorganic, manufactured material that may contain one or more of the essential elements required for crop growth.
- Manure: An organic material that consists of the wastes of plants and animals.
- The most important elements needed for crop growth are nitrogen (N), phosphorus (P) and potassium (K).

Summary

- Straight (simple) fertiliser contains only one of the essential elements.
- Compound fertiliser contains two or more nutrient elements. They are often produced by the combination of two or more straight fertilisers.
- Calcium ammonium nitrate (CAN) is the most widely used straight nitrogen fertiliser in Ireland. It contains nitrogen in two forms: nitrate and ammonium ions.
- A substance is hygroscopic if it can absorb moisture from the atmosphere.
- Urea is a slower acting fertiliser than CAN. It must be converted from urea to ammonium form and then into nitrate, before it is available to crops. Urea undergoes volatilisation.
- Volatilisation: A process where the ammonium ions are converted to ammonia gas, which is then lost in the atmosphere.
- The three numbers listed in a compound fertiliser (18-6-12) represent the percentage of N, P and K found in that fertiliser.
- Teagasc categorises soils in a soil index system. This ranks a soil by its fertility level and its likely response to fertiliser application.
- Fertiliser may be applied by placing it in the soil, by broadcasting it or by top-dressing.
- Farmyard manure (FYM) consists of animal dung, animal urine and straw from winter bedding.
- Slurry is liquid manure that contains animal dung and urine.
- Straw is a green manure, as it is a by-product of crop production.

QUESTIONS

1. What is the difference between a fertiliser and manure?
2. What is a simple fertiliser? What is a compound fertiliser?
3. Name a straight fertiliser that contains (a) nitrogen, (b) phosphorus and (c) potassium.
4. Explain the term *CAN*. What effect does calcium have on soil pH when applied in the form of CAN?
5. Describe the effect that ammonium ions have on soil pH.
6. What does the term *hygroscopic* mean?
7. State one advantage of urea as a nitrogen fertiliser.
8. What is volatilisation? What effect does volatilisation of ammonia have on a growing crop?
9. State a suitable method of applying urea to a crop.
10. Why is ground rock phosphate confined to forest-tree fertilisation?
11. Explain what the numbers mean in the following compound fertiliser: 7-6-17.
12. What is the Teagasc soil index system used for?
13. State two ways in which fertiliser can be applied to land.
14. State two advantages of (a) farmyard manure and (b) slurry as organic fertilisers.

EXAM QUESTIONS

1. (a) Compare and contrast slurry and FYM.
   (b) Suggest two disadvantages of spreading slurry. (LC, HL, 2009)
2. (a) Explain the following terms as they apply to artificial fertilisers: *placement*, *broadcasting*.
   (b) Suggest a crop situation in which one of the above methods is used. (LC, HL, 2009)

Chapter 25

Agriculture, Pollution and the Environment

Many of the agricultural activities carried out on Irish farms result in a waste product. Waste products can be disposed of in many ways. However, if they are not disposed of in a proper manner, or they are dumped, they can cause pollution. Pollutants can affect water, soil, air and the environment in which we live in a negative manner.

☰ Possible Sources of Pollution in Agriculture

If the waste products listed below are disposed of carefully, they do not cause pollution or damage to the environment. Some can be reused and recycled if disposed of in the proper manner. However, they can have an adverse effect on our surroundings and quality of life if disposed of carelessly, or if the proper precautions are not observed when using them, e.g. spreading fertilisers or slurry. The waste products below are all produced from agricultural activities. Can you think of any other waste agricultural products that could be added to the list?

- Silage effluent
- Fertiliser run-off from fields
- Silage/hay wrap
- Sheep dip
- Slurry (cattle, pigs and poultry)
- Farmyard manure
- Pesticides, herbicides and fungicides
- Milk
- Run-off from milking parlours.

Effects of pollution

Littering

Used silage wrap if not collected and disposed of properly can be an eyesore when it ends up in fields and ditches in the countryside. As it is made of plastic, it will not biodegrade and has to be physically removed.

||||| Fig 25.1 Plastic used to wrap bales of silage can be a source of pollution

Eutrophication

Aquatic habitats, in particular, can suffer because of eutrophication. Rivers, streams, lakes and ponds are all examples of aquatic habitats that are at risk. Run-off from fertilisers, slurry, silage

> **Eutrophication:** The enrichment of a habitat or environment with nutrients.

effluent and milk can all cause eutrophication. The nutrients in these substances promote the excessive growth of algae, known as algal bloom. Algae die quickly, producing a high volume of dead organic matter. This organic matter is decomposed by bacteria aerobically. As the bacteria respire, they deplete the oxygen levels in the water. Other aquatic creatures such as fish are unable to survive due to the lack of oxygen and they die. When this happens on a large scale it is known as a fish kill.

Biochemical oxygen demand (BOD)

Some organic materials are more pollutant than others in terms of their BOD value. Clean water has a BOD value of 1–2. Polluted water has a BOD value of 100. Table 25.1 lists BOD values for some common organic pollutants. The higher the value, the more polluting the material.

> **Biochemical oxygen demand (BOD):** The amount of dissolved oxygen needed to break down organic matter in a 1 litre water sample.

Table 25.1 BOD values of agricultural waste	
Organic materials	**mg/L**
Raw domestic sewage	300
Dilute dairy and parlour washings	1 000–2 000
Dirty yard water	1 500
Cattle slurry	17 000
Pig slurry	25 000
Silage effluent	65 000
Whole milk	100 000

Fish kills may also occur during the summer months as water temperatures rise. Oxygen gas is less soluble in water with a rise in temperature. As oxygen levels fall, fish may be deprived of oxygen and die. This is a natural form of fish kill.

Build up of toxins in the food chain

Pesticides and herbicides, like the other agricultural effluents, can be washed into rivers and lakes. This can result in the death of other plant and animal species, due to the build up of these chemicals in their environment.

Some of these toxins build up and are stored in an animal's adipose tissue. In a typical food chain, the level of toxins becomes most concentrated in animals at the top of the food chain, as they feed on organisms that have high concentrations of pesticide. Humans may be affected by a build up of toxins as the final consumer in a food chain.

|||| Fig 25.2 Algal bloom caused by eutrophication

☰ Preventing Pollution

Pollution can be prevented and minimised in an agricultural environment in several ways. Good farm practices, such as following guidelines about spreading effluents and fertilisers, can prevent run-off from fields into waterways, springs and groundwater. Much of the water used for human consumption is from groundwater sourced through wells.

Schemes created by the Department of Agriculture help and encourage farmers to adhere to regulations regarding the disposal of organic wastes and spreading fertilisers. Penalties and fines can be imposed for those who do not comply.

Spreading fertilisers and the Nitrates Directive

There are restrictions on the spreading of fertilisers, enforced by the Nitrates Directive. To minimise run-off, waste and water pollution fertilisers should not be spread in the following conditions:

- If the land is waterlogged.
- If the land is flooded or is likely to flood.
- If the land is snow-covered or frozen.
- If heavy rain is forecast within 48 hours.
- If the ground is steeply sloped, and combined with other factors poses a risk of water pollution.

Run-off from fertilisers can also be minimised by following the guidelines below:

- Do not apply fertiliser within 1.5 metres of a watercourse.
- Do not spread fertilisers or effluents near watercourses, bore holes, springs or wells.
- Do not apply chemical fertiliser between 15 September and 15 January.*
- Do not apply organic fertilisers between 15 October and 15 January.*
- Do not apply farmyard manure between 1 November and 31 January.*

*Dates vary slightly with the region.

Storage of organic waste, effluents and silage wrap

Farmyard manure, slurry, silage effluent, soiled water and fertilisers should be collected and stored on a farm until they can be spread on the land or disposed of appropriately. The storage facilities (e.g. dungstead, silage pit) should be maintained so that they are free from any structural damage that would allow seepage of these materials into groundwater. Silage wrap should be stored until it can be collected for recycling or safe disposal.

☰ Protecting our Environment

Many farmers and those involved in agriculture are already working to protect and improve the environment in which they work and live. Many of the practices in place encourage biodiversity.

> **Biodiversity**: All living organisms within an ecosystem; this includes plants, animals and micro-organisms.

A diverse range of living organisms is important in an ecosystem in order to provide resources such as food, but also for recycling of wastes and nutrients. If habitats are destroyed, ecosystems can collapse and disappear rapidly, which in turn eradicates various plants, animals and other living organisms.

Almost 75 per cent of Irish land is used for agriculture and forestry, which has an enormous influence on biodiversity in this country. Therefore, farmers can play a key role in protecting habitats and the environment to ensure the survival of species that play essential roles in food production, nutrient recycling and waste recycling.

Irish farmers can protect and enhance biodiversity on their farms through their involvement in a number of schemes operated by the Department of Agriculture. These schemes include:

- Rural Environment Protection Scheme (REPS) 1994–2013
- Forest Environment Protection Scheme (FEPS); introduced in 2007
- Agri-Environment Options Scheme
- Organic Farming Scheme.

Some ways in which farmers can enhance biodiversity on their farms include:

- Traditional hay meadows: Allow flowers and grasses to produce seed to benefit wildlife (REPS).
- Nature corridors: Protect and enhance field margins, which are an important source of plant diversity and wildlife habitat.
- Hedgerow maintenance: Retained and manage hedgerows; cutting is prohibited during the bird nesting season.
- Minimise the use of chemical fertilisers and pesticides (Organic Farming Scheme).
- Forestry: Plant both coniferous and deciduous trees, with an emphasis on planting broadleaf species (FEPS).
- Retain existing lakes, marshes, woodland, bogs, and watercourses in areas designated for forestry (FEPS).

Fig 25.3 Traditional hay meadow in Ireland

Hedgerows

Hedgerows are a common sight in the Irish countryside. They also play an important role in maintaining biodiversity within our ecosystem.

Hedgerow habitat: An example of biodiversity.

Hedgerows provide a home for many nesting birds, and also larger mammals and insects. Bees are necessary for the pollination of hedgerow flowers, while hedgerows provide a source of food and shelter for these insects.

Many of these species form important food chains and the removal of hedgerows would be the removal of their natural habitat. Without hedgerows, many species would disappear due to lack of shelter and from the absence of a food source, be it the hedgerow itself or an animal or insect species that lives in the hedgerow.

Hedgerows are also useful in a number of other ways:

- They provide shelter for livestock.
- They form natural land boundaries and enclosures.
- They are aesthetically attractive.
- They improve the growth of plants on the sheltered side of the hedge.

Fig 25.4 A hedgerow sheltering cattle

Environmental schemes

A number of schemes have been put in place by the Department of Agriculture to reduce pollution, encourage environmentally friendly practices and encourage biodiversity and conservation. A number of the schemes are outlined below.

Rural Environment Protection Scheme (REPS)

The Rural Environment Protection Scheme (REPS) was established in 1994 and is set to run until 2013. As of 2009, when the scheme was closed to new applicants, there were 62 000 farmers signed up to REPS 4. The aim of REPS is to improve the environment on Irish farms and reward farmers for their environmentally friendly activities. The main aims of REPS are:

- The establishment of farm practices and production methods that reflect the concern for conservation, landscape protection and wider environmental problems.
- To protect wildlife habitats and endangered species of flora and fauna.
- To produce quality food in an extensive and environmentally friendly manner.

Some of the measures that must be undertaken by farmers in the REPS scheme to improve the environment on their farms include:

- Protect and maintain all watercourses and wells.
- Retain wildlife habitats.
- Maintain farm and field boundaries.
- Cease using herbicides, pesticides and fertilisers in and around hedgerows, lakes, ponds, rivers and streams, except with the consent of the Minister for Agriculture.
- Produce tillage crops without burning straw or stubble; leave a specified field margin uncultivated where no nutrients or sprays are applied.

Forest Environment Protection Scheme (FEPS)

The Forest Environment Protection Scheme was established in 2007 and started in 2008. Like REPS, it will run until 2013. The aim of the scheme is to encourage farmers to establish high nature-value woodland to maximise its contribution to the environment.

The main aims of FEPS are:

- To encourage farmers to establish and maintain high nature-value forestry through measures such as increasing biodiversity and protecting water quality.
- To support, establish or provide habitats for wildlife.
- To encourage the provision of protective forestry, e.g. riparian planting.
- To produce a commercial crop of timber while making an enhanced contribution to the environment.

||||| Fig 25.5 Forestry in Ireland planted with broadleaf

- To increase Ireland's woodland cover to contribute positively towards climate change mitigation.

Other habitats including lakes, marshes, bogs, watercourses, woodlands, fens and swamps must also be retained and conserved under the FEPS scheme. Land designated for forestry under this scheme must be planted with a minimum of 15 per cent broadleaf species.

Organic Farming

Organic farming is agricultural activity that does not rely on chemical fertilisers, pesticides, genetically modified crops and livestock antibiotics. While it does not mean farmers have to return to traditional methods, it does mean farming in harmony with the natural environment. This can involve the use of biological pest controls, green manures, crop rotations, composting and mechanical methods of cultivating the land, and controlling weeds and pests.

Many people today, farmers and consumers alike, are more concerned about where their food comes from. Consumers want to eat good quality produce that is free from chemicals, pesticides and antibiotics. They are concerned about the conditions in which animals are raised. More people are looking for the organic option when they go to the supermarket and are willing to pay extra for organic produce.

Advantages of organic farming:

- Animals are reared on land free from chemicals, fertilisers, pesticides and herbicides.

- Animals are free range and have suitable living conditions while on the farm.

- Crops are not genetically modified.

- Soil structure has been protected by means of rotations, and by the additions of green manures, farmyard manures and mulches.

- As there are no organic or chemical pollutants produced, waterways are not at risk of pollution.

- Habitats are maintained, promoting and encouraging biodiversity.

||||| Fig 25.6 Organic farming in Ireland

Summary

- Examples of waste produced on Irish farms include: silage wrap, silage effluent, slurry, sheep dip and run-off from chemicals such as fertilisers and pesticides.

- Eutrophication: The enrichment of a habitat or environment with nutrients. This is common in aquatic habitats.

- Run-off from fertilisers increases algal bloom in waterways. Bacteria decompose the organic matter produced, as a result using up oxygen. This increases the BOD level of the water. Fish die from lack of oxygen.

- Biochemical oxygen demand (BOD): The amount of dissolved oxygen needed to break down organic material in a 1 litre water sample.

- Toxins such as pesticides can build up in the environment. They enter the food chain and increase in concentration at each level of the food chain. This poses a risk to humans who are at the top of the food chain.

- Pollution of water by fertilisers can be avoided by adhering to practices such as not spreading fertiliser when land is waterlogged, flooded, snow-covered, frozen or when rain is due.

- Run-off from fertilisers can be minimised by not spreading fertilisers near watercourses, springs, and wells, or between September and January.

- Biodiversity is all the living organisms within an ecosystem, i.e. plants, animals and micro-organisms.

Summary

▇ Schemes to enhance biodiversity include REPS, FEPS and the Organic Farming Scheme.

▇ Hedgerows are important for biodiversity. They also provide a habitat and food source for animals. They give livestock shelter and form natural boundaries.

▇ REPS was established to conserve land, protect habitats and endangered species and produce quality food in an environmentally friendly way.

▇ FEPS was introduced to establish high nature-value forestry, increase biodiversity, protect wildlife, conserve land and produce wood while improving the environment.

▇ Organic farming does not rely on chemical fertilisers, pesticides, genetically modified crops and livestock antibiotics.

▇ On organic farms rotations and manures are used to protect soil.

▇ On organic farms animals are reared on land free from chemicals; they are free range and have good living conditions.

QUESTIONS

1 Name three agricultural sources of pollution.
2 What is eutrophication?
3 What is algal bloom?
4 Explain what is meant by the term BOD.
5 Name two substances that have a high BOD value.
6 How do fish kills occur?
7 List one negative effect of spreading fertiliser.
8 List one negative effect of the use of pesticides and herbicides.
9 List three ways to minimise fertiliser run-off.
10 What is biodiversity?
11 Describe two ways in which biodiversity can be encouraged.
12 State two measures farmers must undertake to improve the environment under REPS.
13 How does FEPS encourage broadleaf tree forestry?
14 List three advantages of maintaining hedgerows on a farm.
15 State two advantages of organic farming.

EXAM QUESTIONS

1 Suggest **one** practice farmers could adopt to reduce the carbon footprint of Irish agriculture. (LC, HL, 2009)
2 Explain **two** advantages of the spreading of organic manures on soils. (LC, HL, 2007)
3 Give **one** reason that it is recommended not to spread nitrogen fertiliser during the non-growing season. (LC, OL, 2007)
4 Give **two** reasons that hedgerows are important in the farming landscape. (LC, OL, 2007)

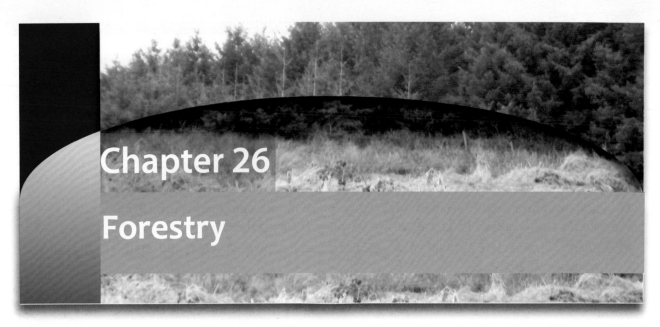

Chapter 26

Forestry

By the beginning of the twentieth century only 1 per cent of the land in Ireland was covered by woodland and forestry. Today forestry accounts for about 10 per cent of the land and covers approximately 750 000 hectares. About 75 per cent of the forestry in Ireland consists of conifers, both commercial (Sitka spruce) and native species (Scots Pine). Broadleaf species such as oak, ash and birch make up the other 25 per cent. This figure is increasing every year. With the help of afforestation schemes such as the Forest Environment Protection Scheme (FEPS), the Native Woodland Scheme and the Afforestation Grant Scheme, 30 per cent of all forestry planted each year in Ireland is now broadleaf species. Many farmers are planting marginal land with forestry where previously the land would have lain fallow.

≡ Soil Types and Forestry Suitability

Trees, like any other crop, have optimum conditions in which they will grow. While some of the better soils in Ireland would support a forestry plantation, they are normally used for intensive tillage production or grassland for livestock production.

Forestry is a long-term crop and it can be planted on poor quality soils, as these soils have no other agricultural purpose. Table 26.1 lists some of the common soil types found in Ireland, showing their suitability for forestry.

||||| Fig 26.1 Coniferous plantation on marginal farmland

Table 26.1 Soils and their suitability for forestry	
Soil types	Forestry suitability
Acid brown earth	Very suitable for broadleaf and conifer plantations
Brown podzolic	Very suitable for broadleaf and conifer plantations
Grey-brown podzolic	Very suitable for broadleaf and conifer plantations
Podzols	Mainly suited to conifer plantations
Peaty podzol	Unsuitable for broadleaf plantation; conifers will grow on this soil
Gleys	Suitable for spruce plantations and a limited range of broadleaves
Peat	When drained, basin peat is suitable for conifers and some broadleaf species

Planting

The first step in ensuring a good quality plantation is the selection of trees for the plantation. Saplings should have a straight stem with a healthy terminal bud and a fibrous root system. They should be stored in cool conditions if not being planted immediately. Trees should be planted into mounds. They should not have their roots exposed and should not be planted into frozen soil.

Broadleaves are planted in November and December and all other species are planted in spring. Trees are normally planted at a rate of 2 500 trees per ha.

||||| Fig 26.2 Trees planted in Ireland

Fertilisation

Nitrogen, phosphorus and potassium are extremely important in forestry. These nutrients are necessary for the healthy growth and establishment of a forestry plantation. Phosphorus is of particular importance as it promotes good root development.

Before planting, a soil test should be carried out to determine the nutrient requirements of the land and to establish which species are most suitable for that soil.

In commercial coniferous plantations, phosphorus is the most important nutrient. It is usually applied in the form of ground rock phosphate. On soils that are suited to broadleaf species, compound fertilisers such as 18-6-12 and 10-10-20 may be applied. Broadleaf plantations that include alder have the added benefit that alder has the ability to fix nitrogen in the same way as clover.

Fertiliser should not be applied after rainfall or within 20 metres of a waterway. It should only be applied between April and August.

Weed and vegetation control

Weed and vegetation control is as important in forestry as it is for any tillage crop. Scrub, weeds and grasses will all compete with newly planted trees for light, space, water and nutrients. Trees will fail to thrive and may die if they do not receive sufficient water and minerals. Growth of scrub can hinder the growth of trees.

Manual control of weeds and scrub is labour intensive. It involves cutting away the weeds and scrub, but it may be suitable on a small-scale farm forest. One of the benefits of this method of control is that it is environmentally friendly.

Chemical control of weeds is also possible in the form of herbicides. Herbicides cannot be applied over the trees if the species are not resistant to the herbicide. Care must also be taken with the volume of herbicide applied. Broadleaf species are more susceptible to damage from herbicides than conifer species.

Harvesting

There are two types of harvesting carried out in Irish forestry: thinning and clearfelling.

Thinning

Thinning is the removal of some trees from a forestry plantation. Thinning is carried out to reduce competition between trees. It creates more space and light. The poorer quality trees may be removed from the plantation or a planned thinning may take place. This is when whole rows of trees are removed to increase space for the remaining trees.

Before thinning, the plantation should be prepared for thinning inspection. Parallel paths should be created through the forest for inspection. The branches on the lower part of the trees should be removed to head height. This is known as brashing. A felling licence must be obtained from the local Garda Station prior to thinning.

The timing of thinning depends on the types of tree in the plantation. Conifers have a faster growth rate than broadleaves, and so in a new plantation, conifers need to be thinned much sooner than a plantation of broadleaves.

Income is also provided from the wood from the thinned trees. Wood pulp and pallet wood is produced from first thinning. Sawlogs are produced from subsequent thinning along with the pulp and pallet wood. The proportion of trees felled for sawlogs increases with the increasing age of the plantation.

Conifer plantations such as Sitka spruce have their first thinning after approximately 20 years. During the first thinning, every seventh line of trees is removed from the plantation. This increases space but also provides access routes to the forest. Subsequent thinning takes place at five-year intervals.

||||| Fig 26.3 Brashing

Thinning in broadleaf plantations takes place at 10-year intervals, as these species have a slower growth rate. In plantations with a mixture of conifers and broadleaves, conifers are often planted as a nurse crop. Fast-growing conifers act as a shelterbelt for the broadleaf species in the early years, but they must be thinned out so as not to hinder the development of the broadleaves in the plantation.

Clearfelling

Clearfelling is the final stage of the forestry crop cycle. It involves harvesting all the trees in an area. In coniferous forests, where Sitka spruce is the main species, this occurs when the trees are approximately 40 years old. In Ireland, this practice is carried out in forests planted for commercial purposes.

Benefits of forestry

- Provides a habitat for birds, animals and plants.
- Provides a food source for animals.
- Can reduce nutrient leaching on a farm.
- Provides an income through the sale of wood.
- Removes CO_2 from the atmosphere, reducing greenhouse gases.
- Provides a natural amenity.
- It is aesthetically pleasing.
- Provides shelter in the form of shelterbelts.

||||| Fig 26.4 Commercial clearfelling of trees

Farm forestry provides shelter for neighbouring fields as it grows. It can work in conjunction with pre-existing or newly planted hedgerows. Shelterbelts increase air and soil temperatures, and decrease ground wind speed. Shelterbelts have the knock-on effect of earlier crop germination, better crop yields and a reduction in heat loss from buildings.

Summary

- Approximately 10 per cent of land in Ireland is used for forestry. Conifers make up 75 per cent of tree species; the remainder are broadleaf species.
- Thirty per cent of all trees currently planted under forestry schemes such as FEPS are broadleaf species.
- Acid brown earths, brown podzolics and grey-brown podzolics are suitable for both broadleaf and conifer species.
- Broadleaf species should be planted in November/December and all other species in spring. They should not have their roots exposed.
- Fertilisers such as 10-10-20 and 18-6-12 can be applied between April and August to provide N, P and K to the plantation. Phosphorus is the most important nutrient in a plantation.
- Weeds and scrub compete for space, water, light and nutrients. They can be controlled by cutting them back, which is environmentally friendly, or by herbicides that do not affect the tree species.
- Thinning is the removal of the poorer quality trees to give the remaining trees more space and reduce competition. Thinning may be planned in a forestry plantation.
- Brashing is a process whereby the lower branches are removed from trees to make a path through a plantation before thinning.
- Conifers have their first thinning after 20 years where thinned trees are used for wood pulp, wood pallets and sawlogs. Subsequent thinning takes place every five years after this, up to 40 years.
- Thinning takes place in broadleaf plantations every 10 years due to their slower growth rate.
- Clearfelling involves harvesting all the trees in one area.
- Forestry provides a habitat and food source for birds and animals. It can reduce leaching and removes CO_2 from the atmosphere. The sale of wood provides an income for farmers.
- Farm forestry provides shelter for neighbouring fields as it grows.

QUESTIONS

1 Name two coniferous species and two broadleaf species of tree found in Ireland.
2 Name two soils which are suitable for broadleaf and conifer plantations.
3 When is the optimum time for planting (a) broadleaves and (b) conifers?
4 What is the average planting rate for a new plantation?
5 Why is phosphorus so important in forestry fertilisation?
6 Which compound fertilisers are most suitable for forestry?
7 Describe two methods of weed control in forestry.
8 In terms of forestry, what is meant by brashing?
9 What is clearfelling? When does clearfelling take place in a Sitka spruce plantation?
10 State an advantage of shelterbelts on a farm.

EXAM QUESTIONS

1 Give a scientific explanation for the inclusion of both conifers and broadleaf trees in shelterbelts. (LC, HL, 2010)
2 Why are thinning operations carried out in forest tree production? (LC, HL, 2002)

●●● UNIT 7

Grassland – Production and Management

Chapter 27
Introduction to Grassland

Grassland covers approximately 20 per cent of the earth's land surface. It is extremely important as a habitat, a source of food for animals and in agriculture. In Ireland, over 3.7 million hectares of agricultural land are under grassland. This accounts for 90 per cent of farmland. It provides a readily available source of food for livestock in the form of grazing land and winter fodder.

Table 27.1 Uses of grassland in Irish agriculture	
Uses of grassland	Hectares ('000)
Pasture	2 092
Silage	1 033.9
Hay	220.3
Rough grazing in use	441.2

≡ Grassland Ecology

Grassland is not the natural vegetation of Ireland. After the Ice Age, almost all of the country was covered in deciduous woodland such as oak, ash and willow. Today about 10 per cent of the land is woodland and forestry; most of this is coniferous forestry for commercial use. Grassland is semi-natural vegetation that thrives in the temperate climate of Ireland, but ultimately is controlled by human activity. If grassland was not grazed by livestock or cut for silage or hay, eventually small shrubs and trees (bramble and blackthorn) would invade the land and become the dominant species. Over a long period, this scrub land would be replaced by the natural vegetation of the country – deciduous forest. The larger trees would create a canopy, which would block out light to the smaller shrubs, preventing their growth.

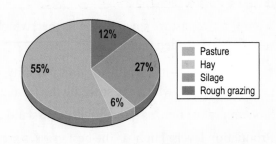

|||| Fig 27.1 Use of grassland in Irish agriculture

As agricultural grassland is used for grazing, grasses are grazed low to the ground, which favours shorter species of grass. These species tend to be leafier. Leafier species are more palatable and nutritious than taller, stemmy species of grass. These taller species of grass, which are of less value agriculturally, can begin to dominate in grassland that is not grazed intensively.

Good grassland management can be the main factor in determining the species of grass present in land used for grazing and conservation as winter fodder. When assessing the value of grassland it is important to consider the following characteristics:

- Botanical composition: The range of grasses, plants and other vegetation present.
- Stocking rate: The number of animals that can be stocked on a set area of land.
- Production levels: Amount of herbage produced by the pasture; a high production level will lead to high production levels in livestock in terms of live weight gain.

The three main categories of grassland are: rough mountain or hill grazing, permanent grassland and leys.

Rough mountain or hill grazing

Rough mountain or hill grazing is a category of land under poor quality grass. It is found on mountains and hillsides, and is often peaty in nature. The land is normally acidic and difficult to cultivate. Where cultivation is possible, land can be improved through liming and reseeding.

- Botanical composition: Highly variable, it consists of poorer grasses such as bent grasses and fescues, heathers and gorse.
- Stocking rate: Nutritional levels are low in the available grassland, so animals cannot be stocked at a high density.
- Production level: Low, as grasses are not productive and livestock will not have a high live weight gain as a result.

Permanent grassland

Permanent grassland is land under grass that is never ploughed. It can be fertilised and limed to maintain and improve quality and productivity.

- Botanical composition: Variable, it consists of a number of grasses – from the highly-productive grasses such as perennial ryegrass (PRG) to the poorer grasses such as fescues and bent grasses.
- Stocking rate: Higher stocking rate than rough mountain grazing due to improved grazing conditions.
- Production level: Higher production levels than mountain grazing as this grassland is of better quality and can be improved through fertilisation and liming.

Leys

A ley is a field or pasture sown by the farmer, which is used for grazing by livestock. Leys are temporary in nature and are reseeded regularly.

- Botanical composition: Little or no variability, one or two species such as perennial ryegrass and clover dominate, which are sown by the farmer.
- Stocking rate: High, as good quality grassland can support a large number of livestock.
- Production levels: High, as the best grasses are sown in leys.

☰ Species of Grass

The following species of grass and clover are found in Irish grassland (see Table 27.1 on page 227). Some species are of more agricultural value than others and will be discussed in detail later in this chapter.

Table 27.2 Grass species

Perennial ryegrass is a highly palatable, productive species	Italian ryegrass is a highly productive, short duration ryegrass	Timothy grass is a palatable, productive species
Meadow foxtail found in hill grazing and permanent grassland	Cocksfoot found in permanent grassland and leys	Yorkshire fog found in permanent grassland
Crested dogstail found in permanent grassland	White clover found in permanent grassland and leys	Red clover found in permanent grassland and leys

Characteristics of Grass

The most important characteristics of grass are its palatability, productivity and digestibility. This is because grass is used as an animal feed both for grazing and winter fodder. In Ireland, it has no other agricultural use. Farmers turn grass into meat and milk through beef and dairy production. They need grass species that will produce the largest volume of grass, which is high in nutrients and is also attractive to their livestock as a foodstuff. Grass species with the highest levels of palatability, productivity and digestibility are the most desirable for grazing and conservation.

Palatability

Palatability is a measure of how pleasant the grass is to taste. Cattle and sheep are selective grazers; they will only eat the grasses that are most palatable to them. If there is a variety of grasses in a pasture, livestock will eat the palatable grasses and ignore the unpalatable species. As the unpalatable species go uneaten, they continue to develop and begin to dominate the pasture. The pasture becomes patchy where certain species have been grazed and, as the unpalatable species replace the palatable ones, the productivity and quality of the pasture is lowered. Perennial ryegrass is the most palatable species to grazing animals.

Productivity

Productivity is a measure of the quantity of plant material (herbage) produced by the grass. The higher the productivity, the more grass is available to livestock for consumption. Higher stocking rates are also possible on grasses that are more productive. Again, perennial ryegrass has one of the highest levels of productivity of all the grass species.

Digestibility

Digestibility represents the proportion of food that can be assimilated and used by the body in comparison to the amount of food consumed. Ideally, digestibility levels should be high as this means there is little waste. The higher the digestibility of a food, in this case grass, the more meat and milk can be produced from that grass.

Grass consists of a number of different constituents (protein, soluble carbohydrates – sugar, cellulose and fibre), each with varying digestibility. The grass that is of most value to the farmer for feeding should consist mainly of the highly digestible constituents: soluble carbohydrates and protein.

The level of digestible constituents varies over the growing season. After germination, a plant enters its second stage of growth, which is described as the vegetative stage. This same stage occurs when grass begins to grow again in spring. The plant photosynthesises, producing a large volume of carbohydrate in the form of sugar and starch, which is stored in the leaves that are produced at this time. This herbage is highly digestible. More than 80 per cent of the grass can be digested by the ruminant animal.

By mid-May, the plant enters its reproductive stage and begins to produce flowering stems. These stems have to support the seed head of the grass. Fibre is needed to provide strength in the stem and so is produced at the expense of protein and carbohydrate.

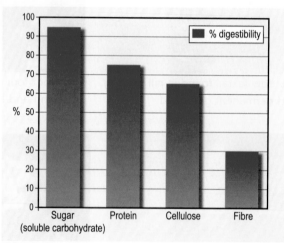

Fig 27.2 Comparison of percentage digestibility of food constituents in grass

As fibre is low in digestibility, this lowers the overall digestibility of the grass plant. The overall digestibility of grass can drop from 80 per cent to 50 per cent within one month.

Digestibility levels vary between grass species. Perennial ryegrass has a higher level of digestibility than any of the other species mentioned in this chapter. When water is removed from the vegetation, the plant material that remains and can be digested is referred to as digestible dry matter.

If the DMD value for grass or silage is low, the dry matter intake of the animal will increase, as it has to

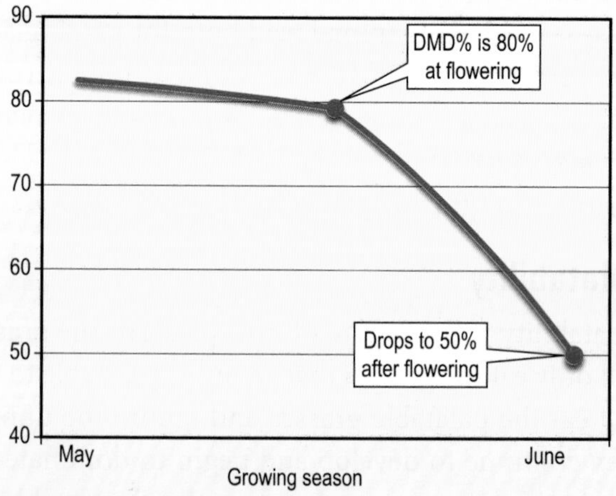

> **Dry matter (DM)**: The matter remaining in a sample of food after the water has been removed. It is usually abbreviated to DM.
> **Dry matter digestibility (DMD)**: The amount (percentage) of dry matter that can be digested by an animal.
> **Dry matter intake (DMI)**: The amount of feed an animal consumes, excluding its water content.

Fig 27.3 Changes in DMD levels of grass over the growing season

consume more feed to get the nutrients it requires. To maximise output a dairy farmer will need to feed grass or silage with as high a DMD value as possible.

Leafy grass will have a high DMD value as it contains a high level of carbohydrates and protein, while stemmy grass has a low DMD value as the stems consist of fibres. This is an important factor to consider when saving grass for silage. Cutting grass at the leafy stage is crucial as the sugars and proteins are contained in the leaves of the plant. As the stems develop, the sugars and proteins are converted to fibre, which leads to a low DMD during conservation.

Experiment 27.1

To determine the dry matter content of grass
Note: This experiment can be used to determine the dry matter content of hay, silage or potatoes.

Materials
Sample of grass, three beakers, scissors, electronic balance, tongs, oven

Method
1 Dry off any excess water on the sample of grass, using a tissue.

2 Cut the grass into short lengths of equal size, using scissors.

3 Weigh each of the empty beakers and record mass.

4 Add a sample of cut grass to each beaker.

5 Weigh each beaker of grass and record its mass.

6 Place all the beakers in an oven at 100°C.

7 Remove the beakers from the oven, using tongs, and re-weigh every 10 minutes until a constant mass is achieved.

8 Record your results in a table similar to the one below and calculate the DM content of the samples.

9 Calculate the average DM content of the grass.

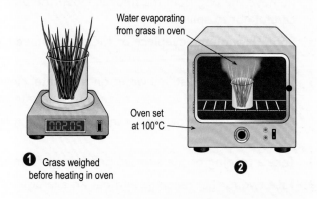

Fig 27.4 Drying grass to determine dry matter content

Results

Table 27.3 Results of DM content of grass			
	Sample 1	Sample 2	Sample 3
Mass of empty beaker (1)			
Mass of beaker + fresh grass (2)			
Mass of fresh grass = (2)−(1)			
Mass of beaker + grass dried to constant mass (3)			
Dry grass = (3)−(1)			
DM% $= \dfrac{\text{Dry grass}}{\text{fresh grass}} \times 100$			

Experiment 27.2

To estimate sucrose concentration in grass

Note: This experiment can also be used to estimate the sucrose content in sugar beet.

Materials
Sample of grass, refractometer, polythene bag, freezer, distilled water

Method
1. Obtain a sample of grass. Dry off any excess water from the grass with a tissue. Water will dilute the sugar concentration.
2. Place the sample of grass in a polythene bag. Remove the air from the bag and seal it.
3. Place the bag in a freezer overnight. Freezing the grass causes the cells to burst. Sap is released from the cells into the bag.
4. Remove the bag from the freezer. Open the bag, being careful not to spill the sap.
5. Look through the eyepiece of the refractometer to check that it is clear.
6. Place a drop of distilled water on the plate, close the cover and adjust the meter to zero to calibrate the refractometer.
7. Place a few drops of sap on the plate of the refractometer, close the cover and look through the eyepiece.
8. Take a reading of the sucrose percentage from the scale, which is visible.
9. Take two further readings and get an average value for the readings.

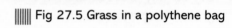

Fig 27.5 Grass in a polythene bag

☰ Choosing Grass Species for Leys

A variety of strains of ryegrass and clover are the most common seed mixtures sown in leys. The most common grass sown is perennial ryegrass and it is usually sown with white clover.

Perennial ryegrass

Almost all grass seed sold for sowing is perennial ryegrass (approximately 95%). Perennial ryegrass is suited to well-drained soils with a pH of 6 or greater. The soil should be fertile and respond well to nitrogen fertilisation. As it is a perennial species, it will persist in a well-managed pasture for many years. Its inflorescence is easily recognised by the presence of spikelets on alternate sides of the stem (see Table 27.2 on page 227).

Advantages of perennial ryegrass:

- It has a higher palatability, productivity and digestibility in comparison to other grasses.
- It has a high DM production.
- Long growing season means reduced costs for winter feed.
- High stocking rate can be maintained because of high productivity levels.
- Good tillering ability leads to sward dominance, good ground cover and weed prevention.

Italian ryegrass

The popularity of Italian ryegrass (IRG) has decreased in Ireland in recent years. It is a biennial plant, which means pastures sown with Italian ryegrass need to be reseeded every two years. Some strains of Italian ryegrass may last for a third year. This means that the management of pastures is more intensive than that of perennial ryegrass pastures. It requires similar soil conditions to perennial ryegrass and can be recognised by the awns on its spikelets (see Table 27.2 on page 227).

Advantages of Italian ryegrass:

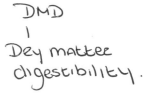

- It has a longer growing season than perennial ryegrass.
- It produces 20 per cent more herbage than perennial ryegrass.
- High production levels make it particularly suitable for silage production.

Hybrid ryegrasses

Hybrid ryegrasses are produced as a result of a cross between different species of ryegrass, usually perennial ryegrass and Italian ryegrass. The aim is to produce a strain of grass with hybrid vigour. This combines the persistence of perennial ryegrass and its longer growing season with the high production levels of Italian ryegrass.

White clover

Clover is a member of the *Leguminosae* family. It is a perennial plant with white flowers. It has smooth stems lacking in hairs (glabrous). As clover produces stolons, it spreads quickly within a sward, as the stolons take root when they are trampled into the soil. This provides good ground cover, preventing weed establishment. It is often included in seed mixtures for leys for grazing or for conservation as silage. Its inclusion is hugely beneficial in a grass-based enterprise.

Advantages of white clover:

- It is a good source of protein.
- Its ability to fix nitrogen, reduces the need for artificial fertiliser, which also reduces costs.
- It provides an increased level of productivity, palatability and digestibility of the sward.
- It reduces the use of chemicals, particularly in organic farming.
- It meets REPS requirements.
- It has a high mineral content.
- It provides good ground cover, which controls the spread of weeds.

Red clover

Red clover is not as popular as white clover in grazing systems. It is often used in seed mixtures sown for silage production. It is a perennial plant and can be recognised by its purple flowers. The leaves and stems of red clover are hairy. It grows in similar conditions to white clover.

Fig 27.6 Red clover

Advantages of red clover:

- It is highly digestible.

- Very productive, it provides a high yield of silage and can be cut a number of times in a season.
- It can fix nitrogen so there is little need for fertiliser, which reduces costs.
- Its tap roots improve aeration and soil structure.

Seed Mixtures

A seed mixture is a combination of a number of different species of grass and clover, or a combination of different strains of the same species of grass often mixed with clover. In the past, it was commonplace to use a variety of species of grass in a seed mixture. However, this practice has shifted in favour of a seed mixture comprising of strains of perennial ryegrass combined with white clover.

> **Heading dates**: The heading date of a grass species is the time when the ear emerges on the grass plant. Grass species are categorised as early, intermediate and late heading.

Table 27.4 Heading dates		
Category	**Heading date**	**Use**
Early	Mid-May	To provide grazing in spring (March/April)
Intermediate	Late May	To provide a good silage yield from May to July
Late	Early June	To provide silage in June to late July and long-term grazing

The key to good grazing management is to have a constant supply of fresh grass available for grazing livestock. If the seed mixture was uniform, all the grass would head out at the same stage and there would be a point in the grazing season where there was very little grass available to livestock. This can be avoided by using a combination of grasses that have different heading dates.

Seed mixtures for grazing

A seed mixture for grazing may include a number of strains of perennial ryegrass of early, intermediate and late heading varieties. Early heading perennial ryegrass will give early growth of leafy grass in spring, so livestock can be let out to graze earlier. The mid and late season varieties will provide grazing pasture throughout the summer and may extend the grazing season into late autumn. Any excess grass produced may be cut for silage.

There are a number of advantages associated with using this type of seed mixture for grazing pasture:

- There is a constant supply of grass over the grazing season from spring to autumn.
- There is always a fresh supply of leafy grass with a high DMD value, as heading dates vary. This ensures the sward has a good feeding value.
- There will not be a dip in production levels at any point in the grazing season as there would be if only one strain of grass was used.
- The whole sward will not go stemmy at the same time leaving unpalatable, poor quality grass, as there is a range of heading dates in the sward.

Fig 27.7 Perennial ryegrass

Seed mixtures for silage

If land is set aside specifically for silage production, the best quality silage will be achieved if all of the grass has a similar heading date, as grass growth will be uniform. To achieve this a seed mixture is used with only one strain of grass or a number of strains of the same type of grass with similar heading dates. This means that all of the grass is ready for silage at the same time and can be cut a number of times in one season.

When land is used primarily for grazing, and excess grass is used for conservation as silage, strains with intermediate and late heading dates are advised for use as a silage crop.

Summary

- Grassland is semi-natural vegetation which, if left unchecked, will be replaced by the natural vegetation of the country, which is deciduous forest.

- Leafy grass species are more palatable and nutritious than taller, stemmy species. Leafy species are more intensely grazed and are found in lowlands. Stemmy species are found on mountains and hillsides.

- The value of grassland is assessed by its botanical composition, stocking rate and productivity.

- The three main categories of grassland are: rough mountain or hill grazing, permanent grassland and leys.

- Rough mountain grass has high variable botanical composition, a low stocking rate and low production levels.

- Permanent grassland has a higher stocking rate and production level than mountain grass and there are fewer species present.

- Leys are sown by the farmer. They have high stocking rates and production levels and are dominated by one or two species of grass.

- The most important characteristics of grass are its palatability, productivity and digestibility.

- Perennial ryegrass has the highest levels of palatability, productivity and digestibility of the common grass species.

- Early in the growing season digestibility is high (80%), but as the grass produces a seed head, carbohydrates are converted to fibre to support the seed head and digestibility decreases to 50 per cent.

- Dry matter (DM): The matter remaining in a sample of food after the water has been removed.

- Dry matter digestibility (DMD): The amount of dry matter than can be digested by an animal.

- Dry matter intake (DMI): The amount of feed an animal consumes, excluding its water content.

- The main species sown in grassland include perennial ryegrass, Italian ryegrass and red and white clover.

- A seed mixture is a combination of a number of different species of grass and clover or a combination of different strains of the same species of grass often mixed with clover.

- The heading date of a grass species is the time when the ear emerges on the grass plant.

QUESTIONS

1 What is the natural vegetation of Ireland?
2 Name the three categories of grassland.
3 List three properties of rough mountain and hill grazing grass.
4 List three properties of permanent grassland.
5 List three properties of leys.
6 What advantages do increased stocking, lime and fertiliser use have on rough mountain and hill grazing?
7 What advantages do increased stocking, lime and fertiliser use have on permanent grassland?
8 List three species of grass you would expect to find in rough mountain and hill grazing.
9 List three species of grass you would expect to find in permanent grassland.
10 List three species of grass you would expect to find in leys.
11 What are the three main characteristics of grass that determine its agricultural importance?
12 What does the term *dry matter digestibility* (DMD) mean?
13 What does the term *dry matter intake* (DMI) mean?
14 Why does the DMD value of a grass decline over the summer grazing period?
15 Explain why DMD value is an important characteristic of grass.
16 What is the function of a refractometer?
17 Explain why perennial ryegrass is considered superior to all other grasses for sowing.
18 What conditions does perennial ryegrass need to grow satisfactorily?
19 Why is Italian ryegrass a suitable grass for sowing?
20 Name the two types of clover found in a grass sward.
21 Describe the appearance of each type of clover and explain how you would tell the difference between both.
22 Why is the presence of clover so important for grazing and grass growth?
23 What does the term *heading out* mean?
24 Seed mixtures used for grazing now use a variety of strains of grass. Give three reasons for this.
25 What type of seed mixture is used for sowing grass for silage? Explain why this seed mixture is used.

EXAM QUESTIONS

1 Suggest a suitable seed mixture that could be used when reseeding a paddock. (LC, HL, 2010)
2 (a) To which plant family does clover belong?
   (b) Give two agriculturally important characteristics of clover. (LC, HL, 2009)
3 Name any two plant species or varieties of herbage to be included in a grass-seed mixture for the production of a permanent pasture. (LC, HL, 2009)
4 Describe how the digestibility of a grass sward changes during the growing season. (LC, HL, 2009)
5 State the benefits of using hybrid ryegrasses over the use of Italian ryegrass on its own. (LC, HL, 2008)
6 Give two reasons for including clover in a seed-mixture for pasture. (LC, HL, 2008)
7 Describe the characteristics of a grass plant at the ideal stage of growth for grazing. (LC, HL, 2007)
8 Explain why the botanical composition of a permanent ley differs from that of a temporary ley. (LC, HL, 2007)
9 Describe a laboratory or field method to determine the percentage of sugar in a sample of grass. (LC, HL, 2008)

Chapter 28

Grazing and Grassland Management

Grassland has two main uses in agriculture: grazing for livestock and conservation of silage and hay for winter fodder. Good management is the key factor in optimising the use of grassland. Farmers must determine how much of the land is to be used for grazing and how much is to be used for conservation. A balance must be achieved to prevent a shortfall in grazing in summer, waste through undergrazing in summer or an inadequate quantity of silage or hay saved for winter fodder.

Farmers must also determine how much grass will be required on an annual basis and how they will achieve this level of production while being cost-effective. Optimisation of production levels can be achieved by good grazing management and by the application of the most suitable fertiliser in the correct quantity.

Livestock units: A livestock unit (LU) is a measurement of livestock grazing. One livestock unit (1 LU) is the equivalent of one dairy cow or one suckler cow. It can be used to determine how much grazing and winter fodder is needed on a farm. One livestock unit requires 12 tonnes (1 tonne = 1 000 kg) of herbage annually. This value can be used to determine the total quantity of herbage required on the farm for the herd.

1 dairy/suckler cow	= 1.0 LU
Cattle <1 year	= 0.4 LU
Cattle 1–2 years	= 0.6 LU
Sheep	= 0.15 LU

Activity 28.1

Calculate how much herbage would be required annually on a farm containing twenty suckler cows, fifteen six-month-old calves, ten 18-month-old cattle and thirty sheep.

☰ Methods of Grazing

There are a number of different methods of grazing. Many of them are based on the concept of a rotational grazing system, where animals are moved around a number of different grazing fields or areas. This allows livestock to graze on fresh grass constantly and allows for re-growth of grazed areas. Grass re-growth takes approximately three weeks. So the best rotational grazing systems operate on the basis that a herd will not return to a paddock during this time to allow the grass to re-grow and reach the vegetative stage of growth. Grass is at its most digestible and is highly palatable during this vegetative growth stage.

Paddock grazing

Paddock grazing is based on dividing the land into 20–30 paddocks. Ideally, each paddock should be of equal size so that it takes the herd one day to graze down the paddock. However, due to a farm's layout, this may not be possible and some paddocks may be created where cattle spend a shorter or longer time grazing. The herd grazes down one paddock each day and is then moved to the next paddock. It will not return to the previous paddock for at least three weeks to give time for the grass to recover. Fertiliser is spread on each grazed paddock after the herd has been moved.

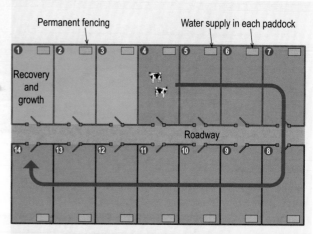

|||| Fig 28.1 Paddock grazing

Advantages of paddock grazing:

▨ Fresh, highly digestible leafy grass is available every day for grazing.

▨ No grass is wasted.

▨ Excess grass produced can be saved as silage.

Disadvantages of paddock grazing:

▨ Expensive to set up. Roadways/access to each paddock need to be created. Fencing and a water supply are needed for each paddock.

▨ If paddocks are small it can be difficult to cut grass for silage.

Activity 28.2

How to calculate the amount of grass available in each paddock

To make this calculation, you need to know the area of the paddock. If the paddocks are of different sizes, the area of the paddock in hectares can be substituted in the equation each time.

Good grassland management requires a precise knowledge of how much grass is available for the grazing herd. Paddocks should be grazed to their optimum level, with no wastage. This measurement can be obtained by going on a weekly farm walk ('walking the land') and taking estimates of the grass cover.

Use the formula on page 237 to determine the grass available for grazing in any paddock and from that how long a herd of cows can be left in a paddock. This procedure can be repeated weekly over the growing season as the output in the paddocks change.

|||| Fig 28.2 Removing grass from inside the quadrat with shears

Materials
Quadrat, shears, plastic bag

Activity 28.2

Method

1 Place a 0.25 m² quadrat in the paddock in an area of grass that is representative of the paddock.

2 Use shears to remove all the grass from within the quadrat. Grass should be cut to the level where the cows should graze.

3 Put the grass in a plastic bag and weigh it, using spring balance scales.

4 Record the weight of the grass.

5 Estimate the DM percentage by squeezing the grass. If water can be squeezed out with one hand, the DM percentage is in the range of 18–20 per cent. Alternatively, a 50 g sample can be dried in a microwave for 30 seconds and weighed. Double the weight of this grass to get the DM percentage.

6 Calculate the amount of dry matter in the grass taken from the quadrat.

Dry matter per 0.25 m² = Weight of grass (g) × DM%

Multiply by 4 to calculate dry matter per m²

Calculate the amount of dry matter available in the paddock by multiplying:

Dry matter per m² × size of paddock (ha)

Calculate the amount of DM available per cow by dividing the dry matter by the number of cows:

$$\frac{\text{Dry matter available}}{\text{herd size}} = \text{DM available per cow}$$

Express this as a fraction of the amount of DM needed per cow. Use this figure to calculate how long the herd can be left grazing in the paddock:

$$\frac{\text{DM available per cow}}{\text{DM needed per cow}}$$

Example

A farmer has a paddock of 0.5 hectares. He has a herd of 50 dairy cows. He would like to determine how long the herd can be left in the paddock so that the entire paddock is grazed completely. His dairy cows will each consume 15 kg of dry matter per day.

Mass of grass removed from 0.25 m² quadrat = 200 g

DM% = 18%

200 g x 0.18 = 36 g of dry matter or 0.036 kg DM per 0.25 m²

0.036 kg of DM × 4 = 0.144 kg DM per m²

0.5 ha = 5 000 m²

0.144 kg DM × 5000 = 720 kg DM/0.5 ha

There are 720 kg of dry matter in the 0.5 ha paddock. The farmer has 50 cows.

$$\frac{720}{50} = 14.4 \text{ kg DM per cow}$$

Each cow normally consumes 15 kg DM per day. $\frac{14.4}{15} \times \frac{100}{1} = 96\%$ of their daily intake.

24 hours × 0.96 = 23.04 hours.

If the herd of 50 cows are put in this 0.5 ha paddock, they will graze down the paddock entirely in 23 hours. Therefore, they should remain in this paddock for 23 hours before moving to the next paddock.

Strip grazing

Strip grazing involves dividing a paddock or field into strips using a movable electric fence. Typically, a strip is created that is big enough to provide enough grazing for the herd for 24 hours. The herd is moved forward to a fresh strip of grass each day. A back fence is used to prevent movement of livestock into the pasture that has previously been grazed.

Livestock are moved around strips in a rotational manner until they return to the first strip three to four weeks later. Each time livestock are moved, the previous strip is fertilised. Strip grazing can be used with a fixed or movable water supply (see Fig 28.3).

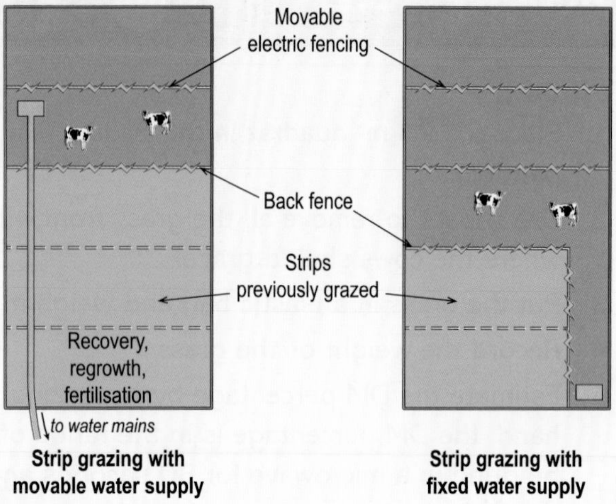

Advantages of strip grazing:

▨ Fresh, leafy grass is available for grazing each day.

▨ There is no wastage of grass as each strip is grazed bare.

▨ Grass is not damaged while re-growing as it is not accessible to livestock.

Disadvantages of strip grazing:

▨ High labour is required to move livestock, fencing and a movable water supply each day.

▨ The use of a fixed water supply means part of a field has to be left as access to the water supply. This land cannot be used for grazing and can be damaged by constant use.

Fig 28.3 Strip grazing

Movable electric fencing

Back fence

Strips previously grazed

Recovery, regrowth, fertilisation

to water mains

Strip grazing with movable water supply

Strip grazing with fixed water supply

Set stocking

Set stocking is the simplest form of grazing management and the least expensive. However, it is the worst form of grazing management and is not associated with intensive farming systems. Stock has access to all grazing land over one continuous area for the grazing season.

Advantages of set stocking:

▨ It is a low-cost system with a minimum of fencing and water troughs required.

▨ Poaching is minimised as livestock are not as densely packed in one area.

▨ Less labour is required.

Disadvantages of set stocking:

▨ In spring, early heading grasses tend not to be fully utilised. In summer, when grass growth is at its peak, it is not grazed efficiently.

▨ Grass is wasted and much of it turns stemmy, leading to a reduced feeding value for the grass and the development of patchy, unpalatable grass with a lower digestibility.

▨ If disease is present in the pasture, livestock are constantly exposed to it.

Fig 28.4 Cattle set stocked on poor quality grazing land

Block grazing

Block grazing is a popular method of grazing in Ireland, particularly on small farms and for part-time farmers where a reduction in labour is preferable. Block grazing consists of dividing large fields into smaller blocks. Livestock graze a block for approximately one week before moving to the next block. Electric fencing can be used to strip graze blocks. Livestock return to a block after three weeks.

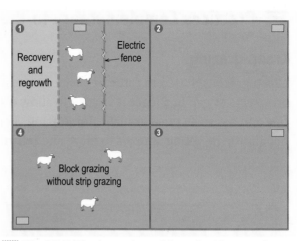

Advantages of block grazing:

- It is cheaper than paddock grazing.
- Less fencing is needed.
- Less labour is required and less movement of animals.

||||| Fig 28.5 Block grazing with and without strip grazing

Disadvantage of block grazing:

- Grazing of blocks is not as efficient as paddock or strip grazing.

Zero grazing

Zero grazing is a system where cattle are housed all year round. Grass or other forage crops are cut and brought to the livestock, where they are fed indoors. Cattle do not graze the land. While the system may be labour intensive there are a number of advantages to using zero grazing:

- Land is not poached by animals.
- Energy is not wasted by animals through movement. Energy can be used for live weight gain and milk production.

||||| Fig 28.6 Cattle housed indoors fed on fresh grass in a zero grazing system

- There is less chance of lameness as livestock are not walking on roads.
- Access to fresh grass at all times means that the cows' feed intake increases.
- The need for silage decreases due to the intake of fresh grass cut from distant fields, which was previously inaccessible to livestock. All fields are accessible for grazing.
- When slurry production increases, the slurry can be spread on the land, reducing the need for artificial fertilisers and cutting costs.
- Topping grass is unnecessary, as all grass is cut at the same time.

> **Topping**: Mowing grass to a height of 5–7 cm. It is carried out post-grazing to remove any remaining grass. Topping cuts grass to the correct post-grazing height and encourages tillering. It can also be used to control weeds.

☰ Practices Complementary to the Grazing Systems

Creep grazing

Creep grazing is used in cattle or sheep systems. It can be used in conjunction with rotational grazing. A creep gate or gap in a fence is created to allow calves or lambs access to another field. This field is disease-free and has fresh grass available for grazing. The gate prevents the older animals from entering the field, but allows the young animals to graze and return to their mothers to suckle.

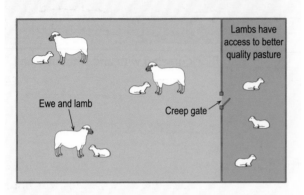

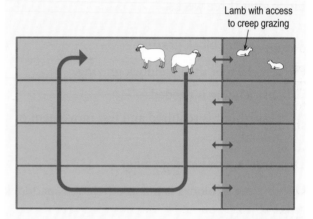

▥ Fig 28.7 Creep grazing is where lambs have access to good quality pasture but can also return to the ewes

▥ Fig 28.8 Creep grazing used in conjunction with rotational grazing

Leader-follower system

The leader-follower system is used in conjunction with paddock grazing where the young animals (calves) are grazed one field ahead of the older animals. Young animals have access to the freshest, leafiest, most digestible grasses as they are always put on fresh pasture. When they are moved to the next paddock, the older animals are moved into the paddock the young animals have just left and graze down the grass that remains. It also means that the young animals are always on fresh, clean grass so there is less chance of them picking up diseases from the grass or from the older animals that have a better immune system. The main difference between leader-follower grazing and creep grazing is that the younger animals do not have access to their mothers.

Mixed grazing

Mixed grazing can be used in conjunction with a rotational grazing system. Mixed grazing is the grazing of cattle and sheep together in the same field or paddock. There are a number of advantages to mixed grazing:

▦ Production levels are increased by 10–15 per cent in both cattle and sheep.

▦ Tillering is increased, as sheep graze closer to the ground. It also reduces the need for topping.

▦ There is less waste of grass due to the sheep's close grazing habit.

▥ Fig 28.9 Mixed grazing of cattle and sheep

- Cows will not eat around their own dung. Sheep will eat this grass ensuring that there is no waste and preventing grass from becoming patchy, stemmy and unpalatable.
- Cows are less selective grazers than sheep, so will eat grass species that sheep will not consume.
- Mixed grazing can reduce the risk of worm infestation in cattle and sheep, as the stocking rate for each is lower when mixed, lowering the risk of infection. In addition, some worms are host specific, so the risk of infestation by endoparasites is reduced.

Tillering

The more side shoots or tillers that are produced by the (grass) plant the greater the quantity of herbage produced. Tillering can be encouraged by grazing pasture with sheep or light stock such as calves. Sheep have a close grazing habit and graze grass low to the base of the stem. When the main shoot of the plant is grazed, this encourages the production of side shoots or tillers. Topping can also encourage tillering.

> **Tillering:** The development of side shoots in a plant.

≡ Fertilisation of Grassland

On grassland where there is little or no clover, nitrogen should be applied to maintain the quality of the grass. Nitrogen should be applied in accordance with the Nitrates Directive. Table 28.1 shows the maximum rates that can be applied. Quantity and timing of application are determined by whether the land is used for grazing or silage. The application of slurry to the land will lead to a reduction in the quantity of N fertiliser needed. The most commonly used N fertilisers are CAN, urea and 18-6-12.

Table 28.1 Application of nitrogen	
Grassland stocking rate (LU/ha)	Maximum N fertiliser (kg/N/ha)
<2	226
2.0–2.47	306
2.47–2.94	279

If slurry is spread on the land, the rate of N application can be decreased. Table 28.2 shows N application levels for first and second cut silage with and without the use of slurry.

Table 28.2 Nitrogen application on grass for silage	
Nitrogen application to first cut silage ground (kg/ha)	
With slurry	Without slurry
115	85
Maximum N application rate	kg/ha
First cut silage	125
Second cut silage	100

Summary

- A livestock unit (LU) is a measurement of livestock grazing. One livestock unit (1 LU) is the equivalent of one dairy cow or one suckler cow.

- A rotational grazing system moves animals around different grazing fields, grazing on fresh grass constantly and allowing for re-growth of grazed areas.

- Paddock grazing divides the land into paddocks of equal size. Livestock are moved to a new paddock each day and grass has re-grown by the time they return to the first paddock.

- Strip grazing divides a field into strips using a movable electric fence. A strip is big enough to provide enough grazing for the herd for 24 hours. The herd is moved forward to a fresh strip of grass each day.

- Set stocking: Livestock have access to all grazing land over one continuous area for the grazing season.

- Block grazing divides up large fields into smaller blocks. Livestock graze a block for approximately one week before moving to the next block. This can be further sub-divided for strip grazing.

- Zero grazing is a system where cattle are housed all year round. Grass or other forage crops are cut and brought to the livestock, where they are fed indoors. Cattle do not graze the land.

- Topping is mowing grass to a height of 5–7 cm. Topping cuts grass to the correct post-grazing height and encourages tillering.

- Creep grazing is where a creep gate or gap in a fence is created to allow calves or lambs access to another field. This field is disease-free and has fresh grass available for grazing.

- The leader-follower system is used in conjunction with paddock grazing where the young animals are grazed one field ahead of the older animals.

- Mixed grazing is the grazing of cattle and sheep together in the same field or paddock.

- Tillering is the development of side shoots in a plant.

QUESTIONS

1. What are the three factors involved in good grassland management?
2. What is a livestock unit?
3. What is rotational grazing?
4. What is paddock grazing?
5. List two advantages and two disadvantages of paddock grazing.
6. A farmer has a herd of 60 cows. Her grazing land is divided into 20 paddocks, each paddock is 0.5 ha. She walks the land to determine how much grass is available for grazing. She removed the grass from a 0.25 m² quadrat. The grass weighed 150 g. The DM value was 20 per cent. Calculate how long she can leave her herd in each paddock before it is grazed down fully. Do you think paddock grazing is suitable for this farm? Give a reason for your answer.
7. Describe strip grazing as a method of grazing.
8. List one advantage and one disadvantage of strip grazing.
9. List two advantages of set stocking. Why is it considered such a poor form of grassland management?
10. Describe block grazing as a method of grazing.

QUESTIONS

11 What is zero grazing? State three advantages of zero grazing.
12 What is meant by the term *topping*?
13 Give one reason topping is carried out.
14 What is creep grazing?
15 Describe what is meant by the leader-follower system.
16 List three advantages of mixed grazing.
17 What is tillering?
18 How can tillering be encouraged?
19 How can the use of artificial N fertilisers be reduced on grazing land?
20 Name two artificial fertilisers used in grassland management.

EXAM QUESTIONS

1   Highlight the main differences between the following: zero grazing and creep grazing. (LC, HL, 2010)
2   (a) Explain the term *tillering*.
    (b) Mention two ways by which the farmer can encourage the tillering process. (LC, HL, 2008)
3   Give two reasons for the process of 'topping' grassland during the grazing season. (LC, HL, 2008)
4   Explain the 'leader-follower' grazing system and give two reasons why it is used by farmers.
    (LC, HL, 2008)
5   With the aid of labelled diagrams, compare and contrast strip growing and paddock grazing on a
    dairy farm. (LC, HL, 2002)

Chapter 29
Sowing and Reseeding Grassland

There are different methods of sowing grass. Many factors determine the sowing method. For example, soil type and depth affect how seed is sown. Farmers must take into account how they want to use the land. For example, if a pasture has been used for grazing or silage for many years and needs to be reseeded then this would also be a factor in choosing the method of sowing.

☰ Reasons for Reseeding Grassland

There are many specific reasons for reseeding grassland. Overall, the aim is to improve the quality of the grass sward.

Weed infestation

After many years, weeds can start to take over a pasture, reducing its overall productivity. Dock leaves, in particular, can be prevalent as their seeds can be spread when slurry is applied. Reseeding can help to remove weeds and improve pasture quality.

Low ryegrass content/high content of poor quality grasses

After a number of years, troublesome weed grasses such as scutch grass and bent grasses can start to dominate a sward. They compete with the good quality grasses such as perennial ryegrass. They lower productivity, palatability and digestibility. These three factors determine how good a grass is for grazing.

||||| Fig 29.1 Grassland infested with weeds

Addition of clover

Reseeding a pasture may allow a farmer to increase the clover content of the pasture. Clover will increase the protein content of the pasture as well as fixing nitrogen in the soil.

Animal activity

Livestock may have poached the land, leading to poor quality pasture. This may be improved by reseeding the land. Establishment of a new sward can improve the root mat system, decreasing the likelihood of poaching.

Livestock can also undergraze or overgraze the land, which can cause problems for pasture quality. Undergrazing, particularly in a pasture with a variety of grasses, can lead to poorer quality grasses dominating, as grasses are selectively grazed by cattle. As the poorer quality grasses dominate, this lowers the overall productivity, palatability and digestibility of the grass, which also leads to lower liveweight gain and milk production.

Overgrazing a pasture down to the roots can prevent the grass growing back properly and hinder its ability to tiller. This will also lower the productivity of the grass.

Poor soil fertility

Before reseeding takes place, soil tests should be carried out and lime and fertiliser requirements should be determined. Perennial ryegrass has an optimum growth rate at a pH of 6.5, so it may be necessary to lime the land to raise the pH to a suitable level. If phosphorus and potassium are lacking, they should be applied to the land in the form of a compound fertiliser or slurry.

Phosphorus is important in the development of plant roots. Soil deficient in phosphorus will lead to poor root development in the grass sward.

Benefits of reseeding:

- Improves grass quality.
- Improves silage quality.
- Increases meat and milk production.
- Higher output allows increased stocking density on land.
- Better response to N fertilisers.
- Longer grazing season reduces the need for winter fodder (silage). This reduces overall costs.
- Excess grass as a result of increased productivity could be cut for silage and sold.

≡ Methods of Sowing and Reseeding Grassland

There are several methods of sowing or reseeding grassland, each with their own advantages. They include direct sowing, undersowing, direct drilling, slurry seeding and slit seeding.

Direct sowing (plough, till and sow)

Direct sowing is the most common method of sowing grass in Ireland. It is also the most consistent method of establishing a sward. Land is ploughed, which has the advantage of burying the weed seeds. It is harrowed to create a fine seedbed. Seed can be sown using a seed drill or by broadcasting the seed onto the soil surface and covering with a harrow.

- **Fertiliser application**: In leys sown in autumn, N fertiliser is not applied until the following spring. In leys sown in spring, fertiliser can be applied during seedbed preparation and harrowed into the soil.
- **Time of sowing**: Seed has to be sown by September in an autumn-sown ley, as frost and winter weather conditions could kill the seedlings. In spring, seed should be sown before May. This will prevent seedlings being killed off due to drought. It will also provide a longer growing season for seed establishment.

Undersowing

Undersowing is used on farms growing tillage crops. It is particularly suitable for tillage/grassland rotations. Undersowing means grass seed is sown with a tillage crop (e.g. barley, wheat). It is not suitable for winter cereals.

Grass seed is sown with the spring cereal. The land is prepared for the cereal crop and the cereal seed is then sown. Cereal varieties with short straw should be chosen to reduce the risk of lodging. Lodging will damage the grass. The grass seed is then sown immediately afterwards. Both grow at the same time. When the cereal is harvested in summer, the grass remains and establishes itself in the field.

Benefits of undersowing:

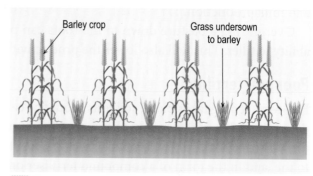

Fig 29.2 Undersowing

- Nitrogen leaching can be prevented or reduced, as the grass will take up any excess nitrogen following the cereal harvest.
- Soil erosion can be prevented as the grass is established after the cereal has been harvested.
- Grass growing alongside the cereal can provide good ground cover and can prevent weed infestation.
- Grassland can be used for grazing after cereal is harvested.

Drawbacks of undersowing:

- As two crops are growing simultaneously they are in competition for water, nutrients and space.
- Undersowing grass to a cereal will lead to a reduction in yield in the cereal crop as it competes with the grass.
- Herbicide use must be restricted if clover is sown with the grass seed.
- Undersowing is not suited to intensive cereal farming where high crop yields are required.

Direct drilling/direct seeding

A direct drilling machine sows the seed. The machine cuts a slit in the soil and drops a seed into it. The land does not have to be ploughed beforehand. Direct drilling is most successful if the land to be seeded or reseeded is grazed bare, or if a herbicide is applied beforehand. This is particularly important if the land was infested with weeds.

Glyphosate (a herbicide) should be applied to the land to remove broadleaf weeds, e.g. dock leaves.

Seeds have the best chance of germination and establishment if they are drilled into bare land.

Fig 29.3 Dock leaf

Benefits of direct seeding:

- This method is most beneficial on soils where ploughing is impossible or is difficult.
- Soils that are easily poached or are shallow are particularly suitable for direct seeding.

Slurry seeding

Slurry seeding is carried out in the same way as direct seeding. After seeding, approximately 10 000 litres of slurry is applied to the land to cover the seed.

Slit seeding/stitching-in

This method of reseeding is very similar to direct drilling. It uses similar machinery to sow the seed.

The main difference is that the grassland is not killed off. Seed is always sown into old grassland.

Slit seeding should take place in spring (March or April) when grass growth is not at an optimum level. This will give the new seed a chance to establish itself in the sward without having to compete with the old sward during the rapid growth periods in the summer months. The old sward should be tightly grazed before seeding. Nitrogen fertiliser may be sown with the seed to encourage establishment.

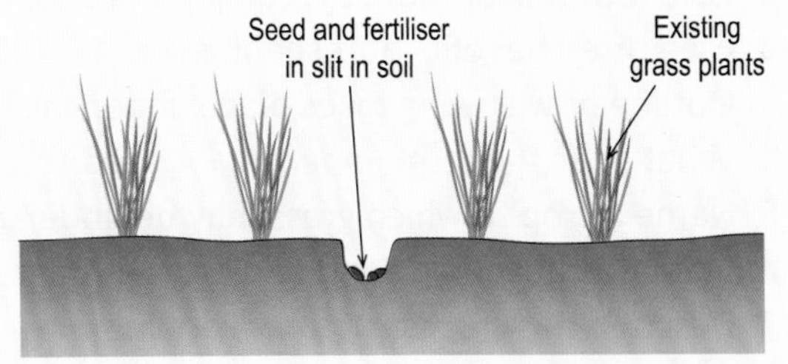

Benefits of slit seeding:

- No need to plough the land.
- Land has not been taken out of use for a prolonged period.
- Increased production level, quality and yield in grass.
- If the seed does not establish itself, the old sward will continue to grow.
- Can be used on poached/shallow soils not suited to ploughing.

Fig29.4 Slit seeding

Summary

- Grass is reseeded due to weed infestation, low ryegrass content and high content of poor quality grasses.
- Reseeding improves palatability, productivity and digestibility. It increases clover content in a sward and improves soil fertility.
- Benefits of reseeding grassland include: improved grass quality, improved silage quality, increased meat and milk production, an increase in stocking density, better response to fertilisers, a longer grazing season and reduced need for winter fodder. Excess silage can be sold.
- Methods of sowing include: direct sowing, undersowing, direct drilling, slurry seeding and slit seeding.
- Direct sowing: Land is ploughed and harrowed and seed is sown with a seed drill or broadcast on the soil. N fertiliser is applied in spring. Autumn-sown leys are sown in September and spring-sown leys are sown before May.
- Undersowing: Grass seed is sown with another tillage crop. When the tillage crop is harvested, grass establishes itself in the field. This is only suitable for spring-sown crops. It provides good ground cover and prevents weed infestation, but competition from the two crops reduces the yield of the main crop.
- Direct drilling/direct seeding: A slit is made in the ground by a direct drilling machine and the seed is dropped into it. The land is not ploughed but it is grazed bare. Herbicides can be used to kill broadleaf weeds. It is useful on shallow soils that cannot be ploughed.
- Slurry seeding: The same process as direct seeding except that slurry is applied to the land after sowing.
- Slit seeding: Similar to direct drilling, grass is sown into a slit in the land, but the grassland is not killed off beforehand. This is carried out in spring to give the new grass the optimum chance of establishment. This can be carried out on soils unsuitable for ploughing, and it helps to improve old grassland.

QUESTIONS

1 Give four reasons for reseeding grassland.
2 Give three benefits of reseeding.
3 Outline how sowing takes place under the direct sowing method.
4 What does the term *undersowing* mean?
5 Name a crop to which grass may be undersown.
6 State one advantage and one disadvantage of undersowing.
7 Describe the process of direct drilling.
8 Where is direct drilling of most use?
9 When is the best time to slit seed? Give a reason for your answer.
10 List two advantages of slit seeding.

EXAM QUESTION

Suggest four reasons why dairy farmers find it necessary to reseed their paddocks on a regular basis.
(LC, HL, 2010)

Chapter 30
Conservation of Grass: Silage and Hay Production

Conservation of Grass as a Winter Feed

Grass is the main source of feed for livestock in Ireland. Cattle and sheep get almost all of their nutrition from fresh or conserved grass. During the summer months there is no shortage of fresh grass for grazing animals. During the winter months, where there is no grass growth, it is necessary to feed conserved grass, which is often supplemented with other concentrated animal feeds. Fig 30.1 shows that excess grass is produced during the summer months, particularly between May and July. This grass can be saved in the form of hay or silage for winter feeding. This provides a relatively cheap source of feed all year without the need to purchase large quantities of expensive animal feeds.

Grass can only be conserved as winter feed if bacterial activity in the grass is inhibited. If bacterial activity was not inhibited, the grass would spoil in a short period and would be of no use as winter feed. Silage making and haymaking are the two main methods of conserving grass. Each uses a different method of inhibiting bacterial activity.

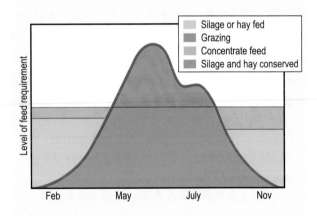

Fig 30.1 Grass production curve

- **Silage**: Fermentation of carbohydrates in the grass produces acids, which lower the pH of the grass and inhibit all microbial activity. Properly fermented and preserved silage can be stored for a few years.

- **Hay**: Grass is dehydrated to remove the majority of the water present. In the absence of water, microbial activity is inhibited.

Silage Production

A number of factors influence when grass is cut for silage. Silage should be cut when the weather is good, in mid to late May and again in July to August. Silage making can be delayed by poor summer weather, and second cut silage can extend into September.

Silage is cut from permanent grassland or ryegrass sown leys. The heading dates of the grasses in these fields can also determine when the silage is cut; an early heading grass may be cut in May, but it will not be possible to cut a late heading grass until June. Farmers must consider this when sowing grass for silage.

The grass must be cut when digestibility is high, to ensure the highest possible feeding value for the silage. Dry matter digestibility (DMD) is approximately 75 per cent at the heading out stage in perennial ryegrass. For each day that cutting is delayed after this point, the DMD value falls by 0.5 per cent. This also affects the quality at ensiling.

Heading out: When half the grass plants have produced seed heads.
Ensiling: The process of storing grass or another crop in a silo, clamp or pit for preservation as silage.

Grass cut for silage should also contain a high level of carbohydrate. Grass is preserved as silage through the process of fermentation. Fermentation is the conversion of carbohydrates (sugars) to acid by bacteria. The acids produced preserve the grass as silage; therefore, carbohydrates are essential for this process to be carried out properly. Farmers can provide the optimum conditions for high carbohydrate levels in ensiled grass by following the guidelines below:

- Water dilutes carbohydrate concentration in grass, so do not cut grass during or after rainfall.
- Cut grass at the vegetative stage when it is leafy and there is a high carbohydrate concentration.
- Wilt the grass for one to two days after mowing. Wilting reduces water content, thereby increasing carbohydrate content.
- Use double chop machinery to cut the grass into smaller pieces. Carbohydrate is more accessible to bacteria for fermentation when the grass is more finely chopped.
- Cut grass in the afternoon as it has been photosynthesising, giving higher carbohydrate content.
- Adding a sugar or molasses solution increases carbohydrate content in the ensiled grass. This ensures fermentation takes place.

☰ The Biochemistry of Silage Making: The Fermentation Process

Fermentation of carbohydrates in grass is carried out by **anaerobic bacteria.** Therefore, the fermentation process cannot begin until all of the oxygen is removed from the cut grass. Grass is rolled when it is brought to the silage pit to remove the air from it. This also prevents the grass from respiring. If oxygen is present, the grass will continue to respire and convert the carbohydrate in the grass to carbon dioxide. This uses up the carbohydrate and lowers the nutritional value of the silage. When the oxygen is removed, the bacteria can begin to respire anaerobically and convert the carbohydrate into acid, which will preserve the silage. The acids produced by fermentation lower the pH to a level that inhibits bacterial activity and preserves the grass as silage for future use.

The concentration of carbohydrate present in the silage has a huge influence on the type of bacteria that will carry out the fermentation, the type of acid produced and the overall quality of the silage. Two different scenarios are summarised below for grass with a high carbohydrate concentration and grass with a low carbohydrate concentration.

Fermentation by *Lactobacillus* produces good quality lactic acid silage, whereas *Clostridium* produces poor quality butyric acid silage.

Table 30.1 Comparison of lactic acid silage and butyric acid silage		
Carbohydrate concentration	High	Low
Bacteria present	*Lactobacillus*	*Clostridium*
Acid produced	Lactic acid	Butyric acid
Silage quality	Good	Poor
Nutritional value	Good	Poor
Palatability	Palatable to stock	Unpalatable to stock
Storage duration	A number of years	A few months

Silage making

Silage can be produced in two ways: in a pit/clamp or in round bales. Both methods are outlined below.

Production of pit silage

Pit silage is more common on large scale farms. A silage pit normally has three concrete walls and a concrete base. A pit can be expensive to construct and may not be financially viable for small farms. The pit also needs to have a storage tank for effluent and channels to bring effluent from the pit to the tank. The tank should be leak proof to prevent pollution. The storage tank and channels should be cleaned out prior to silage production and polythene and tyres should be readily available to cover the pit.

- Close off the field to livestock and fertilise it in the spring.

- Grass is mowed and left in rows called swathes. It is allowed to wilt.

- It is then picked up by a forage harvester, which cuts the grass and blows it into a trailer.

- The cut grass is brought to the silage pit or clamp and heaped. The pit/clamp should not be located by a waterway to prevent pollution from effluent, but should be easily accessible for winter feeding.

||||| Fig 30.2 Mowed grass has been left to wilt

- A tractor rolls over the layer of grass to remove any air from it. If additives are being used in the silage-making process, they can be added to each layer that is rolled. Some additives may have been added during the harvesting process.

- Once the air has been removed by repeated rolling, the pit or clamp is sealed with heavy-duty, black polythene sheeting. The polythene keeps the pit airtight to allow for anaerobic respiration to take place. It also prevents water from getting into the silage.

- The polythene should be weighed down to keep it in place. One of the most common ways to do this is with old tyres. An alternative to this is to use a heavy-duty, polyethylene mesh cover that is weighted down with gravel bags. As it is reusable every year, it removes the need for a large number of tyres.

||||| Fig 30.3 Forage harvester

- The polythene sheet should be inspected after two to three weeks and tightened and resealed as the silage may subside during this time.

Round bale silage

Round bale silage is a very popular method of silage production in Ireland, particularly on small farms.

||||| Fig 30.4 Tyres weigh down a silage pit

- Grass for round bales should be mown and wilted for one to two days, to 30 per cent DM.

- Swathes of grass are then collected by the baler and turned into bales.

- They are then wrapped in polythene by the wrapper. Baling and wrapping can be carried out using separate baling and wrapping machines or by one integrated machine, which completes both tasks. Most polythene used for wrapping is black, but white or pale green film is also available. The light colour reflects sunlight and helps to keep the bales cool, prolonging their storage life.

- The bales should then be transported to where they are to be stored. Care should be taken in transport to prevent damage or tears to the polythene. Any damage should be rectified immediately.
- Bales should be stored standing on the flat part of the bale. This has a thicker layer of polythene and is less likely to burst. The thicker layer of polythene is also better able to withstand attack from birds.
- To comply with REPS, bales should not be stored closer than 20 metres from a watercourse and stacked no more than two bales high.

||||| Fig 30.5 Round bales transported by tractor

Advantages of round bale silage:

- Less dependent on weather conditions.
- Quality of baled silage can be as good as pit silage; usually better when well managed.
- Low aerobic spoilage losses compared to pit silage.
- Ideal for the conservation of surplus grasses and of grass harvested in autumn.
- Lower dry matter losses during production and storage (<5–10%) than pit silage.
- Flexible storage system; bales can be stored in the field or easily transported to any location on the farm.
- Less expensive for the small farmer when the construction of a silage pit cannot be justified; low transport and storage costs.
- If bales are wrapped properly, there is no effluent, which lowers the risk of pollution. Effluent storage facilities and disposal are unnecessary.
- Excess round bales can be sold.

Disadvantages of round bale silage:

- High unit costs.
- Unsuitable for very wet silage.
- Labour/time at feeding out.
- Prone to damage if not properly handled.
- Plastic waste disposal cost and compliance with waste regulations.

Additives in silage production

Additives are used in silage making when poor preservation may occur and carbohydrate concentration in the ensiled grass may be low. Additives cannot turn poor grass into good silage; however, they can enhance the quality of the ensiled grass for a relatively small cost. There are a number of different additives available and each has a different mode of action on the ensiled grass.

Acids

Acids are used to aid preservation. They lower the pH of the silage, inhibiting the fermentation process and preventing bacterial activity. They are applied at a rate of 3 litres/tonne grass.

Sulfuric acid is one of the most common acids used. Their main disadvantage is that they can reduce the palatability of the grass and they can corrode machinery. They would be more commonly used by silage contractors.

Sugars and molasses

Sugar solutions and molasses are added to ensiled grass to increase carbohydrate concentrations in the pit. This extra sugar is used in the fermentation process. Molasses is one of the more commonly used additives in silage making. It should be applied evenly to each layer of grass in the pit.

Bacterial inoculants

The addition of inoculants speeds up the fermentation process and the reduction of pH within the pit. Innoculants can do this more rapidly than acids. They can also aid the preservation of protein.

Enzymes

Enzymes are added to silage in order to break down grass fibres. The breakdown of grass fibres provides additional carbohydrates in the form of sugar for fermentation.

Silage effluent

The fermentation process that takes place in the silage pit releases a liquid known as silage effluent. Effluent is nutrient rich and contains nitric acid. If effluent seeps into a watercourse it can cause pollution as it has a high BOD level (see Chapter 25). To prevent this from happening, silage effluent needs to be collected in a storage tank and stored. It can then be disposed of in a safe manner. Effluent tanks are usually located underground and there is a channel leading from the pit to the tank for efficient effluent collection. Tanks should be leak proof. As effluent contains mineral nutrients, it can be diluted and spread on the land as a fertiliser. This reduces disposal costs and recycles nutrients. As with all fertilisers, care should be taken when spreading effluent to prevent run-off and seepage into waterways.

Effluent can be minimised by wilting grass before conservation for silage. This reduces the volume of liquid effluent produced.

Activity 30.1

Assessing silage quality

Silage can be assessed for quality by examining its colour, texture, smell, pH and DM content. Most of these tests can be done at the silage pit. A sample of silage can also be tested in the laboratory if more appropriate.

Materials

Silage sample, microwave, pH meter probe, beaker, distilled water

Method

1   Colour: Begin with a visual assessment of the silage. Note its colour.

2   Texture: Rub the sample between your fingers. Note the feel of the leaves and the stems.

3   Smell: Smell the silage and record the smell.

4   DM content: Squeeze a sample of silage with one hand. Note if any liquid can be removed from it. Repeat by wringing out a sample of silage with two hands and note if any liquid can be removed from it.

5   DM assessment in lab: Place 50 g of silage in a microwave for 30 seconds. Remove from the microwave and weigh. Multiply its mass by 2 to calculate dry matter.

6   pH: Squeeze the liquid from the silage and put the pH meter probe into the liquid to read the pH. Alternately, if liquid cannot be squeezed from the silage, place a small amount of silage (20 g) into a beaker with 20 cm³ of distilled water. Stir the silage and water. Place the pH meter probe in the water and record the pH.

Activity 30.1

7   Record your results in a table similar to Table 30.2.

Table 30.2 Silage assessment results					
Sample	Colour	Texture	Smell	DM content	pH

8   Compare your results to the table below and determine the quality of your silage, based on your results.

Table 30.3 Characteristics of lactic acid and butyric acid silage					
Silage type	Colour	Texture	Smell	pH	DM content
Lactic acid	Yellow-green	Soft but firm. Fibres do not wear easily	Sharp, acidic, vinegar	<5.0 ideally should be between 3.8 and 4.2	Liquid cannot be removed by hand. DM >25%
Butyric acid	Dark green	Wet and slimy	Putrid or rancid	>5.0 acidic but has not been properly preserved, only clostridial bacteria present	Liquid can be wrung out with two hands. DM 20–25% Liquid can be squeezed out with one hand. DM <20%

☰ Haymaking

About 18 per cent of conserved grass in Ireland is used for haymaking. Its popularity has declined over the years, with more farmers choosing to make silage. As haymaking is heavily reliant on good weather conditions, silage making has become a safer choice. However, hay has the advantage of being a clean, easily transported winter feed that produces no effluent.

Hay production

Timing

Grass for hay production should be cut in late May or early June, weather permitting. Ideally it should be cut when DMD is at its highest. This is normally in May, but weather may not allow for this. Do not allow livestock to graze the field before harvest. The pasture should also be fertilised with N, P and K. Teagasc recommend 65–80 kg/ha N. CAN, 18-6-12 and 27-2.5-5 are the most common compound fertilisers used in hay making.

Weather

Cut grass for hay only when a prolonged period of dry weather is expected. Warm, sunny, dry weather is needed to remove the moisture from the crop. The moisture levels at storage should be less than 20 per cent.

Machinery

Three machines are essential in the production of hay: a rotary mower, a rotary tedder or 'hay-bob' and a baler.

Rotary mower

The rotary mower is the first machine used in the haymaking process. The mower cuts the grass and leaves it in rows. It is particularly useful for cutting lodged crops. The grass is left in rows in the field.

||||| Fig 30.6 Rotary mower mowing grass

||||| Fig 30.7 Grass being tedded

Rotary tedder

The tedder or 'hay bob' shakes out the grass, allowing air to pass through it and speed up the drying process. Grass for haymaking may be tedded twice before it is baled. Grass should be tedded as soon as possible after cutting. The tedder should be set to minimise damage to the cut grass. The tedder can then be used to gather the grass into rows for baling.

Baler

When the grass has dried out, the baler collects the grass and converts it into bales, which are secured with net wrap or baling twine. Unless there is a prolonged period of dry weather, the quantity of grass cut should be equal to the amount that can be baled in one day, as heavy rainfall can damage the crop. Bales should be moved into storage in a hay shed as soon as possible to avoid getting wet.

||||| Fig 30.8 Hay baling

Summary

■ Grass can be saved in the form of hay or silage for winter feeding.

■ Silage: Fermentation of carbohydrates in the grass produces acids, which lower the pH of the grass and inhibit all microbial activity. Properly fermented and preserved silage can be stored for a few years.

■ Hay: Grass is dehydrated to remove the majority of the water present. In the absence of water microbial activity is inhibited.

■ Heading out: Half the grass plants have produced seed heads.

■ Ensiling: The process of storing grass or another crop in a silo, clamp or pit for preservation as silage.

■ Farmers can provide the optimum conditions for high carbohydrate levels in ensiled grass by cutting grass when it is leafy, cutting in dry weather, using double chop machinery, leaving the grass to wilt and adding molasses to the ensiled grass.

■ Fermentation by *Lactobacillus* produces good quality lactic acid silage, whereas *Clostridium* produces poor quality butyric acid silage.

■ Silage produced in a pit needs to be rolled to remove air pockets, so that anaerobic bacteria can begin the fermentation process, and covered with polythene to keep the pit airtight.

■ Round bales are easy to transport, can be sold, are cheaper for the small farmer and produce no effluent.

■ Additives can enhance the quality of ensiled grass. Acids, sugar and molasses, bacterial inoculants and enzymes are all common additives.

■ Effluent is a nutrient-rich liquid, which seeps from silage stored in a pit and can be a pollutant if not stored and disposed of correctly.

■ Hay is a clean, easily transported winter feed which produces no effluent. Its production is heavily dependent on prolonged dry, sunny weather.

■ A rotary mower, a rotary tedder and a baler are all needed in the production of hay.

QUESTIONS

1 How can the activity of bacteria be controlled (two ways)?
2 When can grass be cut for silage?
3 What level of DMD is most desirable in grass for silage?
4 What happens to the DMD value of the grass after heading out?
5 What is meant by the term *heading out*?
6 What is meant by the term *ensiling*?
7 List four ways a farmer can encourage high carbohydrate levels in grass.
8 How does anaerobic respiration help to conserve silage?
9 What are the names of two of the bacteria involved in fermentation?
10 What is the difference between lactic acid silage and butyric acid silage?
11 What stage should grass be at when cut for silage?
12 Describe the steps carried out in the silage-making process.
13 Describe two ways of storing silage.
14 Give four advantages of round bales.

QUESTIONS

15 Give an example of an acid additive and explain why it is used.
16 Why is molasses used in silage making?
17 Why are bacterial inoculants used as additives in silage making?
18 Why is effluent harmful? How can these dangers be avoided?
19 List three ways of assessing the quality of a silage sample.
20 When should grass be cut for hay and at what stage of growth should the grass be?
21 What machinery is needed for haymaking and what is the function of each machine?
22 What is tedding?
23 Why does grass need to be tedded frequently in haymaking?
24 When should baling be carried out?
25 State one advantage of haymaking over silage making.

EXAM QUESTIONS

1   Explain the significance of the leaf-to-stem ratio in relation to silage quality. (LC, HL, 2010)
2   Outline how a farmer can provide the optimal conditions for bacteria to produce high quality silage. (LC, HL, 2008)
3   Explain the importance of each of the following in the preservation of grass as silage:
    (a) Presence of sugars in the grass.
    (b) Absence of air during ensiling.
    (c) Use of additives.
    (d) Wilting the grass. (LC, HL, 2005)

Tillage Crops

Chapter 31

Crops: Production and Principles

Project link

As part of the practical assessment, students are required to complete a project on two crops. They may choose two of the following:

1 Grassland
2 Potato or root crop
3 Cereal crop.

Any two from the list are acceptable, but two crops must be included in the project to be able to attain full marks in this section. Headings for discussion include: varieties, rotation, cultivation practices, establishment, harvesting and yield. Students can include extra information that may be relevant. Students can gain their practical experience of their two chosen crops by visiting a farm where these crops are grown or by growing the crops themselves on a small scale. For an example see Chapter 36, Potatoes, where a description of how to grow potatoes on a small scale has been outlined. Other examples of root crops include: sugar beet, fodder beet, turnips and swedes. Examples of cereals include: barley, wheat, oats and maize. This section of the book will give an overview of six of these crops.

≡ Certified Seed

The Department of Agriculture, Fisheries and Food (DAFF) is responsible for seed certification in Ireland. Potatoes, cereals, vegetables and fodder crops are just some of the crops included in the scheme. Seeds included in the scheme must pass identity and purity tests. The main advantages of using certified seed are that the germination rate is guaranteed and, therefore, a high yield can be guaranteed.

Properties of certified seed:

- Must have a minimum germination rate of 85 per cent.
- Must have a minimum analytical purity rate of 98 per cent.
- The seed must be treated with fungicide/pesticide.
- The seed must be completely free from wild oat seed.

||||| Fig 31.1 Wild oats growing in maize

These standards apply to barley, wheat, oats, grass and maize seed. However, the percentage germination for maize is 90 per cent and for perennial ryegrass and white clover is 80 per cent. The purity rate for perennial ryegrass is 96 per cent.

Experiment 31.1

To determine the percentage germination of certified seed and uncertified seed

Note: This experiment can be performed with any cereal as long as a sample of certified seed and uncertified or home-produced seed is used.

Materials
Sample of certified seed of choice, sample of uncertified seed of choice, petri dishes or seed trays, filter paper, water

Method

1 Count out 100 grains of certified seed and 100 grains of uncertified seed. Do not mix the two samples.

2 Place each sample in a separate labelled beaker; add water and leave to soak for 24 hours.

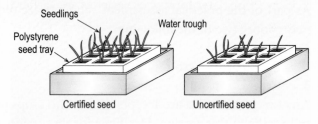

IIIII Fig 31.2 Plant growth

3 Using labelled seed trays, or a set of petri dishes, lay out damp filter paper on the tray. Lay the seeds from each sample in separate trays.

4 Place the trays in darkness for one week. Check on the trays regularly to ensure that the filter paper has not dried out. If it has, add some water to it.

5 After one week, count the number of germinated seeds.

Result
Place the number of germinated seeds in each sample over 100 and multiply by $\frac{100}{1}$ to calculate the percentage germination rate and compare the two results.

Winter sowing v spring sowing

As well as choosing a seed for its certified qualities, farmers may choose to sow a crop (particularly cereals) either in winter or in spring, and so will have to choose a seed type suitable for the seasonal conditions. Both winter and spring varieties of cereal seeds are available, each with their own properties.

Table 31.1 Characteristics of winter and spring seed varieties	
Winter variety seeds	**Spring variety seeds**
Frost resistant	Not frost resistant
Sown September to November	Sown February to April
Harvested mid-July onwards	Harvested August onwards
Longer growing season	Shorter growing season
Higher yield due to longer growing season	Lower yield due to shorter growing season

Ideally, farmers should sow as much as possible of their land with winter varieties, as this produces a high yield with earlier harvesting. It may not always be possible to plant all winter varieties. If there is crop rotation in place, one crop may be harvested in late autumn; sowing a spring variety may be more suitable in these circumstances. However, winter varieties have a number of advantages.

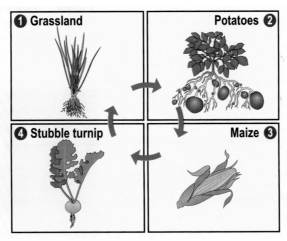

Advantages of sowing winter variety cereals:

▨ In a mixed farming system (tillage and livestock) labour can be spread over the year by sowing winter varieties, as the farmer will be busy with calving and lambing in spring.

‖‖‖ Fig 31.3 Unripe winter wheat

▨ Winter varieties have a longer growing season than spring varieties and, as a result, a higher yield of up to 20 per cent.

▨ Harvesting dates for winter varieties are earlier than spring varieties, so they can be harvested in good weather conditions. Harvesting may prove to be difficult for spring varieties in poor autumn conditions and losses may occur as a result.

▨ Poor weather conditions in spring (late frost and snow, cold temperatures) may delay sowing, germination and the establishment of a crop. This can lead to a delay in harvesting and lower yields than winter varieties.

The suitability of the land that is to be used for growing crops must also be taken into account when planning for tillage. Soils that are lacking nutrients, have poor structure or are infested with pests will not lead to high crop yields. These problems can be overcome by crop rotation.

☰ Crop Rotation

Crop rotation is a system of tillage cultivation where crops are grown in a defined sequence. Each subsequent crop is different from the previous crop: it has different nutritional needs, but also has different pests associated with it.

Crop rotation prevents a build up of pests in a crop over time; it stops the soil being depleted of nutrients and maintains the soil structure.

‖‖‖ Fig 31.4 An example of a four-year crop rotation

Advantages of crop rotation

Prevention of the build-up of pests and diseases

If the same crop is grown in the same field year after year, the pests and diseases that affect that crop will accumulate, which will damage the crop and reduce yields. Some of these pests can live in the soil for many years. To reduce the risk of attack by pests and diseases, crop rotation using several unrelated crops is advised, as the pests that attack each crop will be different, e.g. a root crop followed by a cereal or grassland. This can also help to prevent a build up of weeds specific to a crop.

Nutrient management

Different crops make use of different nutrients at different rates. If the same crop is continuously grown, it will strip the soil of certain nutrients, making it infertile. Crop rotation prevents this and has the added benefit that some plants add nutrients to the

Fig 31.5 Deadly nightshade is a weed associated with maize

soil. For example, planting any leguminous plant (e.g. peas, beans, clover) can fix nitrogen.

Deep-rooted crops can be alternated with fibrous root crops. This allows the use of nutrients that are deep in the soil but unavailable to some crops. For example, the roots of a maize plant can extend up to 1.5 metres underground in good soil conditions.

The fibrous roots of grass help to maintain the organic matter levels in soil. Therefore, grass is often included in crop rotation.

Soil structure

Fibrous plants such as grasses can help bind soil together and improve soil structure. They also help to prevent soil erosion. When the grass is ploughed into the soil to prepare for sowing a new crop, the grass contributes to the fertility of the soil in the form of organic matter.

≡ Control of Pests, Weeds and Diseases

Pests, weeds and diseases can all have an adverse effect on a crop, damaging the crop and reducing its yield. A variety of methods are employed on farms to reduce the effect of pests, weeds and diseases.

Fig 31.6 Leaf roll is a viral disease of potatoes

Biological control

Biological control is the management of a pest, by introducing a predator or parasite of that organism. The predator normally controls the pest organism by consuming the pest, killing it or damaging it. An example of a biological control is that of ladybirds and aphids. Ladybirds are the natural predators of aphids and will keep aphid populations under control.

Fig 31.7 A ladybird eating an aphid

Indirect control

Indirect control is the implementation of agricultural practices that do not eradicate pests and diseases directly; it discourages their establishment.

There are five methods of controlling pests, weeds and diseases indirectly:

1 Crop rotation
2 Sow resistant crop varieties
3 Growth encouragement
4 Timely harvesting
5 Stubble cleaning.

1 **Crop rotation**, which was dealt with in the previous section, prevents the build up of pests, weeds and diseases of a specific crop by sowing dissimilar crops in the same place in subsequent years.

2 **Sowing resistant crop varieties** helps to prevent attack from pests and diseases, as these varieties are not affected by the disease. In some cases, the variety has been developed to resist the disease, particularly when there is no other way of preventing it. For example, some varieties of sugar beet seed are resistant to the Rhizomania virus (see Chapter 37, Sugar Beet), which has an adverse affect on the crop.

Fig 31.8 Beet necrotic yellow vein virus can be prevented by sowing resistant seed varieties

3 **Growth encouragement** promotes the growth of healthy crops, which prevents growth of weeds and attack by pests and diseases. A crop that has the optimum growing conditions to begin with will grow more efficiently and not be as susceptible to pest attack. Growth rate in plants is improved by the availability of nutrients (fertilisers), proper seedbed preparation and when the seed is sown.

4 **Timely harvesting** of the crop ensures that the crop is less susceptible to attack. If a crop is not harvested on time and becomes over-ripe, there is an increased risk of damage to the crop by pests and diseases.

5 **Stubble cleaning** is very important in controlling weeds, pests and diseases. The term refers to the cultivation of the land with ploughs and harrows after harvest. Harrowing the land encourages weeds to germinate. When the weeds have germinated, the land is again harrowed and the weeds are killed.

Direct control (chemical control)

Direct control is the use of chemicals to control or eradicate weeds, pests and diseases. There are three types of chemical control: herbicides, fungicides and pesticides.

Herbicides

There are two types of herbicide available to farmers:

> **Herbicide:** A chemical that kills plants or inhibits their growth.
> **Fungicide:** A chemical that kills or inhibits the growth of fungi.
> **Pesticide:** A chemical used to kill pests (particularly insects and rodents).

1 Selective herbicides
2 Non-selective (total) herbicides.

Most herbicides are applied as a liquid spray.

1 **Selective herbicides** control or kill certain species of plant life without harming other plant species. Many of the herbicides used on crops are selective herbicides. Many are designed to kill broadleaf weeds, particularly in grass and cereal crops. They are effective due to the fact that a broadleaf plant (weed) absorbs more of the herbicide than a grass or cereal because of its foliage. A selective herbicide can become non-selective and kill all plant life if too much of it is applied to the crop.

2 **Non-selective herbicides** are also known as total herbicides. They kill all plant life and do not distinguish between weeds and crops. They may be used to clear an area completely of vegetation. An example of a total herbicide is Roundup.

Pre-emergent and post-emergent herbicides

Herbicides work in a number of ways. Pre-emergent herbicides prevent weed seeds germinating and establishing themselves in a crop. They should be applied before weeds have germinated. The chemical inhibits cell division within the weed seed. Post-emergent herbicides kill weeds after they have germinated. They should be applied after the weed has germinated and can be seen in the crop.

Herbicides have a number of modes of action: contact, translocation and soil acting.

Contact herbicides

Contact herbicides are chemicals that only kill the foliage with which they come into contact, so complete coverage of the plant is important. They are not translocated around the plant and do not affect underground root or rhizome systems. This means that, while on the surface the weed has been killed, underground the root system has not and the weed may grow back. Several applications of a contact herbicide may be necessary as a result.

Contact herbicides are most effective on annual weeds, as perennial weeds have the ability to grow back.

Translocated herbicides

Translocated herbicides are chemicals that are absorbed by the plant and are translocated to the stem, leaves and roots. The herbicide kills each part of the plant with which it comes into contact. This type of herbicide is particularly suitable for perennial weeds that are not killed by contact herbicides and weeds that have well-developed rhizomes or root systems.

Soil acting herbicides

Soil acting herbicides are also called residual herbicides. They are applied to the soil and absorbed by the germinating weed seedlings, killing them as they grow. As they are applied to the soil surface, they do not affect crops with deep root systems.

≡ Fungicides

Fungicides work in a similar manner to herbicides except that they are designed to kill or control fungi rather than plant life. Fungicides are normally applied as a liquid spray. There are a number of types of fungicides; the main types of fungicides are contact, translocated or protective in their modes of action.

Contact fungicides

Contact fungicides work in a similar way to contact herbicides; they kill fungi on application to the crop. They only kill the fungi with which they have come into contact. Therefore, it is important to apply the fungicide to the entire plant.

Systemic fungicides

Systemic fungicides are absorbed by the plant and translocated to the stem, leaves and roots. They kill any fungal infection with which they come into contact. They also provide protection from further attack by fungi.

Translaminar fungicides

Translaminar fungicides are sprayed onto the crop. The upper leaf surface absorbs the fungicide, which is translocated to the lower leaf surface, which in turn gives it protection from fungal attack. It is not translocated to the stem and root system.

Protective fungicides

Protective fungicides work by preventing attack by fungi at the site of application. It is important to apply the fungicide before the crop is attacked by fungi, as it is not effective on an infected crop. It is also advisable to ensure that the entire crop is protected, as this fungicide is not translocated by the plant. Do not apply in wet weather as the fungicide will be washed away.

||||| Fig 31.9 Potato blight is a fungal disease

||||| Fig 31.10 Copper sulfate bluestone is used to prevent potato blight

☰ Pesticides

The main pests of crops include insects, rodents, slugs and snails. Many different chemicals are used to kill and control these pests. Pesticides can be found in solid, liquid or gaseous form, depending on their usage.

Insecticides are used to kill insects, which are pests of plant crops and animals. Crops may be sprayed with a solution of the pesticide. The pesticide may work in contact or translocated form, i.e. it may remain on the surface of the plant or be absorbed by the plant's foliage. When an insect pest eats the plant foliage it will ingest the insecticide and will die. The insect may also be killed by contact with the insecticide. Some pesticides are designed to kill specific pests, e.g. an aphicide is used to kill and control aphids.

Other pesticides are applied in the form of bait. The pest eats the bait, which is poisonous to the pest, and it dies from ingesting toxic levels of the poison. Slug pellets are a common example of bait that is used to kill slugs that eat plant foliage. Slug pellets are spread on the ground around the plant and are eaten by the slugs.

Poisonous gases called fumigants are used also in pest control. They are released in an enclosed space to kill the pests. Fumigants may be used in greenhouses and mushroom tunnels.

||||| Fig 31.11 Spraying pesticides on crops

Summary

▦ Certified seeds are guaranteed to have 98 per cent purity, have an 85 per cent germination rate, be free from wild oats and be treated with fungicide and pesticide.

▦ Winter variety cereals are sown instead of spring varieties because they are frost resistant, have a longer growing season, have a higher yield because of the long growing season, and can be harvested in July in good weather. They lessen the labour load in spring on a mixed farm enterprise.

▦ Crop rotation means that different crops are grown in a defined sequence. It prevents a build up of pests and diseases, it is better for nutrient management as nutrients are not continually depleted and it improves soil structure.

▦ Biological control is the management of a pest by introducing a predator or parasite of the organism.

▦ Indirect controls of pests and diseases discourage the establishment of the pests and diseases.

▦ Methods of indirect control include: crop rotation, growth encouragement, timely harvesting, sowing resistant crop varieties and stubble cleaning.

▦ Direct/chemical control is the use of chemicals (herbicides, pesticides and fungicides) to control weeds, pests and diseases.

▦ Herbicide is a chemical that kills plants or inhibits their growth. A total herbicide kills all plant life.

▦ A selective herbicide kills certain species without harming other plants. Selective herbicides are used to control broadleaf weeds.

▦ Herbicides can work on contact, by being translocated or by action in the soil.

▦ Fungicide is a chemical that kills or inhibits the growth of fungi. The main types of fungicides are contact, translocated or protective in their modes of action.

▦ Pesticide is a chemical used to kill pests. Insecticides are used to kill insects. Bait is spread around a crop and is poisonous when eaten by a pest. Fumigants are poisonous gases that are used in an enclosed space to kill pests.

QUESTIONS

1 Give three advantages of sowing winter variety seeds over spring variety seeds.
2 What are the four properties of certified seed?
3 In an experiment to compare germination rates of certified and uncertified seed, a student sowed two batches of 100 seeds, one batch certified and one batch uncertified. After a week she counted how many had germinated. In the certified batch 88 had germinated and in the other batch 71 had germinated. Account for the difference in the germination rates of the two batches.
4 Give two reasons for the importance of crop rotation.
5 How can pests and diseases of any crop build up in the soil?
6 Name three methods of weed, disease and pest control.
7 Explain how crop rotation can control weeds and pests.
8 What is stubble cleaning?

QUESTIONS

9 Explain how weeds, diseases and pests can be controlled biologically.
10 Direct (chemical) control is an effective way of controlling pests and diseases. What is the difference between a selective and a non-selective herbicide?
11 Describe the following herbicides:
   (a) A contact herbicide
   (b) A translocated herbicide
   (c) A residual herbicide.
12 What is a fungicide?
13 Describe two types of fungicides.

EXAM QUESTIONS

1 (a) Describe two advantages of crop rotation.
  (b) List three methods of weed control in tillage crops.
  (c) What is the difference between a selective herbicide and a total herbicide? (LC, OL, 2009)
2 List three advantages of using certified seed in the cultivation of cereal crops. (LC, OL, 2009)
3 Describe an experiment to show the germination rate of a certified seed sample. (LC, OL, 2009)
4 (a) Describe two non-chemical methods by which each of the following may be controlled in crop production:
     (i) Weeds
     (ii) Pests.
  (b) Suggest four reasons for using certified seed in the sowing of a cereal crop. (LC, HL, 2005)

Chapter 32

Barley

≡ Barley: Facts

Barley (*Hordeum vulgare*) is a cereal and a member of the Gramineae family. It is by far the most widely grown cereal crop in Ireland, with more than 180 000 hectares planted annually. Ninety per cent of the barley grown in Ireland is spring barley.

The Irish barley crop has two main uses: malting barley and feeding barley. Malting barley is used for the production of alcohol in the malting and brewing industry and must be of a very high quality. Feeding barley is used for the production of animal feed. Barley straw is used as animal bedding and occasionally as animal feed.

≡ Cultivation of Barley

Soil suitability

Good drainage is essential for good barley growth. Barley grows best in brown earths and deep, sandy loam soils. The soil's pH is an important consideration. The ideal pH for barley is 6.5, but a crop will grow on soils of pH 6 or greater.

 Fig 32.1 Barley is easily distinguished from other cereal crops by the awns present on the grain

Climate

Moisture is important for barley growth, as drought leads to a lower yield and a poorer quality grain. However, dry conditions are necessary for harvesting; therefore a wet summer can have a detrimental effect on the barley crop. Drier grain is preferable at harvesting.

The south-east region of Ireland is best suited to barley growing, because temperatures are warmer and there is less precipitation.

Preparation of seedbeds

Land should be ploughed in autumn and then harrowed with a one-run harrow. When preparing a seedbed for spring barley, the land may be rolled after sowing seed to ensure good seed–soil contact.

Time, rate and method of sowing

Winter barley is usually sown in September; the optimum sowing date is 1 October. If sown at this time, it reaches the grass corn stage by winter and will survive the winter frost and cold temperatures. If sown any earlier, it grows past the grass corn stage and will grow too tall. When growth recommences in spring, the crop can be prone to lodging, which leads to a reduced yield.

> **Lodging:** The tendency of cereal crops to bend over so that they lie more or less flat on the ground. This makes it impossible to harvest the crop and reduces the yield.

Spring barley is sown between February and April as soon as weather conditions will allow. The later spring barley is sown, the lower the yield will be.

Barley is sown at a rate of approximately 200 kg/ha with a combine drill (corn drill). The drill sows seed and fertiliser at the same time.

Barley varieties

Barley varieties are chosen for their yield, strength of straw, shortness of straw, earliness of ripening, disease resistance and, in the case of winter varieties, winter hardiness. Recommended winter varieties include Saffron, Leibniz and Amerena. Spring varieties include Cocktail, Frontier and Quench. The Department of Agriculture produces a list of recommended cereal varieties based on having tested them for the characteristics listed above.

Fertilisers

The application of N, P and K can vary depending on the fertility of the soil, the region of the country and the field's previous use. Nitrogen is applied by mainly using fertilisers such as CAN and 10-10-20. Phosphorus and potassium are applied mainly by the application of 18-6-12 and 10-10-20. Some farmers are beginning to use more specialised fertiliser compounds based on the results of soil tests.

Table 32.1 Fertiliser application for barley

Average application rates (kg/ha)	N	P	K
Winter barley	150	30	70
Spring barley	120	25	55

Diseases, pests and weed control

Rhynchosporium (leaf blotch or scald)

Rhynchosporium (leaf blotch or scald) is a fungal disease that causes large yield losses and a decrease in grain quality. Leaves affected by the disease have diamond-shaped chlorotic, blue-grey patches. The disease spores are spread by rain splash and it is prevalent in wet weather conditions. It can be treated or controlled by the use of fungicide, which should be sprayed twice during the growing season.

Powdery mildew

Powdery mildew is a fungal disease that affects the leaves of the plant. It can overwinter on volunteer barley or stubble. It forms grey-white patches of fungus on the leaves, while the underside of the leaf turns yellow. It causes a loss of yield in the crop. It should be treated by spraying a fungicide.

Leaf rust

Leaf rust is also known as brown rust. It can be identified by the orange-brown circular spores that are found on leaf surfaces. It causes the premature death of leaves and a reduction in yield. It can be controlled by the use of a fungicide spray.

Barley yellow dwarf virus (BYDV)

Barley yellow dwarf virus (BYDV) is a viral disease transmitted by aphids. It is transmitted to the plant when the aphid feeds on it. The leaves turn bright yellow and the yield is reduced as a result. The disease can be controlled by the use of an aphicide during the growing season.

Wireworms

Wireworms are the larvae of the click beetle. They are yellow-orange in colour. The click beetle lays her eggs near the roots of the plant. When the eggs hatch, the wireworms feed on the seeds, roots and stems of the plants. This can reduce the yield of the plant and cause lodging in cereals. To reduce the threat of wireworm infestation, barley should not be grown after grass in rotation.

Leatherjackets

Leatherjackets are the larvae of the crane fly. They cause damage by eating the roots and underground stems of the plants. Leatherjackets can be controlled by spraying the crop with a pesticide.

Weed control

Selective herbicides can be used to control weeds in a barley crop. Herbicides are chosen on identification of the weeds present in the crop. The crop should be sprayed at the three to five leaf stage for the successful control of the weeds. This is particularly important for spring crops. Other herbicides can be sprayed up to the flag leaf stage.

Crop rotation and stubble cleaning can also help in the control of weeds.

Rotation

Soil-borne pests and diseases do not seriously affect barley. Barley gives higher yields when grown in rotation, particularly in intensive tillage enterprises. The crop can also be affected by pests if grown after grassland. Rotation is considered advantageous as it helps to maintain the soil structure.

Harvest, yield and storage

Barley is harvested with a combine harvester. When the crop is ripe, the ear bends over and lies parallel to the stem. The grains are hard and dry, and the golden colour of the crop fades.

|||| Fig 32.2 A combine harvester

It is important for the grain to have a low moisture level; otherwise the barley will have to be dried. Farmers are paid based on the moisture content of the grain. Winter barley is higher yielding than spring barley and can be harvested earlier in the summer.

Grain is stored in large, ventilated sheds. Grain that is kept in storage is treated with propionic acid. Acid treatment prevents the grain from attack by pests, fungi and bacteria.

|||| Fig 32.3 Barley grain storage

Table 32.2 Barley yield and harvest date		
Crop	Tonnes/ha	Harvest date
Winter barley	7–9	July
Spring barley	6–7	August

Experiment 32.1

To calculate the 1 000 grain weight of a cereal

Note: This experiment can be carried out using any cereal grain, e.g. barley, wheat or oats.

Materials

Electronic balance, beaker or crucible (or suitable container), cereal grains

Method

1 Examine the seed sample and remove any damaged seeds, straw, etc.

2 Count out 1 000 seeds or a specified number of seeds, e.g. 100 seeds.

3 Weigh the seed sample and record the mass.

4 Count out a second sample of the seeds and repeat the procedure eight times.

5 Calculate the average mass of the seed samples.

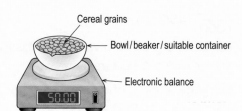

‖‖‖ Fig 32.4 Grain weight

6 For samples that contained less than 1 000 seeds multiply by the relevant factor to get 1 000 grain weight, e.g. for 100-seed weight, multiply by 10 to calculate 1 000-grain weight. The 1 000-grain weight is used to calculate seeding rates for crops. If you know the 1 000-grain weight, and the germination and establishment rates of the seed, it is possible to calculate how much seed will be needed for sowing.

Experiment 32.2

To calculate the seeding rate for winter barley

Note: This experiment can be used to calculate the seeding rate for other cereals once the desired rate of establishment is known.

- Necessary information for calculation: 1 000-grain weight of seed; percentage germination of seed; percentage establishment of seed; required rate of established plants.
- For a winter barley crop, 250–300 plants per square metre is the accepted establishment rate. Calculations are based on attaining this figure. The calculation will be shown by example.

Method

- The 1 000-grain weight of the cereal is given as 50 g.
- The percentage germination is 95%.
- The percentage establishment is 85%.
- The required number of established plants is 250 per m^2.

1 Where the rate of 250 established plants per m^2 equals 85% germination:

$$\frac{250}{85} \times 100 = 294.11 \text{ germinated seeds.}$$

i.e. 294.11 seeds will need to germinate to ensure that 250 plants will be established.

Experiment 32.2

2 The seed was guaranteed to have a 95% germination rate; therefore 294.11 seeds equals 95% germinated seed:

$$\frac{294.11}{95} \times 100 = 309.5 \text{ seeds}$$

i.e. 309.5 seeds will be required to guarantee that 294.11 seeds will germinate, at a rate of 95%.

3 1 000 seeds weigh 50 g (1 000-grain weight given). Calculate the weight of 309.5 seeds:

$$\frac{309.5}{1\,000} \times 50 = 15.475 \text{ g}$$

i.e. 15.475 g of seed will be necessary to sow in 1 m².
10 000 m² = 1 hectare

4 Calculate amount of seed needed per hectare:
15.475 g × 10 000 = 154 750 g = 154.75 kg of seed

Summary

- Barley grown in Ireland is used for malting barley and feeding barley. Malting barley is used for the production of alcohol and feeding barley is used for the production of animal feed. Barley straw is used as animal bedding.
- Barley can be identified by the awns present on its grains.
- Soils such as brown earths with good drainage and a pH of 6.5 are best suited for growing barley.
- Warm temperatures are needed for optimum barley growth and yield. Dry weather is necessary for harvesting.
- When sowing barley, land should be autumn ploughed, harrowed and, in the case of spring barley, rolled. Seed is sown with a corn drill in September; the optimum sowing date is 1 October, so the plant will reach the grass corn stage by winter. This also prevents lodging. Spring barley is sown from February to April.
- Lodging is the tendency of cereal crops to bend over, so that they lie more or less flat on the ground.
- Barley varieties are chosen for their yield, strength of straw, shortness of straw, earliness of ripening, disease resistance and, in the case of winter varieties, winter hardiness. Varieties include Saffron, Cocktail and Leibniz.
- CAN, 18-6-12 and 10-10-20 are the main fertilisers used to supply N, P and K nutrients.
- Fungal diseases that affect barley include Rhynchosporium, powdery mildew and leaf rust; they can be treated and controlled by spraying fungicides.
- Aphids spread the yellow dwarf virus. Control aphids, wireworms and leatherjackets by spraying pesticides.
- Pests and diseases do not seriously affect barley so rotation is not essential. However, it does lead to higher yields.
- Barley is ripe when the grains are dry and hard and their colour has faded. The ear lies parallel to the stem. It is harvested in July (winter barley) or August (spring barley) with a combine harvester.
- Average yields are 7–9 tonnes/ha (winter) and 6–7 tonnes/ha (spring).
- Treat grain with acid to prevent attack from pests and disease. Store grain in a ventilated shed.

QUESTIONS

1 To which family does barley belong?
2 State one way of identifying barley.
3 (a) When are the winter varieties of barley sown?
  (b) What stage do they reach before winter?
4 List two reasons for planting winter barley instead of spring barley.
5 Give two uses for barley.
6 What kind of soils and climate are needed for growing barley?
7 What characteristics of barley (seed) are important when choosing a variety for sowing?
8 Name one winter variety and one spring variety of barley.
9 Describe how land should be cultivated for winter and spring barley.
10 Which machine is used to sow barley seed?
11 Which fertilisers are applied to barley and when and how are they applied?
12 How are weeds controlled in a barley crop?
13 Which diseases and pests are most likely to attack barley and how are they prevented?
14 What signs show that barley is ready for harvest?
15 How is barley harvested?
16 How is barley stored?
17 What is the average yield in tonnes per hectare of (a) winter barley and (b) spring barley?
18 Use the following information to calculate the seeding rate for winter barley for 1 hectare of land:
   - Establishment rate – 300 plants per m^2
   - 1 000-grain weight – 40 g
   - Germination percentage – 90%
   - Establishment percentage – 85%.

EXAM QUESTIONS

1 Describe the cultivation of spring barley or main-crop potatoes under the following headings:
  (a) Soil requirements
  (b) Rotation
  (c) Weed control
  (d) Yield (tonnes per hectare). (LC, HL, 2009)
2 List four factors that are considered by the Department of Agriculture, Fisheries and Food when recommending varieties of cereals to be grown by farmers. (LC, HL, 2008)
3 Give a scientific explanation for the presence of dust-like particles in the air surrounding barley plants showing white raised patches on their leaves. (LC, HL, 2005)

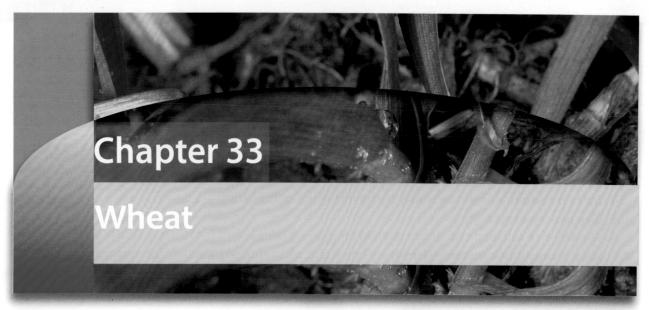

Chapter 33

Wheat

≡ Wheat: Facts

Wheat (*Triticum spp.*) is a member of the Gramineae family. It is the second most popular cereal crop in Ireland and approximately 80 000 hectares are grown each year. About 75 per cent of the wheat grown in Ireland is winter wheat, most of which is used for animal feed.

Wheat is also used for producing flour for baking. Although the majority of wheat produced in Ireland is winter wheat, which gives high yields, some of the spring varieties are more suited to flour production because of their higher protein content.

Wheat straw can be used for animal bedding or for mushroom composting.

≡ Cultivation of Wheat

Soil suitability

Wheat requires well-drained, sandy loam soils or brown earths. It is more tolerant of acidic soils than barley and will grow adequately in soils with a pH of 5.5 to 7.0.

Fig 33.1 The seed head of wheat is easily distinguished from barley or oats

Climate

Wheat is not as tolerant of cool climates as oats or barley. It requires warm temperatures and sunshine. Wheat is mainly grown in the south-east region of Ireland for this reason.

Preparation of seedbeds

Seedbed preparation is similar to that of barley. Land should be ploughed and harrowed to create a fine seedbed.

Fig 33.2 One pass sower

Time, rate and method of sowing

Winter wheat is sown in October and spring wheat in February to March. It is sown using a seed drill or what is known as a one-pass system where both seed and fertiliser are sown at the same time.

Wheat varieties

Like barley, wheat varieties are chosen for their yield, shortness of straw, strength of straw, earliness of ripening and disease resistance. Winter varieties include: Cordiale, Einstein and Lion. Spring varieties include: Sparrow, Raffles and Trappe.

Table 33.1 Fertiliser application rates for wheat			
Average application rates (kg/ha)	N	P	K
Winter wheat (9 tonnes/ha)	160	25	50
Winter wheat (11 tonnes/ha)	200	25	80
Spring wheat	140	25	90

Diseases, pests and weed control

Leaf blotch

Leaf blotch caused by the fungus Septoria is one of the most common diseases of wheat. Symptoms include yellow spots on the leaves, which elongate to form larger yellow-brown patches. The crop can be sprayed with a protective fungicide. Wheat stubble should be ploughed in to prevent attack in the following season.

Powdery mildew

Powdery mildew is another fungus that affects wheat. Its symptoms are similar to those experienced by barley (see page 269). It can be controlled by using fungicides.

Take-all

Take-all is a fungal disease; it is also called root and crown rot. It is prevalent in fields where wheat is continuously grown. Symptoms include stunted growth with white heads. The white heads on the wheat are usually empty of grain. The roots may also be blackened. Spraying with a fungicide or using seed dressings can help to control this disease.

Fig 33.3 Wheat leaf blotch

Weed control

Wheat should be treated with pre- and post-emergent herbicides to prevent weeds in the crop.

Pests

Wireworms and slugs are pests of wheat crops. Wheat should not be grown after pasture as there could be wireworms in the soil. Slugs nibble at the seeds and shoots of the wheat plant. Winter wheat should be dressed once or twice with slug pellets as a control measure.

Rotation

Wheat can be employed in a similar rotation to oats and barley. It is suitable for a cereal-root crop rotation. Wheat grown after a maize crop yields an extra 0.5 tonnes/ha on average.

Harvest, yield and storage

Winter wheat is harvested in late July to early August. Spring wheat is harvested from mid to late August. Wheat is harvested with a combine harvester, which separates the grain from the straw. The grain is transported to a storage bin, while the straw is left in the field for baling. Grain should be stored with an 18 per cent moisture level. If the grain has more than 20 per cent moisture, it must be dried.

Fig 33.4 Harvesting winter wheat, using a combine harvester

Table 33.2 Wheat yield and harvest dates		
Crop	**Yield**	**Harvest date**
Winter wheat	Low yield 9 tonnes/ha	Mid-July to early August
Winter wheat	High yield 11 tonnes/ha	Mid-July to early August
Spring wheat	8.5 tonnes/ha	Mid-August to September

Summary

■ Wheat is a member of the Gramineae family. It is grown for animal feed, flour production and animal bedding (wheat straw). Most wheat grown in Ireland is winter wheat.

■ Wheat grows best in well-drained, sandy loam or brown earth soils with a pH of 5.5 to 7.0. It requires warm temperatures and sunshine.

■ Winter wheat is sown in October and spring wheat in February. It is sown with a seed drill in a seedbed that has been ploughed and harrowed.

■ Varieties are chosen for their yield, shortness of straw, strength of straw, earliness of ripening and disease resistance. Varieties include: Cordiale, Einstein, Sparrow and Raffles.

■ Wheat requires an NPK fertiliser with high levels of nitrogen.

■ Leaf blotch, powdery mildew and take-all are common diseases of wheat. They can be controlled by the use of a fungicide.

■ Wheat is suitable for a cereal-root crop rotation. Wheat yields are higher when it has been planted after maize in a rotation.

■ Winter wheat is harvested in July with a combine harvester. Yields range from 9–11 tonnes/ha.

■ Spring wheat is harvested in September, with a yield of 8.5 tonnes/ha.

QUESTIONS

1 State two uses of wheat grain and two uses of wheat straw.
2 Describe the soil and climate conditions most suitable for growing wheat.
3 When should (a) winter wheat and (b) spring wheat be sown?
4 Name two varieties of wheat and list three characteristics on which wheat varieties are chosen.
5 What is the rate of fertiliser application on winter wheat?
6 Which machine is used to sow wheat?
7 Describe the symptoms of leaf blotch and take-all. Describe how they may be controlled.
8 What is the average yield of (a) winter wheat and (b) spring wheat?
9 When should (a) winter wheat and (b) spring wheat be harvested?

EXAM QUESTIONS

1 (a) Name an insect pest of a cereal crop.
   (b) How does the pest you have named damage the crop? (LC, OL, 2009)
2 (a) Name a fungal disease of plants and name the crop which it affects.
   (b) List two symptoms of the disease in the crop named above.
   (c) Describe one method of preventing this disease. (LC, OL, 2009)

Chapter 34

Oats

The land occupied by oats in Ireland has declined rapidly since the 1950s and 1960s. What was once a major animal feed is now grown in relatively small quantities in comparison to barley and wheat. There is now a greater land area under maize than there is under oats. Every year, 20 000 hectares of oats are sown, a figure that has remained stable for the last decade. Both winter and spring varieties are sown, with winter oats being the more popular.

☰ Oats: Facts

Oats were once grown in large quantities for animal feed, particularly for horses. This level of production declined with the reduction in the number of working horses in agriculture due to mechanisation. Also, barley has replaced oats as an animal feed due to its higher yield and higher digestibility.

Maize silage is also replacing oats as it has higher productivity and a higher feeding value. However, oats continue to be grown on a number of farms across the country, providing animal feed and providing oats for human consumption.

Oats (*Avena sativa*) belong to the Gramineae family. They are easily distinguished from barley and wheat as the oat grains are borne on a panicle. Each grain is called a spikelet.

||||| Fig 34.1 Oats

☰ Cultivation of Oats

Soil suitability

Oats will grow in soils with good drainage. They are tolerant of acidic soils and will grow in soils with a pH of 5.5 or greater.

Climate

Oats are suited to a temperate climate, and have low heat requirements. They will grow in cool climates and are tolerant of rainy conditions. Unlike other cereals, oats are not susceptible to frost damage. This makes them particularly suitable for growing in the north-west of the country, which is not suited to barley and wheat production.

Preparation of seedbeds

Soil should be ploughed and harrowed in the preparation of the seedbed. For spring sowing, rolling may also be carried out.

Time, rate and method of sowing

Winter oats may be sown from late October to early November. Seed is sown at a rate of 130 kg/ha, using a seed drill.

Oat varieties

Like other cereals, oat varieties are chosen for their yield, strength of straw, shortness of straw, early ripening, disease resistance and, in the case of winter varieties, winter hardiness. Recommended varieties include Barra, Binary, Circle and Evita.

Fertilisers

Oats use a high level of nitrogen and this is reflected in the application of fertiliser to the soil.

Table 34.1 Fertiliser application rates for oats			
Avgerage application rates (kg/ha)	N	P	K
Winter oats	12	25	95
Spring oats	95	25	85

Diseases, pests and weed control

Weeds are not a serious problem in oat crops due to the vigorous growth habit of oats. Indeed wild oats are a common weed of other cereal crops. A selective herbicide should be applied to remove broadleaf weed varieties.

Diseases

Oats are affected by similar diseases to barley and should be treated in the same way by applying fungicide or pesticide as appropriate. Eyespot, barley yellow dwarf virus known as red leaf in oats, powdery mildew and rusts all attack the oat crop.

Pests

Aphids and wireworms attack oat crops in a similar way to other cereals and must be treated accordingly.

Rotation

Oats may be grown in rotation with other cereals, root crops and legumes. If oats are sown after a legume crop, the nitrogen applied can be reduced due to N fixation by the legume.

Harvest, yield and storage

Winter oats average 7.5 tonnes/ha and spring oats 6.5 tonnes/ha. They are harvested using a combine harvester and should be stored at 12 per cent moisture. If moisture levels are higher than this, the grain may need to be dried. Winter oats should be harvested from July to August and spring oats from August to September.

Summary

- Oats are a member of the Gramineae family and are grown for both animal and human consumption.
- The grains are known as spikelets and are borne on a panicle.
- Oats need soils with good drainage and a pH of 5.5 or greater. They will grow in temperate to cool conditions.
- Winter oats are sown from October to November, using a seed drill. Before sowing, the soil is ploughed and harrowed.
- Varieties are chosen for their yield, strength and shortness of straw, early ripening, disease resistance and winter hardiness. Varieties include: Barra, Binary, Circle and Evita.
- An NPK fertiliser should be applied to the land when sowing.
- Selective herbicides may be used to remove broadleaf weeds.
- Eyespot and powdery mildew are common diseases of oats.
- Fungicides should be used to prevent diseases.
- Wireworms and aphids are common pests of oats. Rotation and pesticides should be used to prevent attack.
- Winter oats are harvested in July, with an average yield of 7.5 tonnes/ha. Spring oats are harvested in August, with an average yield of 6.5 tonnes/ha.

QUESTIONS

1. Describe the soil and climate conditions most suitable for growing oats.
2. When should winter oats be sown?
3. Name two varieties of oats and list three characteristics on which oat varieties are chosen.
4. What is the rate of fertiliser application on winter oats?
5. Name two diseases of oats and describe how they may be controlled.
6. What is the average yield of (a) winter oats and (b) spring oats?
7. When should oats be harvested?

EXAM QUESTION

Describe the cultivation of a named cereal crop under the following headings:
(a) Soil type
(b) Sowing
(c) Fertiliser
(d) Harvesting. (LC, OL, 2009)

Chapter 35

Maize

Maize (*Zea mays*) is a cereal crop and belongs to the Gramineae family. It is also known as corn. Since its introduction to Ireland as a tillage crop in the early 1970s, it has grown in popularity, and approximately 20 000 hectares of maize are grown every year. This figure is increasing annually and maize production is now on a par with oat production. In other countries, maize is far more popular as a tillage crop; for example, it is the most widely grown crop in the USA.

☰ Maize: Facts

The maize plant is unlike many of the other cereals and grasses grown in Ireland. It can grow between 2 and 3 metres high, depending on the variety of seed sown. Eighty per cent of maize in Ireland is grown specifically for the production of maize silage. This is particularly popular with dairy farmers as a winter feed. The remainder is used for human consumption as sweetcorn.

||||| Fig 35.1 Maize crop

Maize is a self-pollinating plant. The male part of the plant is called the tassel and is located on the top of the plant. The female part is called the silk and is located further down the plant. Pollen falls from the tassels onto the silks, pollinating them. Maize is also susceptible to cross-pollination, as pollen from one plant can be transported by wind on to the silks of another plant.

||||| Fig 35.2 Maize tassel – male

||||| Fig 35.3 Maize silk – female

Maize products

Maize has a number of uses in Ireland, the main one is the production of maize silage for winter fodder. Maize straw is used for animal bedding. Maize is also used for human consumption; it is commonly known as sweetcorn or corn on the cob.

Maize silage v grass silage: Grass silage is the most popular winter feed for livestock in Ireland, but it may be worth considering maize silage for winter fodder.

Table 35.1 Comparison of DM yield and percentage in grass and maize silage		
Silage type	DM yield (tonnes/ha)	DM%
Grass (PRG)	7–8	20–22
Maize	15–20	28–32

Maize, as can be seen from Table 35.1, has a much higher dry matter (DM) yield than first-cut silage. Grass also has a much lower DM content than maize. While maize will only have one cut in the growing season, the subsequent cuts of grass will not produce the same volume as the first-cut silage.

Grass produces a high volume of effluent as is has a low DM. Effluent has to be stored and disposed of carefully due to its potential to pollute waterways. Maize with its higher DM value produces little or no effluent, reducing storage and disposal costs and reducing the potential to pollute. Feeding maize silage to beef and dairy cattle increases their DM intake and live weight, gain reducing the need to feed concentrates. This also reduces feed costs. Maize contains high levels of starch and protein and is palatable to livestock.

Cultivation of Maize

Soil suitability

Maize requires a warm, well-drained soil with a pH of 6.5 to 7.0. While maize will grow in most soils, brown earths and sandy loams are the most suitable soils. Maize will not reach its potential in waterlogged soils. Deep soils are advantageous as maize roots can penetrate the soil up to a depth of 1.5 metres, breaking up the soil, improving its structure and utilising nutrients unavailable to other crops.

Climate

Maize requires a warm climate and is not frost hardy. For this reason, many farmers in Ireland grow maize under plastic, which increases soil temperatures. Maize seed will not germinate until temperatures reach 10°C. Dry weather is important for the sowing and pollination of the crop. Maize grown in coastal areas tends to be more susceptible to eyespot, which is a fungal disease.

Preparation of seedbeds

The soil should be rotovated and ploughed in March. The soil should then be harrowed to produce a fine seedbed.

Time, rate and method of sowing

In Ireland, 70 per cent of maize is grown under plastic. The remainder is grown in the open. When maize is grown under plastic, it can be sown earlier, which results in a longer growing season and a higher yield. The plastic film increases the heat, doubling temperatures. This leads to a germination time of seven days in comparison to a germination time of three weeks in the open. The early germinating maize can take advantage of warm sunny weather in June, which will lead to an increase in grain yield.

Table 35.2 Comparison of maize sown under plastic and in the open		
Method of sowing	Sowing date	Germination time
Under plastic	25 March–10 May	7 days
Open sowing	15 April–10 May	21 days

Maize sown after 10 May will have a lower grain yield and higher forage yield. Maize seed is sown at a rate of 100 000 seeds/ha (25 kg seed/ha), using a precision seeder. If the maize is to be grown under plastic a specialised maize seeder can be used. The maize seeder sows the seed, applies a herbicide and lays the plastic in one run. Two rows of seeds are sown under each sheet of plastic 66–86 cm apart and 4 cm deep.

Table 35.3 Distance between rows when planting maize	
Method of sowing	Distance between rows
Under plastic	66 cm apart
Open sowing	76 cm apart

The plastic is designed to keep soil temperatures warm. It has tiny holes in it to let some heat escape as the crop will die if temperatures reach 50°C. The optimum temperature is 37°C. The plastic prevents the establishment of weeds, but is designed so that the maize plant can break through it. The plastic film is biodegradable, so there is no need to remove it from the growing crop or at harvesting.

Maize varieties

Maize seed is chosen for a number of characteristics including: yield of DM, DM content, starch content, resistance to lodging and forage harvest maturity. Justina and Benicia are varieties that are grown under plastic. Fergus and Nimrod are varieties that are grown in the open.

Fertilisers

Maize has the ability to utilise large volumes of slurry – approximately 65 000 L/ha. If slurry is applied, it is spread in March and ploughed in before sowing. The necessary precautions should be taken when spreading slurry. Slurry will provide the P and K requirements of a maize crop. When spreading inorganic fertilisers 150 kg/ha N, 55 kg/ha P and 150 kg/ha K should be applied.

Diseases, pests and weed control

Maize is not badly affected by weeds, pests and diseases. Controls should be put in place to prevent damage to the crop.

Weed control

Pre- and post-emergent herbicides can be applied at sowing when maize is grown under plastic. Pre-emergent herbicides prevent weeds from germinating and post-emergent herbicides kill weeds at the seedling stage. This is important to prevent weeds from competing with the maize seedlings, as the heat under the plastic encourages weeds to grow as well as maize. One of the main weeds of the maize crop is nightshade.

Wireworms

Wireworms are occasionally a problem in the maize crop when it is grown after grassland. Seed dressings can be used to prevent attack by wireworms.

Eyespot

Eyespot is a fungal disease that attacks mature maize crops. It mainly occurs on open crops. Crops may have to be harvested early to prevent losses.

Eyespot is easy to identify as the leaves of the plant display brown spots, each surrounded by a yellow circle. Spores are transmitted by air. Crops should be sprayed with a fungicide when they are 1 metre high. The fungicide provides a six-week protection from eyespot.

Rotation

Maize is not seriously affected by soil-borne pests and diseases and can be grown continuously in the same place year after year. It is suitable for use in a rotation with other crops.

Harvest, yield and storage

The crop should be tasselled by 10 August. The earlier the tassel appears, the higher the grain yield. Pollination of the silk occurs soon after. Maize is harvested from September to October. Ideally, the crop should be harvested by 1 October as frost kills the crop.

Maize grown under plastic will be ready for harvest before maize grown in the open. If sown under plastic in March, maize can be harvested by mid-August. The main advantage is that the crop is harvested during good weather conditions and before the risk of autumn frost. When the maize crop is fully ripe, the leaf around the grain turns yellow-white and sugar transfer to the cob has stopped. The optimum date for harvest is when there is 50–55 per cent DM in the cob and 32 per cent DM in the whole crop (for ensiling).

||||| Fig 35.4 An unripe maize cob with silk attached at the end of the cob

Maize can be ensiled in much the same way as grass. As maize has such a high DM content it produces virtually no effluent. This reduces the cost of disposal of effluent for farmers. No additives are needed as the sugar content of the maize is so high. Sugars are converted to lactic acid as they are in grass silage production. Stabilisers may be added to keep the temperature of the ensiled maize cool.

Table 35.4 Yield of DM and starch content of maize at harvest

Method of sowing	Yield of DM (tonnes/ha)	DM content	Starch content
Under plastic	15–20	32%	28%
Open sowing	13–14	30%	22%

Maize can also be baled using a specialised round baler. This system of storage is not very common in Ireland and is usually carried out by maize contractors.

Summary

- Maize is a member of the Gramineae family.
- In Ireland, 80 per cent of maize is used for maize silage production.
- Maize is self-pollinating. The male part is called the tassel and the female part is called the silk.
- Maize has a higher DM yield and content than grass. It produces little effluent, which reduces storage and disposal costs.
- It is high in protein and starch and palatable to livestock.

Summary

- Maize requires well-drained, sandy loam or brown earth soils with a pH of 6.5 to 7.0
- Maize requires frost-free, dry conditions, with warm temperatures. Maize will not germinate until temperatures are 10°C.
- Soil needs to be ploughed and harrowed in March. Seeds are sown under plastic, which increases the heat in the soil and leads to earlier germination. Seed is sown from late March to early May.
- Seed is sown using a precision seeder at the rate of 100 000 seeds/ha.
- Maize seed is chosen for a number of characteristics including: yield of DM, DM content, starch content, resistance to lodging, and forage harvest maturity. Justina, Benicia, Fergus and Nimrod are common varieties.
- An NPK fertiliser or slurry can be spread on maize to provide nutrients.
- One of the main weeds of maize is nightshade. Most weeds are killed using herbicide.
- Eyespot is a fungus that affects maize. The crop should be sprayed with a fungicide to prevent attack when it is 1 metre high.
- Harvest takes place from September to October, using a maize harvester. When the maize crop is fully ripe, the leaf around the grain turns yellow-white and sugar transfer to the cob has stopped. The optimum date for harvest is when there is 50–55 per cent DM in the cob and 32 per cent DM in the whole crop (for ensiling).
- Under plastic maize yields 15–20 tonnes/ha.
- Maize can be ensiled in much the same way as grass. Maize is baled using a specialised round baler.

QUESTIONS

1. What are the two main uses of maize in Ireland?
2. Name the male and female parts of the maize plant.
3. Explain how pollination occurs in the maize plant.
4. Give three advantages of the use of maize silage instead of grass silage.
5. What types of soil condition are necessary for maize production?
6. What climatic conditions are best suited to maize production?
7. When is the optimum time for sowing maize? Give one advantage of sowing maize under plastic.
8. List three characteristics on which maize varieties are chosen. Name one variety of maize seed.
9. How are weeds controlled in the maize crop? Name a weed of the maize crop.
10. When should maize be harvested?
11. What yield can be expected from a maize crop (a) under plastic and (b) in the open?
12. How is maize stored for winter feed?

EXAM QUESTIONS

1. Account for the increasing popularity of maize silage as a feed for dairy cows. (LC, HL, 2010)
2. Give a scientific explanation for the use of plastic in the cultivation of maize. (LC, HL, 2009)

Chapter 36

Potatoes

Potatoes are believed to have been first cultivated in Ireland around the 1600s. By the 1700s, they were part of the staple Irish diet, especially of the poor. This had devastating consequences when blight destroyed the potato crops between 1845 and 1852; this period of history is now remembered as the Great Famine. Regardless of this, the potato is one of the most popular vegetables in Ireland. Potatoes are an excellent source of starch and vitamin C and are fat free (as long as no butter is added). They belong to the family Solanaceae. Other members of this family include tomatoes and tobacco.

A potato tuber is a modified stem used for food storage by the plant.

≡ Categories of Potato

Potatoes are classified as:

- First earlies
- Second earlies
- Maincrop.

First and second earlies are planted as early as February. However, potatoes are not frost resistant and for this reason they are grown in coastal areas of counties Cork and Wexford. The soils in these regions are sandy soils and they warm up early in spring.

Earlies are harvested immaturely from May onwards. As a result, there is a lower yield but they obtain a higher price. Home Guard and British Queen are the most popular early varieties grown in Ireland.

Maincrop potatoes are harvested fully mature in September and October and give higher yields than early varieties. Maincrop potatoes are used to supply the consumer market until May of the following year.

||||| Fig 36.1 Potato plant with flowers

Kerrs Pink, Roosters, Records and Golden Wonder are the most popular maincrop varieties in Ireland, as these varieties have high dry-matter content and produce floury tubers. In contrast, Cara, a variety that is popular on the Continent, has low dry-matter content but is very high yielding. Production of maincrop potatoes is mainly confined to counties Meath, Dublin, Louth, Cork and Wexford.

Table 36.1 Potato varieties and characteristics		
Category	**Variety**	**Characteristics**
First earlies	Home Guard	Good eating quality, good yield
	Epicure	Good eating quality and yield
Second earlies	British Queen	Excellent eating quality
	Maris Piper	Good yield
Maincrop	Kerrs Pink	Good eating quality, high yield
	Golden Wonder	Excellent eating quality, low yield
	Cara	Low dry matter, poorer eating quality, very high yield

|||| Fig 36.2 Home Guard potatoes

|||| Fig 36.3 Kerrs Pink potatoes

☰ Seed Production

Commercial potato production can be divided into two categories:

1 Certified seed potatoes

2 Ware production (potatoes for human consumption).

Seed potato production is centred in Donegal. The windy conditions keep the aphid population low and it is isolated from other potato growing counties, preventing the spread of diseases. Certified seed potatoes that are distributed to commercial ware growers are grown under strict regulations. Seed potatoes can only be produced from fields free from potato cyst nematode and they must be free from plant viruses, e.g. leaf mosaic virus, leaf roll and virus Y.

Certified seed is also produced using micropropagation (see Chapter 18, Applied Genetics). Some growers reduce the cost of producing their ware potatoes by using their own potatoes for seed, which can produce a good yield. However, it is advisable to purchase certified seed every three years as viruses can build up in a producer's stock.

|||| Fig 36.4 Aphids are carriers of a number of viral diseases that affect potatoes

≡ Cultivation Practices

Soil suitability

Potatoes are grown on a wide variety of soils. However, deep, well-drained loams and sandy loams are ideal. Potatoes prefer a pH of 5.5 to 6. If the pH of the soil is very alkaline (pH >7), it can cause scab on potatoes. For this reason, potatoes are not grown in recently limed fields. If the soil's pH is less than 5.5, then the availability of trace elements is affected and, as a result, this affects crop growth. When potatoes are grown in sandy or sandy loam soils, irrigation may be required if drought occurs in late summer.

Drought affects tuber development and reduces crop yield. Adding manure to the soil helps it to retain more water, especially in sandy soils, and this helps prevent drought damage to the potato crop.

Rotation

Rotation is vital in the production of potatoes as it prevents the build up of potato cyst nematode and other soil-borne pests and diseases. Ware potatoes should not be grown in the same area for more than one year in four and in seed production that is increased to one year in five.

Preparation of seedbeds and sowing

Potatoes need deep and well-cultivated soil. In the past, farmers were encouraged to autumn plough their soil, as frost action over the winter months kills slugs and fungi and helps break up the soil, making further cultivation easier. However, under the Nitrates Directive, autumn ploughing is prohibited if a crop is not sown immediately after. Ground left without vegetation on it over the winter months is susceptible to nitrogen leaching. As

|||| Fig 36.5 Potato cystnematode on the roots of a potato plant

a result, ploughing to a depth of 22 cm, rotovation and bed formation occur in spring to produce a fine seedbed. Each seedbed will be 172–182 cm wide and will contain two drills.

Commercial growers also practise stone and clod removal. This prevents bruising and contamination of the potatoes at harvesting. The stones and large clods are removed, using a machine similar to a potato harvester, and are placed in a line at the side of the machine. The following year the land is ploughed at a right angle to distribute the stones again. Drill formation is the final cultivation and it is done either before sowing or when the potatoes are sown.

|||| Fig 36.6 'Gimme' de-stoner

|||| Fig 36.7 Drill formation

Potatoes are sown 10 cm below the ridge. The spacing between the seed potatoes is determined by the size of the seed. It is recommended that seeds 35–45 mm should be spaced 20–25 cm apart giving a sowing rate of 60 000 per ha, and seeds 45–55 mm should be spaced 30–35 cm apart giving a sowing rate of 40 000 per ha. Seeds can be planted by hand, but commercial farmers use an automated planter.

Sprouting

Seed potatoes can be sprouted before planting. This process is also known as chitting, and it involves exposing the potato seeds to light so that they develop shoots. Sprouting gives the potato seeds a head start and is an essential practice if growing early varieties.

Fig 36.8 Sprouted potatoes

To sprout potatoes, the seeds are placed in shallow trays that are kept in a greenhouse, or in a building using artificial light at a temperature of 5.5°C. Sprouting seeds speeds up growth, plant emergence and yield.

Fertiliser application

As with any crop, it is important to establish first the inherent fertility of a soil. Do this by carrying out a soil test to establish the N, P and K content of the soil. Most growers apply a compound fertiliser such as 10-10-20 to their potato crop before planting the seed. This is done by broadcasting the fertiliser and then incorporating it into the soil in one of the final cultivations.

Commercial growers place the fertiliser in two bands, one either side of the potato drill. Placing the fertiliser in bands ensures an even distribution between the potato plants that promotes uniform growth. This method is a more beneficial and cost-effective mechanism of fertiliser application, with less wastage than broadcasting the fertiliser.

The amount of fertiliser added to potatoes must be judged carefully. Excess nitrogen depresses the dry matter content of the tuber and produces a more watery tuber. Likewise, excess phosphate also depresses dry matter. The addition of sulfate of potash (a source of potassium) increases dry matter. Adding FYM improves the soil structure and helps to prevent drought damage.

Weed control and earthing up

Once 15 to 20 per cent of the potato plants has emerged after sowing, the potato crop is sprayed, usually with a contact and a residual herbicide. The contact herbicide kills all plants including the potatoes; however, the potato crops will quickly recover. The residual herbicide prevents any weed seeds germinating. Weeds are controlled by shading once the potato crop has become established. At this point, the haulms (shoots and leaves) of the potatoes meet across the ridges and prevent sunlight reaching the soil, which prevents any weed seeds present in the soil from germinating.

Weeds can also be controlled by earthing up. This covers the growing haulms with more soil and prevents light getting to the tubers and turning them green. Green tubers cannot be sold, as these tubers contain poisonous alkaloids.

Earthing up also supports the growing haulms and helps prevent blight spores being washed from the leaves down onto the tubers. However, earthing up is no longer practised by commercial farmers as the potatoes are sown deep enough in the drills to prevent the tubers being exposed to sunlight.

☰ Diseases

Potato blight

Potato crops can be attacked by a number of pests and diseases, but by far the most common is potato blight. Blight is caused by an airborne fungus called *Phytophthora infestans*. Its spores can travel from fields up to 1.6 km away. The spores germinate in humid weather when the temperature is greater than 10°C. The first signs of blight are yellow spots that turn black on the leaves. If the underside of the leaf is inspected a white furry growth should be visible; these are the sporangia. The fungus produces more spores on the infected leaves of the plant and these spores can be washed down into the soil by rain where they will then infect and rot the tubers. The most reliable way to prevent fungal infection is to spray the potato crop with a fungicide.

|||| Fig 36.9 Leaf showing potato blight

The meteorological service issues blight warnings when weather conditions are right for the spread of blight. When blight warnings are issued, commercial growers spray their crop and continue to spray it every 10 days until the crop is harvested. In severe cases of blight, farmers are advised to spray every seven days. As blight is not a risk until the summer months, farmers who grow earlies do not usually have a problem as their crop is harvested before blight becomes a threat.

Blight is a problem for organic farmers, who cannot spray their crop with any chemicals. If blight strikes, the infected haulms should be removed and burnt to prevent further spread of the fungus. Blight-resistant potato varieties are available.

Blackleg

Blackleg is an increasingly worrying disease for commercial potato growers. It is caused by the bacteria *Erwinia carotovora subsp. atroseptica*, which is also responsible for causing the soft rot of tubers. The bacteria can affect the potato seed and prevent emergence of the plant, but more commonly it affects the established crop, causing the leaves to turn yellow and the stems to turn black just above or below ground level. The disease itself is spread through contaminated seed potatoes.

The multiplication of the blackleg bacteria is totally weather dependent. Cool, wet weather favours the multiplication of the bacteria, which spreads to developing tubers. Therefore, blackleg outbreaks are more common in wet springs rather than drier springs. Poor draining soils that retain water also facilitate the spread of the disease.

|||| Fig 36.10 A potato plant with blackleg

Seed potatoes need careful inspection for blackleg as the bacteria spreads from the infected tubers to others during storage. Damaged or bruised seeds or sprouts allow entry of the bacteria more easily and for this reason damaged seeds should not be sown.

To prevent blackleg, growers should only plant clean, disease-free certified seed. If an outbreak of blackleg occurs, the infected stems and tubers including the original seed potato should be removed. The original seed potato was probably the source of the infection. Removal of all tubers at harvest will prevent any diseased potatoes harbouring the disease for the following year. The bacteria itself does not survive very long in the soil, so crop rotation will help in controlling the disease.

Pests

Wireworms, the insect larvae of the click beetle, can sometimes be a problem if potatoes are planted after pasture. They attack tubers, eating them and lowering tuber yield and tuber quality. This can be treated using an insecticide. Some varieties are more prone to slug damage than others. Slugs eat tubers and they can be a problem in wet summers, when the slug population rises. These pests are killed using slug pellets. Aphids not only cause damage to the crop but also are vectors of viral diseases. Control of aphids is vital in seed potato production. The potato crop should be sprayed with a suitable insecticide.

> A **vector**, usually an insect, is a carrier of a parasitic agent (bacteria, fungi, protozoa or virus).

Harvest and Storage

Early potatoes are harvested from late May onwards and maincrops are harvested in late September or October. The haulms are first killed off using a contact herbicide. The potatoes are then left in the ground for up to three weeks to allow the skins of the tubers to harden; this prevents them from being bruised when harvesting. The potato crop is then harvested with a potato harvester, usually an elevator digger. This machine separates the potatoes from the soil and either leaves the potatoes on the top of the soil to be gathered by hand or carries them to a storage bin. Care is taken to remove all potatoes, so that none are left behind. If potatoes remain after the harvest, they are called groundkeepers and they can be a source of disease for future potato crops.

|||| Fig 36.11 A potato harvester

Potatoes must be stored in purpose-built buildings that are well-ventilated, leak proof, insulated and frost proof. They must allow easy access to a tractor and trailer. Potatoes are stored in stacks. If the stock is 1.8 metres high, natural ventilation is adequate to dry out the potatoes. However, if potatoes are stored in stacks higher than this, then a forced draught ventilation system is required. Any heat generated by the stacks must be allowed to

|||| Fig 36.12 Potatoes stacked in a refrigeration shed

escape or otherwise the potatoes will start to sprout. To further reduce the risk of sprouting, potatoes are often sprayed with a sprout inhibitor. Sprouted potatoes are unsellable. As the demand for potatoes is year round, many commercial growers store their potatoes in refrigerated units and this further extends the availability of the potatoes.

Yield

First and second earlies yield around 7–10 tonnes of potatoes per hectare. Maincrops have a much higher yield of 30–40 tonnes per hectare as they are harvested when they are fully mature.

Activity 36.1

Practical crop project

For the practical coursework, students must demonstrate that they have gained practical experience in crops. This can be achieved by growing some potatoes. Potatoes are one of the easiest plants to grow and require only a little care and attention. You do not need to have a garden to grow your own potatoes; a large pot or a potato grow bag is perfect. Seed potatoes can be purchased from your local garden centre. Use the following steps to write up your project and include photographs. Finally, enjoy cooking and eating your own homegrown potatoes and you will be surprised just how tasty they are.

||||| Fig 36.13 Potatoes growing in a grow bag

1 **Selecting the plot**

   Find a sunny spot in your garden to dig your ridges or to place your grow bag. Identify what type of soil it is by carrying out a soil feel test. Take a sample of soil to school to test the pH. Was there any other crop grown here last year?

2 **Cultivation**
   - Give a detailed account of how you prepared your seedbed. Did you dig ridges, remove stones, etc?
   - Which fertiliser did you add? Potatoes benefit greatly from the addition of farmyard manure, which also improves the soil structure.
   - Compare the preparations that you made to those made by commercial farmers.

3 **Choosing and sowing the seed**
   - Which variety and category of seed did you use? Discuss the varieties and categories available.
   - Did you use certified seed? Discuss the advantages of using certified seed.
   - How deep did you sow your seeds and how far apart were they?
   - Were the seeds sprouted beforehand or did you sprout them? How did you sprout them?
   - Compare what you have done to that of commercial farmers.

4 **Establishment of the crop**
   - How did you control pests and diseases?
   - Was blight a problem? How would you prevent blight?
   - Did you earth up your potatoes and why?
   - Remember to keep your potatoes well watered, as the tubers require a lot of water to swell.

5 **Harvesting**
   - Once the flowers have gone and the foliage turns yellow and begins to wilt you can harvest your potatoes. The process where the plant starts to die back is called **senescence** by commercial farmers.
   - Give a brief description of how you did this. If you grow earlies, harvest them just before you are going to cook them as they taste so much better.

Summary

- Potatoes belong to the family Solanaceae.
- Potatoes are classified as: first earlies, second earlies and maincrop.
- Earlies are harvested immaturely from May onwards.
- Maincrop potatoes are harvested fully mature in September to October and give higher yields than early varieties.
- Certified seed potatoes are produced in Donegal. The windy conditions keep the aphid population low and prevent the spread of diseases.
- Potatoes prefer to grow in deep, well-drained loam soils and sandy loam soils with a pH between 5.5 and 6.
- Rotation is vital as it prevents the build up of potato cyst nematode and other soil-borne pests and diseases.
- Potatoes need deep and well-cultivated soil.
- Soil cultivation for potatoes involves ploughing to a depth of 22 cm, rotovation to produce a fine seedbed 172–182 cm wide, each containing two drills.
- Commercial growers remove stones and clods; this prevents bruising and contamination of the potatoes at harvesting.
- Potatoes are sown 10 cm below the ridge. The seed's size determines the spacing between the seed potatoes.
- In the sowing of early varieties the seed potatoes are sprouted before planting. Sprouting seeds speed up growth, plant emergence and yield.
- Fertiliser requirements are determined by soil tests.
- Excess nitrogen depresses the dry matter content of the tuber and produces a more watery tuber.
- Weeds are controlled initially by using a contact and residual herbicide. Once the crop becomes established, shading prevents the growth of weeds.
- An airborne fungus causes blight.
- To prevent fungal infection farmers spray the potato crop with a fungicide.
- Blackleg is caused by a bacterium, which is also responsible for causing soft rot of tubers and affects the established crop, causing the leaves to turn yellow and the stems to turn black.
- To prevent blackleg, growers should only plant clean, disease-free certified seed.
- The potato crop is harvested with a potato harvester.

QUESTIONS

1. Identify the family to which potatoes belong.
2. Potatoes are classified according to harvest date. What are the three main categories of potatoes?
3. Production of early potatoes is mainly confined to coastal regions of counties Cork and Wexford. Give a reason for this.
4. Identify the location in Ireland where certified seed potatoes are produced. Give one reason why seed potatoes are grown there.
5. Potato growers are recommended to use certified seed. Give a reason for this.
6. Why is crop rotation important in the production of potatoes? Give a suitable rotation for (a) certified seed production and (b) maincrop.

QUESTIONS

7 Outline the cultivation of potatoes under the following headings:
 (a) Seedbed preparation
 (b) Sowing of the seed
 (c) Use of fertiliser
 (d) Weed control
 (e) Pest control
 (f) Harvesting the crop.
8 Which factors determine the amount of dry matter in potato tubers?
9 What is earthing up and why is it carried out?
10 Blackleg is becoming a common problem due to our favourable climate in Ireland.
 (a) What type of organism causes blackleg?
 (b) What effect does blackleg have on the established crop?
 (c) What precautions should a farmer take to prevent blackleg occurring in their crop?

EXAM QUESTIONS

1 The photograph shows potato tubers affected by blight.
 (a) What weather conditions help the spread of the disease in the potato crop?
 (b) Which type of organism causes this disease?
 (c) Describe two ways in which the disease affects the potato plant.
 (d) Give two ways that this disease can be controlled. (LC, OL, 2006)
2 Consumer demand in Ireland is for floury (high dry matter) potatoes.
 (a) Suggest a suitable compound fertiliser for the production of floury tubers.
 (b) Give three causes of low dry matter in potato tubers. (LC, HL, 2009)
3 (a) Name two viral diseases of potatoes.
 (b) In the case of one disease state how it is spread.
 (c) Mention one method used to prevent the spread of the disease. (LC, HL, 2006)

||||| Fig 36.14

Chapter 37

Sugar Beet

In 2006, the last sugar-processing plant, based in Mallow, was closed for good. This brought an end to sugar production in Ireland. It also meant that growing sugar beet was no longer commercially viable for over 3 500 farmers in the south and south-east of Ireland, as all sugar beet growers grew sugar beet on contract. This crop had been an important root crop for the tillage industry in those regions for approximately 80 years. It was used in rotation with cereal and grassland production.

≡ Sugar Beet: Facts

Sugar beet (*Beta vulgaris*) is a member of the Chenopodiaceae family. Other members of the family include fodder beet and beetroot, all of which descend from sea beet. It is a biennial plant and has 15–20 per cent sucrose content by dry mass weight. While sugar is the main product associated with sugar beet processing, it has a number of by-products of agricultural importance.

By-products of sugar beet

- **Molasses**: Black syrup is left over after the crystallisation process in sugar production. It is approximately 50 per cent sucrose. It also contains vitamins and minerals. It is an additive in animal feeds and can be used to increase the palatability of silage. When it is used as a silage additive, it acts as a stimulant in the fermentation of grass.

- **Beet tops**: During beet harvesting, the tops are cut from the sugar beet and left in the field. These can be fed to sheep or cattle.

- **Beet pulp**: This is the remains of the root material after the sugar extraction process. It is dried and shredded and can be used as a livestock feed.

||||| Fig 37.1 Sugar beet plant

||||| Fig 37.2 Molasses

≡ Cultivation of Sugar Beet

Soil suitability

Deep, well-drained sandy soils are necessary for sugar beet production. Poor drainage leads to a low rate of establishment. Compacted soils lead to root forking. Beets with forked roots cannot be processed. Sugar beet also needs a soil environment with a pH of 6.5 to 7.0. The crop will not tolerate acidic soils.

Climate

Beet is best suited to a temperate climate as it is not a frost-resistant plant. Sunshine also plays a major role as it has an influence on the level of sucrose produced and stored in the beet. The south-east of Ireland has a warm, sunny climate in comparison to other regions of the country, which made it ideal for sugar beet production.

Preparation of seedbeds

Land should be autumn ploughed and then rotovated in spring for production of a fine seedbed.

Time, rate and method of sowing

Sugar beet is sown in spring where it can avail of water and avoid frost damage. This also allows for a long growing season, which can lead to a high yield. Seed is sown at a rate of 100 000 seeds per hectare by a precision seeder.

Fertilisers

Fertilisers containing nitrogen, phosphorus and potassium were provided by sugar companies to farmers. Beet fertilisers also contained boron (B) and sodium (Na). A lack of boron causes heart rot/crown rot in sugar beet. Sodium was necessary as sugar beet is descended from sea beet, a salt-loving plant found in coastal habitats. Another deficiency disease found in sugar beet is speckled yellows, caused by a manganese deficiency. Fertiliser specific to sugar beet is broadcast onto the soil and ploughed in during cultivation.

Diseases, pests and weed control

The two main diseases of sugar beet are viral diseases. Virus yellows is transmitted by the aphid and causes chlorosis of the plant. Aphid populations can be reduced by spraying an aphicide during the spring and summer seasons. Rhizomania (root madness) is caused by beet necrotic yellow vein virus (BNYVV), which is transmitted by a soil-borne fungus. It stunts root production, increases root hair production and prevents N uptake, which results in a loss of up to 80 per cent sugar yield. Sowing rhizomania-resistant varieties slows the spread of the virus.

The beet cyst nematode is the main pest of sugar beet. It can be controlled by crop rotation. Weeds in the crop can be controlled by spraying a herbicide twice before full leaf cover.

Rotation

Beet should only be grown one year in three. This helps to prevent the build up of the beet cyst nematode. Ideally, it should be grown in a cereal-grassland rotation. It should not be grown in rotation with other chenopods, such as beetroot or brassica crops, as they are also susceptible to infestation by beet cyst nematode.

||||| Fig 37.3 Sugar beet harvester

Harvest, yield and storage

Harvesting of sugar beet takes place between September and December. Specialised sugar beet harvesters are used for this purpose. Tops are removed from the plant and left in the field while roots are transferred to a trailer. Roots yield 40 tonnes per hectare and tops yield 25 tonnes per hectare. Roots can be stored in clamps and covered with straw to prevent frost damage. Beet tops left in the field can be fed to livestock in situ. The tops need to be wilted for a week as they contain oxalic acid. This causes scour in animals. Wilting the beet tops reduces the acid concentration.

Experiment 37.1

To estimate sucrose concentration in sugar beet

Note: This experiment can also be used to estimate sucrose concentration in grass.

Materials
Sample of sugar beet, refractometer, distilled water

Method

1   Look through the eyepiece of the refractometer to check that it is clear.

2   Place a drop of distilled water on the plate, close the cover and adjust the meter to zero to calibrate the refractometer.

3   Place a few drops of sap/sugar solution on the plate of the refractometer, close the cover and look through the eyepiece.

4   Take a reading of the sucrose percentage from the scale.

||||| Fig 37.4 Refractometer

Summary

▨   Sugar beet (*Beta vulgaris*) is a member of the Chenopodiaceae family.

▨   The main product associated with sugar beet is sugar; its by-products include beet tops and beet pulp which are both used as animal feed, and molasses which is used in animal feed and as a silage additive.

▨   Soils for sugar beet production should be deep, well-drained sandy soils with a pH of 6.5.

▨   As the crop is not frost resistant it needs a warm, sunny climate. Sucrose production in the beet plant is dependent on sunshine. As a result, it was mainly grown in south-east Ireland.

▨   Land should be autumn ploughed and harrowed. Seed is planted in spring, using a precision seeder.

▨   An NPK fertiliser such as 10-10-20 is used in sugar beet production. Boron is added to the fertiliser to prevent heart rot in sugar beet, and sodium is added as sugar beet is related to sea beet.

▨   Virus yellows is transmitted by aphids and signs include chlorotic leaves. Rhizomania, a virus, is transmitted by a soil-borne fungus and stunts root production.

Summary

- The beet cyst nematode is the main pest of sugar beet. Sugar beet should be grown in a three-year rotation to prevent the build up of the nematode in the soil.
- Harvesting takes place between September and December. A sugar beet harvester is used, which cuts the tops off the beets and leaves them in the field. On average 25 tonnes/ha of tops and 40 tonnes/ha of roots are produced.
- Tops can be fed to cattle in situ once they are wilted for a week as they contain oxalic acid which causes scour.
- Roots can be stored in clamps and covered in straw to prevent frost damage.
- The percentage of sugar in a beet plant can be measured using a refractometer.

QUESTIONS

1. What is the Latin name for sugar beet?
2. To which family does sugar beet belong?
3. (a) Name three by-products of sugar beet production.
   (b) Describe a use for each of these by-products.
4. What causes forking in sugar beet?
5. Which types of soil are suitable for sugar beet growth?
6. What weather condition affects the sugar content of the sugar beet plant?
7. What is the average sugar content of a sugar beet plant in Ireland?
8. Rotation is practised in sugar beet growing to avoid which pest?
9. How often can sugar beet be grown in a rotation?
10. Which machine is used for planting sugar beet?
11. At what time of year is sugar beet sown?
12. What is the seeding rate per hectare?
13. Which two minerals are added to sugar beet fertilisers? Why is each mineral added?
14. How is the virus yellows disease transmitted to the sugar beet plant? How can it be prevented?
15. How is rhizomania spread in sugar beet plants?
16. What is the average yield per hectare of sugar beets and tops?
17. Describe one way of storing sugar beet.
18. Why do sugar beet tops need to be wilted for a few days before feeding?
19. Which instrument can be used to measure sucrose concentration in sugar beet?

EXAM QUESTIONS

1. (a) Name two crops that can be grown as a suitable root break in a cereal rotation.
   (b) State any one use for one of the crops that you have mentioned. (LC, HL, 2008)
2. Speckled yellows is a disease of sugar beet caused by a deficiency of a trace element.
   (a) Name the trace element involved.
   (b) Name another disease of sugar beet caused by a deficiency of a named trace element.
      (LC, HL, 2005)

Chapter 38
Catch Crops

≡ Catch Crops: Facts

Catch crops, also known as fodder crops, are fast-growing crops that are grown between two main crops.

> **Catch crops:** Fast-growing crops grown between two main crops when land would otherwise lie idle.

Catch crops are cultivated primarily for animal feed. They are usually incorporated into a crop rotation, where they can provide some quickly grown livestock feed. For example, a gap between the harvest of winter sown barley and sowing a spring ley provides farmers with the opportunity of growing a catch crop, thus providing farmers with additional winter fodder. Ploughing a catch crop back into the soil can also help to improve soil structure.

Advantages of catch crops

▦ Catch crops are fast growing.

▦ Catch crops are high yielding.

▦ Provide farmers with additional winter feed; less risk of fodder shortage in winter months.

▦ Reduce winter feed costs; less concentrated feeds purchased.

▦ Feed is fully traceable as it is grown on the farmer's own land.

▦ Break crop between grass and cereals.

▦ Help prevent nitrogen leaching.

▦ Early bite for dairy cows when grazed in February.

▦ Some crops, e.g. kale, have high crude protein contents.

Disadvantages of catch crops

▦ Catch crops are labour intensive if strip grazed or zero grazed.

▦ Many catch crops are low in fibre; therefore hay or silage must be fed with the catch crop.

▦ Catch crops are vulnerable to attack from pests and diseases; crop rotation must be employed.

▦ It is uneconomical to plough a productive perennial ryegrass pasture for sowing a catch crop unless reseeding is planned.

▦ Risk of poaching land if a catch crop is grazed in situ during wet winter months on heavy soils.

▦ Iodine deficiency can occur when livestock are fed on brassica crops, as brassicas are low in iodine, and chemicals produced by the plants can inhibit the uptake of iodine in animals.

≡ Stubble Turnip

Stubble turnip is a fast-growing, nutritious and highly palatable catch crop. It has a shorter growing season than kale and is ready for grazing 12–14 weeks after it is sown. The following table shows the nutritional value and yield of stubble turnip.

||||| Fig 38.1 Sheep grazing stubble turnip

Table 38.1 Yields and feed quality of stubble turnip	
Average DM yield	3.5–4 tonnes/ha
Average fresh yields	38–40 tonnes/ha
Dry matter	8–9%
Crude protein	17–18%
Digestibility	68–70%
Metabolisable energy	11 MJ/kg DM

(Source: Limagrain UK)

||||| Fig 38.2 Stubble turnip variety Dynamo

Cultivation practices and feeding

Soil suitability and sowing

Stubble turnip prefers free-draining loam soil with a pH of 6.5 or more. The soil must be suitable for grazing, as this crop is not suitable for harvesting. Soil cultivation is not always required as stubble turnip can be broadcast onto cereal stubble after harvesting followed by rolling. Alternatively, plough and harrow the soil to produce a fine seedbed followed by direct drilling of the seeds. It is important not to over-cultivate the soil, as this increases soil moisture loss, which can lead to poor crop establishment and lower yields.

Stubble turnip can be sown in spring, summer or early autumn. If sown in spring (April to June) the crop can be used to finish lambs, while stubble turnip sown in late June to August is used for winter fodder in November. Stubble turnip is not very winter hardy.

Samson, Delilah, Rondo and Tyfon are common varieties of stubble turnip.

Rotation

Stubble turnip is a member of the Cruciferae family and as a result is vulnerable to club root. Club root is caused by a soil-borne fungus and can be prevented by crop rotation. Therefore, stubble turnip should not be grown in the same area for more than one in every three years. Some varieties of stubble turnip show good club root resistance.

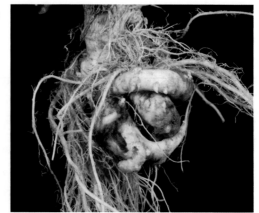

||||| Fig 38.3 Club root

Fertiliser requirements

A soil test should be completed before applying fertiliser. Stubble turnip requires 70 kg/ha of nitrogen, 35 kg/ha of phosphorus and 35 kg/ha of potassium at planting. A top dressing of 70 kg/ha of nitrogen is applied three to four weeks after sowing.

Pests and diseases

The flea beetle is a common pest of stubble turnip. They are small, black or striped beetles that jump from plant to plant. They eat small round holes in the seed leaves, and young seedlings are especially vulnerable to attack.

The larvae of the flea beetle are white with a dark head. The larvae feed on the roots of the plant. The crop should be sprayed with an insecticide at first sign of attack. Slugs can also be a problem.

Fig 38.4 Flea beetle

Fig 38.5 Flea beetle larvae

Feeding livestock

Stubble turnip should be introduced gradually into the diet of sheep and cattle. Both leaves and roots are edible. Strip grazing using an electric fence should be utilised to minimise waste. Silage or hay must make up 25 per cent of the diet of an animal grazing stubble turnip. This ensures proper saliva production and helps maintain the pH of the rumen within its normal pH range.

Bales should be placed in the field when the land is dry; this prevents damage to the soil structure caused by tractor tyres during wet winter months.

It is recommended that dairy cows graze stubble turnip after milking, as grazing stubble turnip before milking can taint the milk. Livestock must also be provided with a run back, with some shelter. A dry area is important as it allows the animals' feet to dry, thus reducing the incidence of lameness.

≡ Kale

Kale is another popular catch crop grown in Ireland. It has a longer growing season than stubble turnip, and if a farmer is planning to use it as winter fodder it must be sown between April and early July. Kale gives its maximum yield after a growing period of five to six months.

Table 38.2 on page 302 outlines the nutritional value and yield of kale.

Fig 38.6 Kale variety Maris Kestral

Table 38.2 Yields and feed quality of kale	
Average DM yield	8–10 tonnes/ha
Average fresh yields	6–65 tonnes/ha
DM	14–16%
Crude protein	16–17% fresh; 19–25% ensiled
Digestibility	68%
Metabolisable energy	10–11 MJ/kg DM

(Source: Limagrain UK)

Cultivation practices and feeding

Soil suitability and sowing

Kale grows best on a free-draining loam or sandy soil with a pH of 6.0 to 7.0. Land must be suitable for grazing if a farmer plans to graze the kale in situ; otherwise kale can be zero grazed or harvested in August to September and baled like silage to produce kaleage.

A fine, firm seedbed is required for the sowing of kale. Usually the land is ploughed and then power harrowed to produce the final seedbed. Kale can be broadcast, or it can be sown with a

||||| Fig 38.7 Direct drilling of kale

precision drill or by direct drilling. Seeds should be sown at a depth of 10 mm.

Caledonian, Grampian, Keeper and Maris Kestrel are common varieties of kale.

Rotation

Like all members of the Cruciferae family, kale is prone to club root. For this reason, kale should not be grown continuously in the same field. Ideally, it should be incorporated in a five-year rotation. Varieties with club root resistance are available.

Fertiliser requirements

Soil tests should be carried out to determine the fertiliser application. Nitrogen is applied at sowing at a rate of 75–85 kg/ha. Nitrogen application can be split, with some applied at sowing and the rest applied as a top dressing. The application of phosphorus and potassium depends on the soil index.

||||| Fig 38.8 Dairy cows strip grazing kale

Pests and disease

Kale is susceptible to flea beetle and aphid attack. The crop should be sprayed with a suitable insecticide. Also seedlings can be prone to slugs; slug pellets can be used if necessary.

Feeding livestock

Kale can be strip grazed by livestock, using an electric fence allowing a space of 3 metres per cow.

IIIIII Fig 38.9 Suckler cow eating mineral supplements

If fed to dairy cows, kale should make up only 30–35 per cent of the cows' dry matter intake, as the excessive intake of kale can lead to anaemia. Kale can also cause red water in livestock, as it contains a non-protein amino acid that is converted into a compound in the rumen, which damages red blood cells. The damaged cells release haemoglobin and the haemoglobin appears in the urine of the animal, similar to red water fever. In order to prevent this happening, livestock should be gradually introduced to kale and the crop should not be grazed if it is in flower as red water is more common then.

When grazing kale, provide livestock with hay or silage at all times. Kale is high in calcium but low in phosphorus, manganese and iodine; therefore provide mineral supplements to livestock. Kale is suitable for zero grazing and can be harvested and fed indoors to animals.

Summary

- Catch crops are fast-growing crops, grown between two main crops when the land would otherwise lie idle.
- Catch crops are cultivated primarily for animal feed.
- Ploughing a catch crop back into the soil can also help to improve soil structure.
- Advantages of catch crops include: fast growing, high yielding and reducing winter feed costs.
- Disadvantages of catch crops include: labour intensive, low in fibre and vulnerable to attack from pests and diseases.
- Stubble turnip is a fast-growing, nutritious and highly palatable catch crop.
- Stubble turnip requires free-draining loam soil with a pH of 6.5 or more. Soil must be suitable for grazing as this crop is not suitable for harvesting.
- Rotation is important when growing stubble turnip and kale, as both varieties are vulnerable to club root.
- Stubble turnip requires 70 kg/ha of nitrogen, 35 kg/ha of phosphorus and 35 kg/ha of potassium at planting. A top dressing of 70 kg/ha of nitrogen is applied three to four weeks after sowing.
- Kale is another popular catch crop grown in Ireland. It has a longer growing season than stubble turnip.
- Kale grows best on a free-draining loam or sandy soil with a pH of 6.0 to 7.0.
- Kale is susceptible to flea beetle and aphid attack. The crop should be sprayed with a suitable insecticide.
- Kale can be strip grazed by livestock, using an electric fence, or harvested and baled like silage to produce kaleage.
- Livestock should be provided with hay or silage at all times when grazing kale.
- Kale is high in calcium but low in phosphorus, manganese and iodine; therefore mineral supplements should also be given to livestock.

QUESTIONS

1. Define catch crop. Give two examples of catch crops.
2. Give three advantages and three disadvantages of growing catch crops.
3. To which family do kale and stubble turnip belong?
4. Describe the cultivation of a named catch crop under the following headings:
   (a) Soil requirements
   (b) Rotation
   (c) Fertiliser requirement
   (d) Pests and diseases.
5. Hay and silage must be fed to livestock when on kale or stubble turnip. Explain why this is important.
6. Briefly describe how catch crops may be fed to livestock as winter feed.
7. Identify the type of organism that causes club root in kale and explain how the disease can be prevented.

EXAM QUESTIONS

1. Give two reasons why the intake of fodder crops (e.g. rape and kale) in the diet of a farm animal should be limited. (LC, HL, 2007)
2. Describe the production of a named catch crop on a tillage farm. (LC, HL, 2007)
3. In relation to fodder crops, other than grass:
   (a) State three advantages of growing fodder crops.
   (b) Describe two methods used in feeding these crops to animals. (LC, HL, 2006)
4. Identify the type of organism which causes club roots in turnips and explain how this disease could be controlled or prevented. (LC, HL, 2008)

Livestock Production and Management

Chapter 39
Animal Nutrition, Feeds and Body Condition

☰ Animal Nutrition

In order to maintain a healthy body an animal must have a diet composed of carbohydrate, protein, fat, vitamins, minerals and water. The functions of these nutrients are given in the table below.

Nutrient	Function
Carbohydrate	Energy and fibre (roughage)
Protein	Growth and repair of cells, energy
Fat	Insulation and energy
Vitamins	Control many metabolic processes
Minerals	Bone and teeth building, energy production, milk production
Water	Solvent, aids in temperature regulation, lactation and other metabolic processes

Table 39.1 Nutrients and their functions

Like humans, cattle, sheep and pigs require all of these nutrients from their feed to maintain good health. As cattle and sheep are ruminants, their animal feeds can be divided into two categories:

1   Bulky feeds
2   Concentrates or formulated rations.

Bulky feeds

Bulky feeds are high in water or fibre. Grass, silage, hay, root crops and forage crops (kale) are all classified as bulky feeds. Both cattle and sheep need to have adequate levels of fibre in their diet to ensure that the rumen (first division of the stomach) functions correctly.

Acidosis can occur when their diet is high in easily digestible starches and sugars and low in fibre. Sheep and cattle must be fed silage, hay or straw when concentrates are added to their diet.

||||| Fig 39.1 Silage

||||| Fig 39.2 Hay

||||| Fig 39.3 Grass

Concentrates

Concentrates are feeds that are low in water and fibre. Cereals, fats, oil, molasses, beet pulp and feed supplements are all classified as concentrates. Concentrate rations are formulated to give the correct balance of protein, carbohydrates, fibre, minerals and vitamins.

Cereals very often make up a substantial part of concentrates. Barley, wheat and maize are commonly used. Cereals have many advantages in a formulated ration:

- They are high in carbohydrates and energy.
- Their seed coat contains fibre.
- They can be used to supplement poor quality silage or other fodder crops.
- They can ensure production targets are met.

||||| Fig 39.4 Barley

||||| Fig 39.5 Wheat

||||| Fig 39.6 Maize

Table 39.2 below and Table 39.3 and Table 39.4 (see overleaf) are examples of some formulated rations for dairy cattle, beef cattle and pigs.

Table 39.2 Dairy rations	
Component	**Percentage**
Crude protein	18
Crude fibre	8
Crude oil	2.8
List of ingredients	
Barley, wheat, rapeseed extraction, malt culms, maize, cane molasses, beet pulp, palm kernel, vitamin A, vitamin D, magnesium, copper, calcium, selenium	

||||| Fig 39.7 Ration bag

Energy and protein are very important elements in a formulated dairy ration. The cereals wheat, barley and maize are sources of carbohydrate and, therefore, energy. Malt culms is a by-product of malting and along with rapeseed extraction is a source of protein. Cane molasses is a source of sugars; molasses is normally used to bind the meal together into a nut. Palm kernel is the residue of the palm nut once the oil has been removed. Palm kernel and beet pulp (left over beet once sugar is extracted) are high in fibre.

Vitamins and minerals have been included in this ration to prevent diseases caused by deficiencies. Vitamin A is required for the maintenance of healthy tissues while vitamin D is required for healthy bones. Deficiencies in selenium and copper have been linked with infertility in dairy cows. Magnesium is added to prevent grass tetany and calcium to prevent milk fever.

An animal's diet can also be supplemented with minerals, using the following methods:

▦ Dusting mineral supplements onto silage.

▦ Providing the animals with mineral licks.

▦ Dressing the pasture.

▦ Added to the drinking water.

▦ As an oral dose or as a mineral bullet.

||||| Fig 39.8 A cow using a mineral lick

Table 39.3 Beef ration

Component	Percentage
Crude protein	15
Crude fibre	7.5
Crude oil	4.5
List of ingredients	
Barley, maize, rapeseed extraction, wheat feed, palm kernel, beet molasses, citrus pulp, vegetable oils, maize gluten, vitamin A, vitamin D, vitamin E, copper, selenium	

||||| Fig 39.9 Beef nuts

Some components of the beef ration are the same as the dairy ration. Citrus pulp (a by-product of the citrus fruit) and maize are included in this ration as sources of carbohydrate. Palm kernel and maize gluten are sources of fibre. Beet molasses is used to bind the components into a nut as well as a source of sugars. Vitamin E plays an important role in maintaining a healthy immune system.

Unlike cattle and sheep, pigs are monogastric animals. Their feeds have less fibre than cattle or sheep, as pigs are unable to digest fibre. Table 39.4 is an example of a pig ration. Note the addition of lysine in this feed, an essential amino acid required by pigs.

Table 39.4 Pig ration

Component	Percentage
Crude protein	18
Crude fibre	3.5
Crude oil	4
List of ingredients	
Soya bean (dehulled and toasted), rapeseed, barley, animal fat, lysine, calcium, vitamin A, vitamin D, selenium, copper	

Soya is included in this ration due to its high-energy value and high protein content. The soya bean is dehulled to remove the seed coat; this reduces fibre. It is toasted to improve the biological value of the protein. Rapeseed meal is also a source of protein. However, the amount of rapeseed used in the ration must be limited due to the presence of anti-nutritional factors present in the rapeseed. The animal fat in this ration is a high source of energy.

Barley is used in both the ruminant and pig rations. However, the barley must be treated differently when used in these rations. The barley seeds must be rolled when fed to ruminants. Rolling breaks the seed coat, allowing the ruminant's digestive system to break down the contents of the seed. If the seeds are not rolled, then undigested seeds are present in the faeces. When barley is fed to pigs, the barley must be ground down so that it can be easily digested.

Fig 39.10 Soya beans

Experiment 39.1

To compare the digestibility of rolled barley versus whole barley when fed to cows

Materials
Two dairy cows, 1 kg of barley seeds (500 g of which is rolled and the other 500 g is left whole), hose, sieve

Method
1 Cows must be housed indoors for the duration of the experiment, approximately 12 hours with one hour loose.

2 Feed one cow 500 g of the rolled barley and the other cow 500 g of whole barley.

3 Both cows are given access to water and hay or silage.

4 Collect dung samples separately from both cows.

5 Wash the dung through a sieve.

6 Collect and count any whole barley grains.

Result
The cow fed unrolled barley will have more undigested barley grains in its dung compared to the cow fed the rolled barley.

Conclusion
Rolling improves the digestibility of barley.

☰ Food Tests

Animal feeds can be tested for the presence of nutrients, using the following experiments.

Experiment 39.2

Test for starch

Materials

Five test tubes, starch solution, iodine solution, pestle and mortar, oats, wheat, potato

Method

1 Label five test tubes A to E. Add water to test tube A. Add the starch solution to test tube B (Fig 39.11).

2 Place a small amount of oats in the pestle and mortar and add some water. Grind up the oats and water together. Repeat with the wheat in a separate pestle and mortar. See note at the end of this experiment.

3 Add 5 cm³ of the oat solution and 5 cm³ of the wheat solution to test tube D.

4 Cut up the potato into small pieces.

5 Add a small piece of potato to test tube E.

6 Add 1 cm³ of iodine solution to each test tube.

7 Record the results.

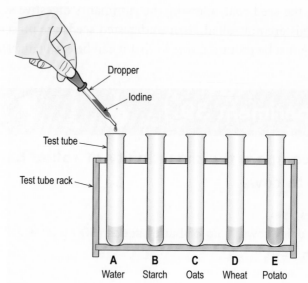

Fig 39.11 Test for starch

Result

		Table 39.5 Results of starch test	
Test tube	Contents	Observation
A	Water	
B	Starch	
C	Oats	
D	Wheat	
E	Potato	

Conclusion

The test tubes containing starch, oats, wheat and potato all turned the iodine a blue-black colour, indicating that starch was present.

Note: If wheat is unavailable use some flour and porridge to supply oats for this experiment.

Experiment 39.3

Test for reducing sugars

Materials

Two test tubes, glucose solution, beaker, Benedict's reagent, Bunsen burner, tongs, tripod, gauze mat

Method

1 Add a small amount of water to the first test tube and a small amount of glucose to the second test tube.

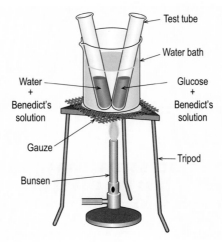

||||| Fig 39.12 Test for reducing sugars

2 Add 3 cm³ of Benedict's solution to each test tube.

3 Place in a beaker of water and heat over a Bunsen burner as shown in Fig 39.12.

4 Record the results.

Results

Table 39.6 Results of test for reducing sugars		
Test tube	Contents	Observation
A	Water	
B	Glucose	

Conclusion

The Benedict's solution turns a brick-red colour in the presence of glucose.

Experiment 39.4

Test for fats

Materials
Two pieces of brown paper, oil or butter, water

Method
1 Place a drop of water on one piece of brown paper and rub it in.
2 Place a drop of oil on the second piece of paper and rub it in.
3 Allow both pieces of paper to dry.

Result
Hold both pieces of paper up to the light and record the result.

Conclusion
Fat leaves a translucent spot on brown paper.

Experiment 39.5

Test for protein

Materials
Four test tubes, copper sulfate solution, dilute sodium hydroxide solution, milk, yoghurt, egg albumin

Method
1 Label four test tubes A to D.

2 Add 5 cm^3 water to the first test tube and add 5 cm^3 of the milk, yoghurt and egg albumin to the other three test tubes, as shown in Fig 39.13.

3 Add 2 cm^3 of copper sulfate and 4 cm^3 of dilute sodium hydroxide to each test tube.

4 Record the results.

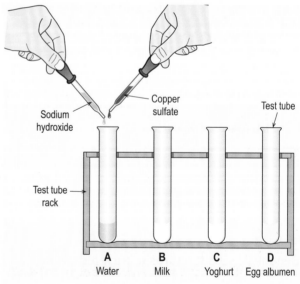

Fig 39.13 Test for protein

Experiment 39.5

Result

		Table 39.7 Results of protein test	
Test tube	**Contents**	**Observation**
A	Water	
B	Milk	
C	Yoghurt	
D	Egg albumin	

Conclusion

Milk, yoghurt and egg albumin all turn a purple or lilac colour, indicating the presence of protein.

Experiment 39.6

Test for vitamin C

Materials

DCPIP (a blue dye that goes colourless in the presence of vitamin C), freshly squeezed orange, lemon or lime juice, two test tubes

Method

1   Add 5 cm^3 of water to test tube A and 5 cm^3 of juice to test tube B.

2   Add 1 cm^3 of DCPIP solution to both test tubes.

Result

The blue dye turns colourless in the fruit juice, indicating the presence of vitamin C.

☰ Metabolisable Energy

When an animal eats forage and feed, only part of the total energy of the food can be used by the animal. Energy loss occurs in animals in the following way:

▨   Undigested materials in faeces.

▨   Production of urine.

▨   Formation of methane gas by ruminant animals.

▨   Production of heat.

The remaining energy, which is used by the animal to put on live weight gain (LWG) or to produce milk, is known as metabolisable energy. It is measured in MU/kg (megajoules per kilogram) of dry matter.

> **Metabolisable energy:** The energy from feed that an animal can convert into LWG, milk and wool and is measured as MU/kg.

313

Experiment 39.7

To demonstrate that food contains energy

Materials
Test tube, graduated cylinder, tongs, thermometer, Bunsen burner, cracker, stand and clamp

Method

1 Add 20 cm³ of water to the test tube and set up the apparatus as shown in Fig 39.14.

2 Record the temperature of the water using the thermometer.

3 Light the food using the Bunsen burner.

4 Hold the burning food under the test tube.

5 Record the change in temperature of the water.

Conclusion
Chemical energy in the food is converted to heat energy, which heats the water causing the temperature of the water to rise.

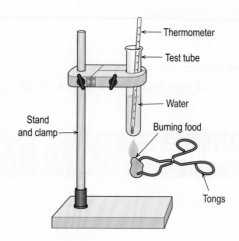

||||| Fig 39.14 To demonstrate that food contains energy

☰ Maintenance and Production Diets

The diet of dairy cows, sheep and pigs changes throughout the course of the year. For part of the year, a production animal can be placed on a plane of low nutrition, commonly called a maintenance diet. At other times, the animal must be fed on a high plane of nutrition to meet high energy demands during breeding, giving birth and producing milk. At these times, the animal is fed a production diet.

Maintenance diet: The amount of feed that allows an animal to maintain a constant body weight.
Production diet: The extra amount of feed required to produce 1 kg of LWG, 1 L of milk, 1 kg of wool, or to produce a calf or lamb.

Conformation

Conformation refers to the shape of an animal and is important in the grading of carcasses under the EUROP classification system (see Chapter 48). Conformation traits vary greatly between dairy and beef breeds of cattle.

Conformation: The shape of an animal and the distribution of fat and muscle around its body.

Beef breeds have a block-shaped conformation, with wide shoulders and hindquarters that are well-fleshed (see Fig 39.15).

The top and bottom lines of a beef breed should be parallel and the neck of the animal is short and wide. On the other hand, a purebred dairy animal has a triangular or wedge-shaped conformation (see Fig 39.16).

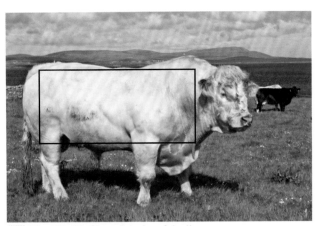

||||| Fig 39.15 Charolais beef bull

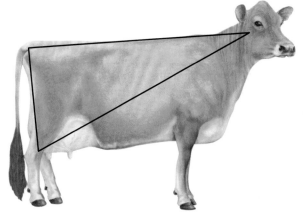

||||| Fig 39.16 Jersey cow dairy breed

In dairy breeds, the shoulders are narrow and not well-fleshed and the neck is long and thin. The hindquarters are wide but are not well-fleshed. Dairy cows have a wide chest and a large lung capacity, which supports their ability to produce lots of milk.

Factors affecting conformation

- **Breed**: Continental beef breeds have the best conformation, while purebred dairy breeds have the worst conformation.

- **Sex**: The sex of the animal affects conformation, with bulls having the best conformation, followed by steers and heifers. Cows have the worst conformation.

Body condition score (BCS)

Body condition scoring is a routine procedure used to assess the level of fat reserves that an animal has at various stages of its production cycle (before mating, giving birth and during lactation).

Animals are assessed both visually and by handling in order to assess their body reserves. It is particularly important to handle sheep when assessing their BCS as the presence of the fleece can often impair visual assessment.

BCS ranges from 1 to 5. A condition score of 1 indicates an extremely thin animal while a score of 5 indicates an extremely fat animal. Body condition scores of animals should be assessed regularly so that a farmer can adjust feeding and management to ensure that the animal is at the correct BCS.

In the BCS of dairy cows, the animal is assessed in the following areas: the loin (between the hip bone and the first rib) and the tail head.

> **Body condition scoring** of cattle, sheep and pigs allows the animal producer to assess the level of fat reserves that an animal has at various production stages.

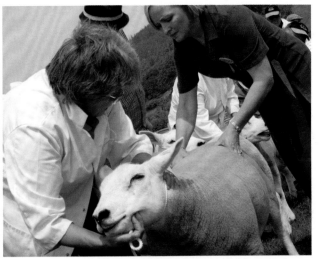

||||| Fig 39.17 A sheep judge evaluating BCS at a show

315

The figures opposite illustrate the fat cover on dairy cows with a score of 1, 3 and 5. Notice how the layer of fat cover increases as you go from a BCS of 1 to a BCS of 5.

A dairy cow with a BCS of 3 is classified as an animal in good condition. Moorepark Dairy Research Centre recommends the following body condition scores for a dairy herd (Table 39.8).

Table 39.8 Body condition scores for dairy cows	
Stage of production cycle	**Average BSC for herd**
Drying off	3.0
Precalving	3.25
Start of breeding	2.9

Extremes of body condition should be avoided (BCS of 1 and BCS >4). Cows that calve down too thin will have difficulty reaching the correct target BCS prior to mating, thus delaying these cows going back into oestrus and increasing the risk of metabolic problems and diseases. On the other hand, dairy cows that are too fat are more prone to calving difficulties, milk fever, lameness and developing fatty liver disease.

Sheep are also assessed between a range of 1 and 5 for body condition. The level of muscle and fat cover above the vertebrae bone (spinous process) and around the horizontal bone (transverse process) in the loin region is assessed by hand.

A ewe's BCS depends on what stage she is at in her productive cycle. A BCS of 3 indicates good condition and, like dairy cattle, it is essential that the ewe is at the correct BCS before mating and at lambing.

BCS for pigs range between 1 to 5 and pigs should be kept within a range of 2.5 and 4.5 over their productive cycle.

Keeping the correct body condition score is necessary to maintain the health, productivity and reproductive efficiency of any animal production system.

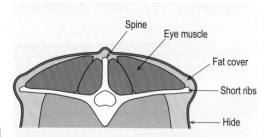

Fig 39.18 Dairy cows with a BCS of 1

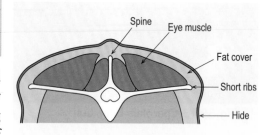

Fig 39.19 Dairy cows with a BCS of 3

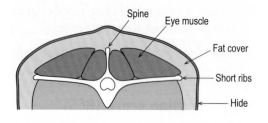

Fig 39.20 Dairy cows with a BCS of 5

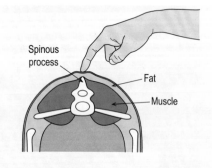

Fig 39.21 Assessing the level of fat cover above the vertebrae bone (spinous process)

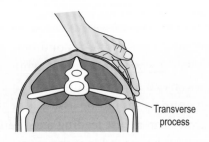

Fig 39.22 Assessing the level of fat cover around the horizontal bone (transverse process)

Summary

- In order to maintain a healthy body an animal must have a diet composed of carbohydrate, protein, fat, vitamins, minerals and water.
- Feeds for ruminants can be divided into two categories: (i) bulky feeds and (ii) concentrates or formulated rations.
- Bulky feeds are high in water or fibre, e.g. grass, silage, hay, root crops and forage crops (kale).
- Concentrates are feeds that are low in water and fibre, e.g. cereals, fats, oil, molasses, beet pulp and feed supplements.
- Cereals have advantages in a formulated ration, e.g. high in carbohydrates and energy, seed coat contains fibre; used to supplement poor quality silage or other fodder crops.
- Vitamins and minerals are included in concentrates to prevent diseases caused by deficiencies.
- Concentrates for pigs have less fibre than cattle or sheep, as pigs cannot digest fibre.
- If barley is included in a pig ration it must be ground down, while in a ration for sheep or cattle it must be rolled so that it can be digested.
- Metabolisable energy is the energy from feed that an animal can convert into LWG, milk and wool and is measured as MU/kg.
- A maintenance diet is the amount of feed that animals need to maintain constant body weight.
- A production diet is the extra amount of feed needed to produce 1 kg of LWG, 1 L of milk, 1 kg of wool, or to produce a calf or lamb.
- Conformation is the shape of the animal and the distribution of fat and muscle around its body.
- Beef breeds have a block-shaped conformation, wide shoulders and well-fleshed hindquarters.
- Dairy breeds have a triangular or wedge-shaped conformation, long thin necks and narrow shoulders that are not well fleshed.
- Body condition scoring of cattle, sheep and pigs assesses the level of fat reserves an animal has at various production stages.
- Body condition scores of animals should be assessed regularly so that farmers can adjust feeding and management to ensure that the animal is at the correct BCS.

QUESTIONS

1 Give a function for each of the following nutrients in the diet of an animal:
   (a) Carbohydrate
   (b) Protein
   (c) Vitamins
   (d) Water.

QUESTIONS

2 Explain the difference between a bulky feed and concentrates. Give an example of each type of feed.

3 Explain why ruminants fed concentrates as part of their diet must also be fed silage, hay or straw.

4 Give two reasons why cereals are used in concentrates.

5 Give a reason why the following feeds are added to formulated rations:
   (a) Barley
   (b) Maize
   (c) Malt culms
   (d) Palm kernel
   (e) Soya bean
   (f) Selenium.

6 Explain the difference between a formulated ration for dairy cows and a ration for pigs.

7 Give one advantage and one disadvantage of using rapeseed meal in concentrates.

8 Compare the treatment of barley seeds before feeding to (a) a ruminant animal and (b) a monogastric animal.

9 Describe an experiment to investigate the digestibility of rolled and unrolled barley in a ruminant's diet.

10 Explain the difference between a maintenance ration and a production ration.

11 Complete the following table on food tests.

Table 39.9 Food tests			
Test	**Chemicals added**	**Heat required (yes/no)**	**Result**
Starch			
Glucose			
Protein			
Fat			
Vitamin C			

12 List three ways animals lose energy from their food.

13 (a) Define metabolisable energy.
   (b) Which unit is used to measure metabolisable energy?

14 Define conformation. Distinguish between the conformational characteristics of a beef animal and a purebred dairy animal.

15 Explain the meaning of 'body condition score'. How is body condition score measured?

16 Identify the correct body condition score for a dairy cow at each of the following stages:
   (a) At mating
   (b) Calving.

17 Extremes of body condition score (BCS 1 and BCS 5) should be avoided. Give reasons for this statement.

EXAM QUESTIONS

1 Why are minerals and vitamin supplements used in the diet of farm animals? How are these supplements supplied to the farm animal? (LC, HL, 2008)

2 The following table outlines the constituents of a ration that is fed as a supplement to hay or silage to a pregnant ewe.

Table 39.10

Constituent	Percentage of ration by weight
Beet pulp	40%
Rolled barley	40%
Soya bean meal	20%
Mineral mixture	

(a) Give reasons, in each case, for the inclusion of the four constituents in the diet of a pregnant animal.

(b) What would be the consequences if the ration were to be composed of 40% soya bean meal and 20% rolled barley? (LC, HL, 2007)

3 The following table shows the effect of body condition score (BCS) at calving on milk production in early lactation.

Table 39.11

Treatment	BCS	Milk yield kg/cow/day	Milk fat %	Milk fat kg/cow/day	Milk protein %	Milk protein kg/cow/day
A	2.73	25.50	3.71	0.94	3.14	0.80
B	3.00	26.50	3.81	1.01	3.18	0.84

(a) What is meant by a body condition score?
(b) What is the relationship between body condition score and milk yield in the data above?
(c) What is the total yield of fat plus protein under treatment A?
(d) State two factors, other than BCS, that may influence the percentage fat in milk.
(LC, HL, 2007)

4 Suckler cows can be fed for *maintenance* for much of the time but they must be fed on a higher plane of nutrition for 6–7 months of the year.
(a) Explain the highlighted term.
(b) Give three reasons for the 'higher plane of nutrition'. (LC, HL, 2006)

5 Distinguish between a maintenance ration and a production ration for dairy cows. (LC, HL, 2004)

6 Explain the term *conformation*. Describe the difference in conformation between beef cattle and dairy cattle. (LC, OL, 2010)

Chapter 40

Animal Health and Welfare

Notifiable Diseases

A notifiable disease is one that, under the Diseases of Animals Act 1966, must be immediately reported to the district veterinary office. These diseases are notifiable because they are normally infectious and highly contagious.

Notifiable diseases can cause significant economic hardship, through loss in productivity and the death of affected animals. In addition,

Infectious diseases: Diseases caused by micro-organisms (bacteria, fungi or virus) or other agents that enter the body of an organism.
Contagious diseases: Diseases easily transmitted by contact through bodily fluids, or through the the contamination of buildings, clothing or vectors.

many notifiable diseases are zoonoses and pose a significant threat to human health. According to the World Health Organisation, zoonoses are defined as: 'Diseases and infections that are naturally transmitted between vertebrate animals and man.'

Table 40.1 lists some notifiable diseases in Ireland.

Table 40.1 Some notifiable dieases in Ireland			
Notifiable diseases	**Animal it affects**	**Infectious agent**	**Comment**
Anthrax	All mammals	Bacteria	Zoonose, fatal disease
Avian influenza	Poultry	Virus	Zoonose
BSE (Bovine Spongiform Encephalopathy)	Cattle	Prion	Zoonose, spread through contaminated meat and bone
Bluetongue	Ruminants	Virus	Virus spread by midges. Vaccination available
Brucellosis	Cattle	Bacteria	Zoonose, causes undulant fever in humans. Herd testing and eradication programme in place
Contagious bovine pleuropneumonia	Cattle	Bacteria	Affects the lungs
Foot and mouth disease	Cattle, sheep, pigs	Virus	Highly infectious blisters occur in the mouth and on the feet of infected animals. Causes economic loss
Newcastle disease	Poultry	Virus	Highly contagious
Rabies	Mammals	Virus	Zoonose, spread through saliva
Scrapie	Sheep and goats	Prion	Same symptoms as BSE
Bovine tuberculosis	Cattle	Bacteria	Herd testing and eradication programme; zoonose

||||| Fig 40.1 No entry
warning sign of foot and
mouth disease

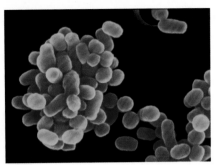

||||| Fig 40.2 Scanning electron
micrograph of Brucella abortus
bacteria

||||| Fig 40.3 Poultry is inspected for
signs of avian influenza (bird flu)

When a notifiable disease is identified on a farm, the movement of animals and animal products is restricted to prevent the spread of the disease. The animals are slaughtered humanely and the carcasses are disposed of by incineration or burial. For many years, Ireland has had eradication programmes for bovine tuberculosis and brucellosis, with regular testing of the national herd. These eradication programmes have had considerable success with Ireland being declared brucellosis free in 2009.

Non-infectious diseases

A non-infectious disease is a disease that is not caused by a pathogen (micro-organism). Milk fever and grass tetany are examples of diseases that are caused by environmental factors. Milk fever is due to low calcium levels in a mammal's blood after giving birth and commencing lactation. Grass tetany is caused by low levels of magnesium in lush spring grass.

☰ Biosecurity

Prevention is always better than cure, particularly in the case of notifiable diseases, as the treatment of these diseases is normally impossible. The following is a list of measures that farmers should take to prevent the entry of disease onto their farms.

- Maintain a closed herd; breed all replacement stock where possible and only buy in stock from herds certified disease free.
- Quarantine all bought-in stock. Farmers should have a separate building away from their own stock animals for bought-in animals.
- Erect good fencing to prevent the contact of stock with animals from neighbouring farms.
- Limit access of the farm to people and vehicles. Both can carry disease onto a farm through clothing, footwear, tyres, etc.
- Control of vermin. Prevent vermin and wildlife having access to animal feed and bedding.
- When using AI, ensure semen and embryos have disease-free status.
- Cattle and sheep should never be housed together. Cattle can become infected with malignant catarrhal fever during lambing time.
- Ensure all newborn animals receive colostrum from their mother.

☰ Welfare of Animals

The health and the welfare of agricultural animals are intertwined and ultimately are the responsibility of the farmer. In 1965, the Brambell Report was published. It studied the welfare of animals kept under the intensive livestock husbandry system in the UK. From this report came the **five freedoms**. These describe the conditions required to ensure the good physical health and mental state of farm animals.

321

1. **Freedom from hunger, thirst and malnutrition**: Animals should have access to fresh water and food to maintain good health and vigour.

2. **Freedom from discomfort**: Animals should be provided with shelter and a comfortable resting area.

3. **Freedom from pain, injury and disease**: By preventing disease and the prompt diagnosis and treatment of animals when a disease occurs.

4. **Freedom to express normal patterns of behaviour**: Animals should have sufficient space, proper facilities and the company of their own kind.

5. **Freedom from fear and distress**: To avoid causing an animal mental stress by ensuring good conditions and treatment.

Fig 40.4 Free-range chickens

≡ Farm Buildings

The type of farm building that a farm needs is dictated by the type of farming, e.g. tillage or animal production, or a mixture of both.

Fig 40.5 Battery hens

Slatted house

The most common type of housing for cattle in Ireland is a slatted house. This building can accommodate both the animals and animal waste (slurry). In a slatted house, cattle can be grouped according to age (weanlings), body condition and calving date. Slatted houses incorporate a feeding area, a lying area and, in some cases, a calf creep area (especially useful when housing suckler cows).

The main disadvantage of slatted houses are that they are expensive to build and unsuitable for calving. The recommended space for a cow in a slatted house is 2.5–3 m^2 per cow and an additional 1 m^2 if a suckler cow is housed with her spring-born calf.

Fig 40.6 Housing for cattle in a slatted house

Cubicle house

Another common winter house for cattle is the cubicle house. There is one cubicle per cow, with a recommended width of 1.2 metres and a length of 2.3–2.6 metres. This ensures that the cow has adequate space to stand up and lie down. Cow mats can be used to reduce pressure on the cows' knees when they stand up and lie down.

The cubicles are raised and sloped to provide drainage, so that urine and dung fall into a central passage. This passage is scraped clean of waste every day. The dung passageway can be replaced with slats and slurry storage.

Fig 40.7 Cow cubicle house

Project link

For the practical examination, you are required to draw a farm layout identifying the various buildings found on the farm. Fig 40.8 on page 324 is an example of a farm layout. Guidelines for producing the farm layout are contained in the practical activity section.

Activity 40.1

Animal production project

As part of the practical examination in the Leaving Certification, students are expected to complete an animal production project on one of the following, e.g. beef, dairy, sheep, pigs or horses. The following is a list of suggested headings that students might consider when putting together their animal production project. It is important to have access to a farm when doing this project so that you have practical experience. Bring a camera whenever you visit the farm and take plenty of pictures for your project. If you live on a farm, you might consider keeping a farm diary of all the week-to-week activities that occur on your farm during the year.

Headings for animal production project

- **Type of farming**: Sheep, mixed, beef, dairy and tillage. Total acreage, arable acreage under grass and under tillage (include root crops) and non-arable land (woodland, scrub etc). Are you a member of REPS? Include REPS' plans where available.

- **Overview of the production system**: Description of the management of a dairy herd or suckler herd, pigs or a mid-season lamb production system. This should include some of the following: the breeds, crosses, numbers, sourcing of replacement, sires used and AI. It should also include livestock management and general husbandry, e.g. feeds, amounts fed, disease prevention, parasite control and dosing programme.

- **General layout of farm**: Include the types of building relevant to the chosen animal production. Include photographs of winter housing, calving or lambing sheds, storage sheds and handling facilities for animals.

- **Machinery**: Functions of machines.

- **Crops grown**: Varieties, reason for choice, rotation, cultivation, fertiliser usage, weed control, pest control, disease control, yields and use of products. One or both of the crop projects could also be completed here.

- **Grassland management**: Grazing management, stocking rate, grass conservation (hay or silage), fertiliser application, liming, high/low clover swards, weed control, reseeding programme and long-term/short-term lays.

- **Plan or suggested improvements**: Breeding policy, increasing stocking rates, etc.

Farm layout

In addition, a student must produce a farm layout plan (see overleaf). The following are some guidelines to consider when drawing a farm plan.

Structures to include on the farm plan

- **Farm layout**: Aspect (direction of north), topography, shelter (hedgerows), roads, gates and water supply.

- **Farm buildings**: Animal houses – general or purpose built; sheep or cattle handling facilities (crush, foot bath, dipping, etc.), crop storage (winter feed, concentrates, etc.), silos, silage storage (pit or bale), and grain storage.

- **Grassland**: Grazing fields and system of grazing, silage/hay fields and crop fields.

It is advisable to draw the plan on an A3 sheet or larger.

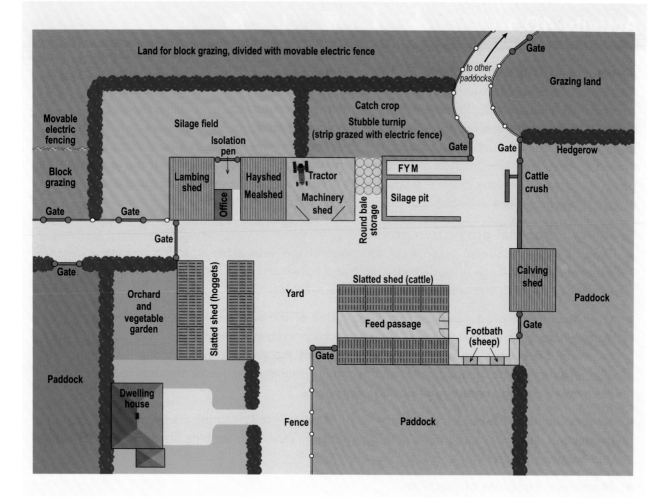

IIIII Fig 40.8 A farm plan

Summary

- Under the Diseases of Animals Act 1966, a notifiable disease must be immediately reported to the district veterinary office.
- An infectious disease is caused by a micro-organism (bacteria, fungi or virus) or other agents that enter the body of an organism.
- A contagious disease is easily transmitted by contact through bodily fluids, or through the contamination of buildings, clothing or vectors.
- Zoonoses are diseases and infections that are naturally transmitted between vertebrate animals and man.
- Bovine tuberculosis, brucellosis and BSE are zoonoses and notifiable diseases.
- If a notifiable disease is identified on a farm, the movement of animals and animal products is restricted to prevent the spread of the disease.
- A non-infectious disease is not caused by a pathogen (micro-organism). Milk fever and grass tetany are diseases that are caused by environmental factors.
- The five freedoms describe the conditions required to ensure the physical welfare and mental state of farm animals.

QUESTIONS

1 Define a notifiable disease.
2 Explain the difference between an infectious disease and a non-infectious disease. Give an example of each.
3 Name a notifiable disease and identify the agent that causes the disease.
4 Identify three precautions a farmer can take to prevent the entry of disease onto a farm.
5 Explain the meaning of the term *zoonose* and give an example.
6 List the five freedoms and explain any two.

EXAM QUESTIONS

1 Write a brief note to explain notifiable diseases in farm animals. (LC, HL, 2002)
2 Notifiable diseases must, by law, be reported to the authorities. Place a tick (√) in the correct box in each case to indicate if a disease is notifiable or not. The first one has been completed as an example. (LC, OL, 2010)

Table 40.2

Name of disease	Notifiable	Not notifiable
Foot and mouth disease	√	
Mastitis		
Swine fever		
Brucellosis		
Liver fluke		
Tuberculosis (TB)		

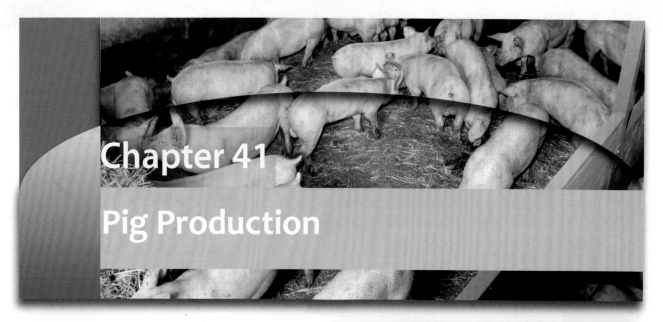

Chapter 41

Pig Production

Pig farming is quite different to cattle and sheep farming. In Ireland, the vast majority of pig production takes place indoors in specialised pig production units. There are only a small number of farmers involved in pig production nationwide. In 2010, 85 per cent of all pigs reared on Irish farms were produced on fewer than 400 pig farms. The remainder were reared in smaller units. A small number of farmers rear pigs in a free-range, outdoor production system.

Fig 41.1 Pigs reared outdoors

Pig Breeds

There are two main breeds used for commercial pig production in Ireland: Large White and Landrace. Purebred pigs are used to produce crossbred sows and pigs for meat production. Both the Landrace and Large White have a number of desirable characteristics.

Landrace

- Danish breed
- Good conformation
- Long body, small shoulders, large hams.

Large White

- British breed
- Highly prolific
- Fast growth rate
- Good meat quality
- Good food conversion ratio.

Other pig breeds such as the Duroc are used on a smaller scale. However, the Landrace and Large White are the most widely used breeds for commercial pork and bacon production in Ireland.

Fig 41.2 Landrace pig

Fig 41.3 Large White pig

A Landrace–Large White crossbreed is desirable as it should inherit the best characteristics of both breeds. It is less expensive to buy and rear crossbred pigs than purebred pigs. To produce crossbred pigs of this type a breeding strategy known as criss-cross breeding is used in many pig production units.

≣ Criss-Cross Breeding

Criss-cross breeding is a cost-effective method of pig breeding. Ideally, all breeding pigs would be a Landrace–Large White crossbreed. However, maintaining a herd of purebred pigs for crossbreeding purposes is expensive and therefore not cost-effective. Criss-cross breeding reduces the cost of producing quality pigs, with characteristics from both breeds, while maintaining hybrid vigour.

First generation

A number of crossbred gilts are purchased for mating with a purebred boar. The boar can be either Landrace (LR) or Large White (LW). As crossbred gilts were the offspring from two purebred pigs, one

> **Gilt:** A female pig that has not yet had a litter.

Landrace and one Large White, they should have 50 per cent of their genes from one breed and 50 per cent from the other breed. This should confer the traits of both breeds on the gilt and thus maintain hybrid vigour. In this example, the boar used is a Landrace boar. When crossed with the LW–LR crossbred gilt, the offspring produced will have both Landrace traits from the boar and Large White and Landrace traits from the sow.

The best females from the litter are kept for breeding purposes, while the remaining females along with all of the males are fattened for slaughter.

Second generation

When the gilts chosen from the litter are mature, they are mated with a Large White boar, as a Landrace was used in the first generation. This ensures hybrid vigour is maintained and keeps the desirable traits inherited from both breeds around the 50 per cent mark.

Third generation

As in the previous generation, the best gilts are chosen from the litter for breeding. The remaining males and females are fattened for slaughter. The breed of purebred boar used for mating is switched again to maintain hybrid vigour. However, some hybrid vigour is lost with each generation as the gilts used are not purebred. However, the pigs produced are of an acceptable standard for meat production.

Boars must be replaced every two years to prevent inbreeding. It is also less expensive to replace a boar than to replace all the gilts/sows in the breeding herd.

Table 41.1 Criss-cross breeding in pigs				
Sire	**Crossed with**	**Dam**	**Progeny/Offspring**	
LR	x	LW-LR	LR	-LW-LR
LW	x	LR-LW-LR	LW	-LR-LW-LR
LR	x	LR-LW-LR-LW	LR	-LW-LR-LW-LR

The highlighting in Table 41.1 denotes which traits were inherited from the sire and which were inherited from the dam. The most suitable females from the first generation are used for breeding in the second generation, and those produced in the second generation are used for breeding in the third generation.

Many pig production units are now using AI (artificial insemination) instead of boars, but continue to employ a criss-cross method of breeding.

☰ Bacon Pig Production

Sow and bonham production and management

About 85 per cent of all pigs produced in Ireland are produced on fewer than 400 farms. Most of these farms are large commercial farms known as integrated pig production units. All breeding, rearing, and fattening processes are carried out on the farm, rearing the pigs for slaughter. This means there is less movement of pigs overall and less risk of disease entering the farm. In integrated pig production units, pigs are exclusively raised indoors. A small number of farms concentrate on breeding or fattening only. In addition, a few producers rear pigs outdoors in a free-range or organic enterprise.

The next section will examine pig production in an integrated pig production unit.

The importance of the sow in pig production

The role of the sow is to produce as many quality bonhams as possible in her litters. Ideally, a sow can produce 2.39 litters per year, but realistically the average is lower. In reality, a sow should be able to produce 2.0–2.3 litters per year. A litter can range between 5 and 22 bonhams. The average litter size produced is 11.

Dry sow house: housing for young sows and gilts

Sows and gilts are housed in the dry sow house. Sows that are thin from rearing a litter are given extra feed to bring them back to their normal weight. A sow that has weaned a litter will come back into heat five to seven days later. A boar is used to detect sows in heat. Physical signs of heat in sows and gilts include: a swollen, red vulva, erect ears and loud grunting.

Oestrous cycle

The length of the oestrous cycle in pigs is 21 days. The duration of oestrous is two to three days.

When heat is detected, a sow is double served. This means she is served twice in 24 hours. This can be done by the appropriate boar, by AI or a combination of both. In pig production units 90 per cent of all servings are now by AI. Double serving increases conception rates and the size of litters. If the sow comes back into heat again after 21 days, she is served again. If she repeats, she will be culled from the herd.

A gilt should not be served on her first heat as she will produce a small litter. When she comes into heat for a second time, she should be served twice in 12 hours to increase conception rates and litter size.

Sows and gilts must be loose housed (kept in groups) from four weeks after service until one week before farrowing. The pens must have lengths of 2.6 metres or greater for groups of six or more sows/gilts.

The young sows and gilts are fed 2.5 kg of dry sow ration per day. Sows should not be overfed in the first three weeks of gestation as this can cause them to come back into oestrous. In the final three to four weeks of gestation, sows are fed an extra 0.5 kg of ration per day. Dry sow ration typically contains 17.5 per cent crude protein, 4 per cent crude fibre, 1 per cent lysine (an essential amino acid) and vitamins A, D and E.

Gestation

The gestation period in pigs is 115 days or three months, three weeks and three days. One week before farrowing the sow is moved to the farrowing house.

Farrowing house

Sows and gilts must be cleaned and disinfected and treated for internal and external parasites before moving into the farrowing house. The sow or gilt is placed into a farrowing crate in the farrowing unit. The farrowing crate allows for the movement of the sow but prevents her from crushing the bonhams. It also allows the bonhams to suckle the sow with ease, while having access to an infrared lamp and a creep area. The farrowing unit is maintained at a temperature of 20°C. Plastic slats help to prevent foot injuries, and heat pads ensure a warm environment for the litter.

Fig 41.4 Bonhams suckling a sow in a farrowing crate

Fig 41.5 Bonhams under an infrared lamp

Birth, Suckling and Weaning

Bonhams weigh 1.0–1.5 kg at birth. Tooth and tail clipping may be carried out in accordance with pig welfare legislation to prevent damage to the sow's teats and to prevent tail biting among the litter. Clip teeth within 24 hours of birth. Dock tails in the first week after birth. In the first two to three days, the bonhams should be given an iron injection to prevent anaemia. Ear notching may also be carried out to identify future replacement gilts for the breeding herd.

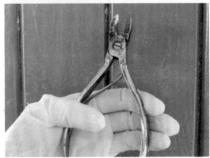

Fig 41.6 Tooth clipper

Fig 41.7 Tail docker

Fig 41.8 Ear notcher

The sow suckles the bonhams for four to five weeks. The minimum time in which bonhams can be weaned is 28 days (four weeks). Five weeks may be necessary for larger litters. Sows are fed 1.8 kg of suckling ration daily with an extra 0.5 kg of ration per bonham. Creep ration containing 21 per cent protein and 1.5 per cent lysine is introduced after approximately one week to the bonhams. Bonhams are weaned after four to five weeks.

The sow is returned to the dry sow house and will come into oestrous five to seven days later when she will be served to start her next gestation period. A sow will produce litters in this manner for four to five years until she is culled.

Overview of Sow Production Year

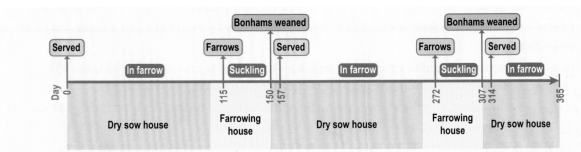

Fig 41.9 Sow production year

Weaner management and feeding

Weaners are moved to the first stage weaner house. Litters that have been weaned at the same time are mixed and grouped according to size and weight. Weaners are normally 9 kg on entering the first stage weaner house. They are fed link ration ad lib for the first two weeks in the weaner house. Link ration contains 21 per cent crude protein and 1.45 per cent lysine. They are then moved onto weaner rations that contain 18–20 per cent protein and 1.3 per cent lysine.

After one month in the first stage weaner house, the weaners are moved to the second stage weaner house, where they remain for another month. They are regrouped again by size and weight. Temperatures in the weaner house are kept at 24°C. When weaners reach 32 kg, they are moved to the fattener house.

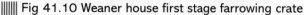 Fig 41.10 Weaner house first stage farrowing crate   Fig 41.11 Weaner house second stage

Fattener management and feeding

Fatteners, like weaners, are grouped by size and weight. They are fed fattener ration ad lib, which contains 14–16 per cent protein and 1.1 per cent lysine. Water is also available. Temperatures are kept at 22°C in the fattener house. Fatteners remain in the fattening house for approximately three months. Feeding may be restricted before slaughter to prevent fat deposition. Pigs are 'finished' when they weigh 80–82 kg. They are approximately six months old.

Pigs that have been selected as replacement gilts for breeding are housed for a further four to six weeks until they reach a weight of 100–140 kg. They are then moved to the dry sow house to enter the production cycle.

Summary

- Most pig production in Ireland takes place indoors in integrated pig production units.
- The two main breeds used in commercial pig production are the Landrace and the Large White.
- Landrace are chosen for their good conformation, long body, small shoulders and large hams.
- Large Whites are chosen for their prolificacy, fast growth rate, good meat quality and good food conversion ratio.
- Criss-cross breeding is used to produce a Landrace–Large White crossbreed, which has the desirable characteristics of both breeds. This is cheaper than rearing purebred pigs.
- In criss-cross breeding, crossbred sows are mated with purebred boars. Their offspring are mated with a boar of the other breed the following season. Each season the breed of the boar is alternated to keep the characteristics of the offspring half Landrace and half Large White.

Summary

- Boars are replaced every two years to prevent inbreeding.
- A sow can produce an average of 2.39 litters per year, with an average litter size of 11.
- Sows are housed in the dry sow house after their litter is weaned. They come back into heat one week later and are served twice by the boar within 24 hours.
- Oestrous cycle: 21 days; duration of oestrous two to three days; gestation three months, three weeks and three days.
- Sows eat 2.5 kg of ration per day. In the final four weeks of gestation 0.5 kg extra ration is fed. It contains 17.5 per cent protein.
- Sows are moved to the farrowing house one week before farrowing where they are cleaned and deloused. The farrowing house is kept at 20°C.
- Bonhams weigh 1.0–1.5 kg at birth and have their teeth and tails clipped. They are given an iron injection to prevent anaemia and are weaned at five weeks. At this point, they are consuming creep ration with 21 per cent crude protein and 1.45 per cent lysine.
- Weaners live in the weaner house, which is kept at 24°C. They are 9 kg at weaning and leave the weaner house when they reach 32 kg. They eat weaner ration (20 per cent protein and 1.3 per cent lysine) and are grouped by size.
- Fatteners (32–80 kg) live in the fattener house, which is kept at 22°C. They are grouped by size and eat fattener ration (16 per cent protein and 1.1 per cent lysine). Pigs are finished for slaughter at 80–82 kg. Pigs for breeding are kept until they weigh 100–140 kg.

QUESTIONS

1. What are the two main breeds of pig used in pig production in Ireland?
2. List three desirable characteristics for each breed.
3. What kind of sow is an ideal sow for breeding purposes?
4. What is criss-cross breeding and how does it work?
5. What are the advantages of criss-cross breeding?
6. What is a gilt?
7. What is the average litter size?
8. What are the physical signs of oestrous (heat) in a sow or gilt?
9. What is the length of the oestrous cycle?
10. What is the duration of oestrous?
11. What is double serving and why is it carried out?
12. How long is the gestation period?
13. Why would a sow be thin in early pregnancy?
14. Where is the in-young sow housed?
15. When is the sow moved to the farrowing house?
16. What happens to the sow in the farrowing unit?
17. At what temperature is the farrowing house maintained?

QUESTIONS

18 What weight is a bonham at birth?

19 Why are bonhams' teeth and tails docked after birth?

20 Why are bonhams given an iron injection after birth?

21 When are bonhams weaned?

22 What happens to the sow after bonhams are weaned?

23 Which house are the bonhams moved to after weaning?

24 Describe the feeding regime employed in this housing unit.

25 What type of weight gain is expected in the weaner house?

26 Where are the weaner pigs sent for finishing?

27 Describe the feeding regime employed to get a pig to its slaughter weight.

28 How old are pigs when they are sent to slaughter?

29 At what weight are pigs slaughtered?

EXAM QUESTIONS

1 Give the approximate value of each of the following for pigs:
   (a) Weight at birth (kilograms)
   (b) Age at puberty (months)
   (c) Length of oestrus cycle (days)
   (d) Length of gestation period (days)
   (e) Recommended temperature for farrowing unit (°C). (LC, HL, 2008)

2 Give a scientific explanation for 'The practice of housing a boar near sows and the double-serving of sows in a pig breeding enterprise'. (LC, HL, 2007)

Chapter 42

Pig Management

A number of factors can affect pig production levels on farms. Feeding makes up 70 per cent of the costs associated with pig production. Efficient feeding strategies need to be employed to reduce costs and make pig production a cost-effective enterprise.

Disease control and housing management are also important factors in pig production. If disease is not properly controlled it can lead to an increase in mortality rates, high treatment costs and a reduction in output from the pig production unit. First we will look at feeding management.

☰ Feeding Management

Feed conversion ratio

Feed conversion ratio (FCR) is also known as feed conversion efficiency (FCE). It is a measure of an animal's efficiency in converting a mass of food into body mass or live weight. It is expressed as a ratio of the food consumed in comparison to the live weight gained. An FCR value of 3.0 would mean that an animal would have to consume 3.0 kg of food to gain 1.0 kg of weight or body mass. The lower the FCR value the better, as a low value indicates that a greater proportion of the food consumed is being converted to body mass or live weight. This is especially important in pig production, as feeding costs account for a large proportion of overall pig production costs.

WEANER RATION

COMPLETE FEEDSTUFF FOR WEANER PIGS

Crude protein	23%	Lysine	1.2%
Crude fibre	2%	Vitamin A	
Ash	6.5%	Vitamin D	
Crude fat	10%	Vitamin E	

List of Ingredients

Soyabean, Whey Powder, Wheat, Maize, Oat Flour, Soyabean Protein Concentrate, Whey Protein Concentrate, Soyabean Oil

For animal use only. Keep away from children.
USE IN ACCORDANCE WITH VETERINARY PRESCRIPTION

||||| **Fig 42.1 Weaner ration**

Target FCR values in pig production units	
Weaners	1.75
Fatteners	3.25

FCR values increase with age, as in the early stages of development most of the food consumed by pigs goes towards growth and muscle development. In the latter stages of development, growth has slowed and the pig is feeding for maintenance.

A number of factors affecting FCR values are listed below:

- **Diet**: Feed an appropriately balanced ration to pigs at the different stages of growth. It should contain protein, vitamins, minerals and essential amino acids such as lysine. It should also provide energy. If a pig is not getting enough protein from the ration provided it will consume more food, thereby increasing its FCR value.

- **Breed**: Certain breeds such as the Large White can confer a good FCR value on their offspring. A fast-growing breed will have better FCR. Choosing a breed that can confer a good FCR value will mean that the offspring produced will reach slaughter weight faster and will cost less to feed in comparison to a pig with a poorer FCR, kept under similar conditions.
- **Health**: A healthy, disease-free animal will have a low FCR. If an animal is not at its optimum level of health or is fighting illness it will not use the energy supplied from its food for weight gain. Instead, energy is used to fight illness.
- **Housing**: FCR values in a pig herd can be maintained using well-insulated housing. If pigs are kept in a warm environment they will not have to use energy to keep warm and will use it instead for weight gain. Housing for pigs should be draught free, with low roofs to maximise temperatures.
- **Management**: The management ability of the farmer can have a great effect on FCR within a herd. A farmer who maintains a pig production unit with an efficient feeding regime and proper disease control will have a healthy herd with a good FCR.

Carcass grading of pigs

Pigs are graded according to estimated lean meat percentage content. They are classified according to the scale below and assigned the appropriate grade letter (see Table 42.1).

Profits in pig production are small and the higher the carcass quality, the higher the profitability. The majority of carcasses are graded using the Hennessey Grading Probe. Back fat thickness and muscle depth are measured, using this instrument. Lean meat percentage can then be estimated, using a standard formula.

Carcass quality is influenced by breed and diet. Terminal sire lines that are used for breeding pigs for slaughter have included the superior Large White lines and the Pietrain breed. Similarly, the Duroc has been used in dam lines to improve quality in criss-cross breeding mainly dominated by the Landrace and Large White breeds.

Table 42.1 Carcass grading of pigs	
Lean meat as percentage of carcass weight	Letter grade
60 or more	S
55 or more but less than 60	E
50 or more but less than 55	U
45 or more but less than 50	R
40 or more but less than 45	0
Less than 40	P

||||| Fig 42.2 Pietrain pig

||||| Fig 42.3 Duroc pig

Housing

The management and upkeep of housing is especially important as pigs in integrated pig production units are reared indoors. A properly managed unit minimises illness, injury and disease and maximises FCR values.

Guidelines for housing management and disease control

- Maintain housing units at appropriate temperatures, e.g. dry sow house at 20°C, weaner house at 24°C, fattener house at 22°C.
- Insulate housing to maintain temperatures and keep well-ventilated to minimise airborne diseases.

- Make available isolation units/housing with comfortable bedding for sick, injured or bullied pigs. Each isolation unit should have water. Wash and disinfect units after the pigs have returned to the herd.

- Power wash and disinfect all housing pens between batches. Create partitions between pens to prevent contact between batches.

- Pigs should only move in one direction. Do not return stage two weaners to the first stage house. One way movement reduces the risk of infection.

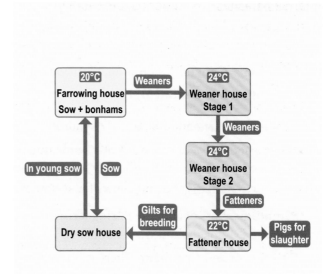

Fig 42.4 One way movement of pigs in a pig production unit

Diseases of Pigs

Pigs in integrated pig production units live in an indoor environment that is strictly regulated. The regulation of their environment minimises disease. However, disease can spread rapidly through a housing unit if it enters the unit at all.

Common diseases of pigs

Anaemia of bonhams

Anaemia of bonhams is a nutritional disease caused by a lack of iron. It is most frequently seen in indoor production environments, as pigs reared outdoors can get sufficient iron from rooting in the soil.

- **Symptoms**: Pale skin, rapid breathing, weakness, and scour. Poor growth in the first two to three weeks of life.

- **Prevention**: A soluble iron injection is given to two- to three-day-old bonhams to prevent anaemia.

- **Treatment**: An iron injection may be given to bonhams with anaemia, but treatment of anaemia is uncommon as iron injections are given as standard practice to all newborn bonhams.

Fig 42.5 Pig rooting in soil

Enteroviruses (SMEDI)

Enteroviruses are gut-borne viruses specific to pigs. Bonhams are normally protected from these viruses by the antibodies from the sow's colostrum. In the absence of these antibodies, the viruses multiply in the intestines and travel through the bloodstream and cross the placenta.

- **Symptoms**: Stillbirth, mummification of embryos, embryonic death and infertility can be caused by the viruses entering the uterus and crossing the placenta.

- **Treatment**: There is no form of treatment for this disease.

Internal parasites (roundworms, tapeworms)

Roundworms and tapeworms live in the internal organs of pigs and can be caught by exposure to infected faeces.

- **Symptoms**: Coughing, vomiting, diarrhoea and loss of condition.
- **Prevention and treatment**: Dose pigs every six months for worms.

Porcine reproductive and respiratory syndrome (PRRS)

Porcine reproductive and respiratory syndrome is a virus that was first identified in 1991. It kills the macrophages that exist in the body to ingest and remove invading bacteria and viruses. This lowers the pigs' ability to fight disease and allows for secondary infection by bacteria and other viruses.

- **Symptoms**: Loss of appetite during farrowing period, respiratory problems, early farrowing, increased stillbirths and weak bonhams.
- **Prevention and treatment**: There is no treatment for this virus; however, antibiotics may be administered to prevent secondary infection by bacteria.

Post-weaning multisystemic wasting syndrome (PMWS)

Post-weaning multisystemic wasting syndrome (PMWS) is a disease seen in weaners. Signs are usually observed between six and eight weeks when weaners start to lose weight. PMWS will not be seen in pigs unless porcine circovircus (PCV2) is present.

- **Symptoms**: Weight loss, emaciation, slow growth rate (wasting) and secondary bacterial infections.
- **Treatment and control**: There is no effective treatment. However, a strict hygiene policy in a pig unit, low stocking densities and the prevention of cross-contamination between pig batches can control the spread of the virus.

Coliform scour

Coliform scour is caused by E. coli bacteria. Weaners and bonhams are most commonly affected by this disease. It is usually caused by a lack of hygiene in the housing unit.

- **Symptoms**: Diarrhoea, dehydration and weight loss in weaners, and loss of condition.
- **Prevention**: Disinfect the farrowing house and the weaner house regularly, keep environmental conditions stable; housing should be warm, well-insulated and draught-free. Avoid a sudden change in diet, introduce a gradual change of feed; reduce stress as much as possible.
- **Treatment**: Treat pigs with a course of antibiotics and rehydrate with a fluid replacement solution.

Summary

- Feed conversion ratio (FCR) is a measure of an animal's efficiency in converting a mass of food into body mass or live weight. It is expressed as a ratio of the food consumed in comparison to the live weight gained.
- FCR values in pigs: weaners – 1.75, fatteners – 3.25.
- Factors affecting FCR are: diet, breed, health, housing and management.
- Pig carcasses are graded according to estimated lean meat percentage content using the Hennessy Grading Probe. Back fat thickness and muscle depth are considered when grading a carcass.

Summary

- Disease can be controlled in housing by maintaining houses at the correct temperature, placing sick animals in isolation units for treatment, insulating housing and keeping housing well-ventilated, disinfecting housing between batches of pigs, and ensuring pigs move in one direction. Pigs being reared for slaughter should never return to a house they have left.
- Pigs are susceptible to a number of diseases.
- Anaemia is an iron deficiency that can be prevented by giving iron injections.
- SMEDI are gut-borne viruses for which there is no treatment.
- Roundworms and tapeworms can be prevented by dosing pigs every six months.
- Porcine reproductive and respiratory syndrome lowers the pig's ability to fight disease. There is no known treatment but antibiotics can be administered to prevent secondary infection.
- Post-weaning multisystemic wasting syndrome (PMWS) leads to weight loss and emaciation and can be controlled by lower stocking densities and by preventing cross-contamination. There is no effective treatment for the virus.
- Coliform scour is caused by E. coli bacteria in bonhams and weaners. This can be treated with antibiotics and rehydration.

QUESTIONS

1 What is meant by the term *feed conversion ratio* (FCR)?
2 Why is FCR so important in relation to pig production?
3 What are the five factors affecting FCR?
4 How does each of these factors affect FCR?
5 On what factors are pigs' carcasses graded?
6 At what temperatures should the dry sow house, weaner house and fattener house be maintained?
7 List two ways to reduce the risk of disease in pig production units.
8 Why are pigs subject to fewer diseases than cows or sheep?
9 Describe the following two diseases under the following headings: Effects; Symptoms; Prevention; Treatment: Anaemia of bonhams; Coliform scour.

EXAM QUESTION

Most of the bacon pigs produced in Ireland are reared in **integrated pig production** units.
Explain the highlighted term and give two advantages of these units. (LC, HL, 2006)

Chapter 43

Sheep Breeds and Production

In Ireland, sheep are bred solely for their meat. It is an important export market, with Bord Bia estimating that it contributed roughly €166 million to the Irish economy in 2009. Ireland is the fifth largest exporter of sheep meat within the EU; the UK and Spain are the largest exporters. Ireland exports roughly 50 per cent of its sheep meat to France, 10 per cent to the UK and 2 per cent to Mediterranean countries. The Irish population consumes just less than 30 per cent of the sheep meat produced here.

Under EU regulations, the Department of Agriculture must carry out an annual sheep census. The 2008 census shows that sheep numbers have been declining in Ireland since the first census was carried out in 2005. It reports that in 2008 there were just over 3 million sheep, and that the numbers of sheep had decreased in Ireland by 23 per cent since 2005. Estimates by Bord Bia suggest that this trend continued into 2009, with reportedly just over 2.4 million breeding ewes in the country. Poor lamb prices and competitiveness due to increasing imports of New Zealand and Australian lamb into the European markets can be partly blamed for this decrease. In order for sheep farmers to be profitable within this industry, it is necessary to show high levels of skill and management.

≡ Sheep Production in Ireland

Sheep production in Ireland can be divided into two categories: mountain or hill sheep and lowland sheep. Table 43.1 summarises the main points of these two industries.

Historically, lowland sheep farming is more intensive, with higher production targets than mountain and hill. Better pastures and rotational grazing are used to ensure lambs are finished off for the Easter and mid-season lamb markets. Mountainous and upland locations are exposed to harsh weather conditions where sheep graze commonage over large areas.

Table 43.1 Comparison of mountain/hill and lowland sheep enterprises	
Mountain and Hill	**Lowland**
Extensive farming	Intensive
Low production targets	High production targets
Rough grazing	Rotational grazing
Ewe and lamb mortality rates can be high	Lambing indoors reduces ewe and lamb mortality
Ewes generally only have one lamb	More ewes give birth to twins and triplets
Sheep breeds suited to exposed conditions	Larger, muscular sheep used to produce meat
Blackface Mountain, Wicklow Cheviot	Suffolk, Texel, Galway, Charollais

The botanical composition of commonage is highly variable as it is composed of heathers and poorer quality grasses.

Hill and mountain lambs are in demand in some Mediterranean countries due to their smaller and

Commonage: Land where two or more farmers have rights to graze.

lighter carcasses. Their meat is slightly darker due to their diet of varied mountain flora and it has a distinct flavour, which accounts for the growing popularity of this meat. Mountain ewes are also in demand by lowland farmers as breeding stock.

Sheep breeds

Mountain and hill breeds

Blackface Mountain sheep, also known as the Scottish Blackface, and the Wicklow Cheviot are the two most popular mountain sheep breeds in Ireland. Mountain ewe breeds are used to produce crossbred ewes for lowland sheep farmers. Blackface Mountain sheep are a small, extremely hardy breed with long wool, black faces and horns. Blackface Mountain ewes are known for their good mothering ability and good milk production. This variety of mountain sheep is extremely popular along the west coast of Ireland.

Wicklow Cheviots originate from Scotland. These sheep are a hardy mountain breed; they have white faces and are medium-sized. The ewes are good mothers. It is a popular breed along the east coast of Ireland.

Fig 43.1 Blackface Mountain sheep

Fig 43.2 Wicklow Cheviot sheep

Lowland sheep breeds

Prolific breeds

Border Leicester is a large, long wool, white, hornless breed easily recognisable by its upright ears. This breed is known for its prolificacy as it produces many offspring and the breed imparts its prolificacy on its offspring.

The Bluefaced Leicester is another popular prolific breed in Ireland and, like the Border Leicester, it originates from England. It is a large breed, with a white head and a slight roman nose. It is also known as the Hexham Leicester. It acquired the name Bluefaced as its skin appears dark blue through its white hair.

Fig 43.3 Border Leicester sheep

Fig 43.4 Bluefaced Leicester sheep

Terminal sires for meat production

In Ireland, the most popular lowland breeds used as terminal sires for the production of lamb for meat are the Suffolk and the Texel.

> **Terminal sire:** A ram that is used to produce offspring with high growth rate and good carcass quality for slaughter.

The Suffolk originates from England and has a distinctive black head and legs. It is a short and solid breed known for its good carcass quality. The Suffolk has excellent conformation and fast growth rates. Suffolk cross lambs are early maturing, reaching slaughter weight in less than 14 weeks, making the Suffolk ram an ideal terminal sire for lambs for the Easter market.

||||| Fig 43.5 Suffolk sheep

||||| Fig 43.6 Texel sheep

The Texel originates from the Netherlands. It has a white wide face, with short ears, and it lacks wool on its head and legs. The breed has good conformation and carcass quality and is particularly noted for muscle leanness. The Texel has a slower growth rate than a Suffolk and it is used as a terminal sire for mid-season lamb.

The Charollais is a French breed and was bred alongside Charolais cattle. It is a medium-sized, heavy sheep with a long loin and muscular hindquarters. It is a popular terminal sire and produces lean, fast-growing lambs.

||||| Fig 43.7 Charollais sheep

Irish sheep breeds

The Galway is the only native sheep breed (see Fig 43.8). It is a large, white, polled lowland sheep. It has long wool and is predominantly found in Galway and some surrounding counties. It has a good growth rate and when crossed with Suffolks or other Continental breeds it can produce good early lambs.

Teagasc undertook research to improve the Galway breed by crossing Galway ewes with the Finnish Landrace, a breed known for its extremely high prolificacy. The ewes were then crossed with a Lleyn ram, a Welsh breed known for high prolificacy, a strong mothering instinct and good conformation. The resulting breed was called the Belclare Improver.

Belclare Improvers (see Fig 43.9) have improved prolificacy in comparison to the Galway. The Belclare ewes normally produce twin lambs, have little lambing difficulty and have good mothering ability. When Belclare Improver rams are crossed with Galway ewes the resulting offspring are known as the Improved Galway and display hybrid vigour in comparison to the native Galway.

| Fig 43.8 Galway sheep

| Fig 43.9 Belclare Improver sheep

Breeding Strategy in Ireland

In mountain and hill farming, purebred mountain ewes are always crossed with purebred mountain rams. Due to the harsh conditions in these regions and the poor quality of the grass, mountain ewes usually only produce a single lamb. These lambs are either kept as replacements or fattened and sold to the Italian market. The fertility of the mountain ewes decreases under these harsh conditions after a few years. They are sold as cast or draft ewes to lowland sheep farmers. Mountain ewes are renowned for their good mothering ability and as a result are in demand by lowland sheep farmers.

> A **cast** or **draft ewe** is a ewe whose fertility has declined due to the harsh conditions experienced in mountainous areas. It is sold to a lowland farmer where once on an improved plane of nutrition will continue to produce lambs for many years.

The cast ewes are the start of the three-breed crossing system used to produce lamb for meat. Other countries such as Australia and New Zealand use similar three-breed crossing systems. Ram selection is a vital part of this breeding programme. A common statement used is that 'a ram is half the flock'. The reason for this is that the ram genes will spread over a greater proportion of the offspring than a ewe. Rams of superior genetic merit should be used to improve the genetic merit of the flock.

In Ireland, purebred rams are used to improve prolificacy, growth rates and carcass quality of the offspring. Table 43.2 outlines the breeding strategy used in Ireland to produce lambs for slaughter.

Table 43.2 Three-breed crossing system to produce lambs for meat

Step 1

Scottish Blackface ewe

Border Leicester

Step 2

Greyface ewe

Suffolk

Early lamb

Texel

Mid-season lamb

Step 1

Once cast ewes are moved to better quality grass, their fertility improves. In step 1 of Table 43.2 a Border Leicester ram is crossed with a mountain ewe; the resulting offspring are referred to as crossbreds. In this case, the crossbred ewe is called a

> **Prolificacy** is calculated as the number of lambs reared per ewe mated. Therefore, if 100 ewes were mated and 160 lambs were produced the prolificacy of the flock would be 1.6.

Greyface. Crossbred ewes show hybrid vigour, having the best characteristics of both parents. They have the hardiness, good mothering ability and good milk production from their mountain dam and good prolificacy from the sire, with an average litter size of 1.60.

Increased prolificacy is extremely important for lamb meat production. As a female ewe has two teats on her udder, she can raise two lambs if fed adequately. Therefore, theoretically, if each ewe had twins instead of a single lamb, this would considerably increase the sheep farmer's profits. However, this is not always possible, but most farmers will aim for a litter size of 1.7 or 1.8 lambs per ewe. How do you increase litter size? The answer is in the careful selection of the ram crossed with the mountain ewe in step 1.

Table 43.3 shows the litter size produced by crossbred ewes from Scottish Blackface mothers. Thus crossing a mountain ewe with a Belclare ram increased the litter size that the crossbred ewes produced. The ram with the poorest score for prolificacy was the Scottish Blackface ram. By increasing the prolificacy of a flock, you increase the number of twins, triplets and even quads that the crossbred ewes will produce. Examine Table 43.4 to see the various types of crossbreds produced from mountain ewes by lowland ram crosses.

Table 43.3 Effect of ram breeds on litter size	
Sire of ewe	**Litter size**
Belclare	1.89
Bluefaced Leicester	1.71
Border Leicester	1.60
Wicklow Cheviot	1.51
Galway	1.63
Suffolk	1.65
Texel	1.58
Scottish Blackface	1.48

(*Source: Teagasc*)

Step 2

In step 2 of Table 43.2 the crossbred ewe is crossed with a terminal sire to produce lambs that will be slaughtered for meat. The terminal sires that are used in this step are selected because their traits include good conformation, good carcass quality, fast growth rates and leanness of meat.

Table 43.4 Progeny of mountain ewes crossed with lowland rams		
Mountain ewe	**Ram breed**	**Crossbred**
Scottish Blackface	Border Leicester	Greyface
Scottish Blackface	Bluefaced Leicester	Mule
Wicklow Cheviot	Border Leicester	Halfbred
Wicklow Cheviot	Suffolk	Brownface

The lambs produced from this cross are sold as early lamb or mid-season lamb. When a farmer is aiming for early lamb production, such as the Easter market, then a Suffolk ram is used, as it has the fastest growth rates; therefore the lambs reach slaughter weight in time.

When a farmer is aiming for mid-season lamb, a Texel ram is used. A Texel ram's progeny do not mature as quickly as a Suffolk ram's progeny, but they have higher carcass quality. Teagasc in Athenry compared the effect of terminal sire breeds on their progeny performance and concluded that the three best terminal sire breeds are the Suffolk, Texel and Charollais rams. A Suffolk cross lamb will reach slaughter weight 12–14 weeks after it was born.

Table 43.5 The effect of terminal sire breed on progeny performance			
Sire	Weaning weight (kg)	Extra days to finish	Kill out (g/kg)
Suffolk	31.8	0	438
Charollais	31.0	5	449
Texel	30.6	9	446
Vendeen	30.0	14	445
Belclare	29.3	15	442

(*Source: Hanarahan 1994 and 1997, Teagasc, Athenry*)

Replacement ewe

When selecting breeding ewes farmers should look for the following:

> **Percentage (%) kill out** is the weight of the dressed carcass in relation to the weight of the live animal before slaughter. A dressed carcass will have the head, feet and internal organs removed.

- Age of the ewe.
- Health of the ewe.
- Body condition of the ewe; aim for a BCS of 3.5 at mating.
- Good conformation.
- Mouth of the ewe; no overshot or undershot jaw that could affect the ewe grazing.
- Teeth – sheep need good molar teeth for grinding their food.
- Sound feet and legs.
- Udder, two functioning teats, no lumps in udder, no discharges from udder, good milk supply.
- A ewe that will consistently produce twins.

Criteria for selection of rams

- The type of breed.
- Pedigree and performance tested (lamb plus euro star rating index: 5 stars best ram, 1 star worst ram).
- Age of the ram.
- Conformation especially for terminal sire, good muscle distribution.
- Body condition score of 3.5 to 4.0. Rams must have a higher BCS than ewes at mating as they lose a considerable amount of body weight during mating.
- Sound feet and legs; lameness will affect the ram's performance during the mating season.
- Mouth – no jaw defects as this could potentially affect many lambs.
- Testicle size – there is a direct relationship between testicle size and semen production. A mature ram should have a scrotal circumference of 32 cm. Testicles should be firm, the same size and free from lumps.

Summary

- Sheep production in Ireland can be divided into two categories: mountain and hill, and lowland.
- Hill and mountain lambs are popular in some Mediterranean countries due to their smaller and lighter carcasses.
- The Blackface Mountain and the Wicklow Cheviot are the two most popular mountain sheep breeds in Ireland.
- Blackface Mountain sheep are a small, extremely hardy breed with long wool, black faces and horns.
- Wicklow Cheviots are hardy, white-faced and medium-sized.
- The Border Leicester, the Bluefaced Leicester and the Belclare Improver are prolific breeds that are used to increase litter size.
- Prolificacy is calculated as the number of lambs reared per ewe mated.
- A terminal sire is a ram that is used to produce offspring with high growth rate and good carcass quality for slaughter.
- The most popular terminal sires in Ireland are the Suffolk, Texel and Charollais.
- The Galway is the only native sheep breed.
- Teagasc developed the Belclare Improver from the Galway by crossbreeding it with the Finnish Landrace and the Lleyn.
- A cast or draft ewe is a ewe whose fertility has declined due to the harsh conditions experienced in mountainous areas.
- Use rams of superior genetic merit to bring about improvement in the flock.
- A ram is 'half the flock'. The reason is that the ram's genes will spread over a greater proportion of the offspring than a ewe's genes.
- Suffolk rams are used to produce lambs for the Easter market due to their fast growth rate.

QUESTIONS

1. Outline the main differences between mountain and lowland sheep production.
2. Name a breed of mountain sheep. Describe two characteristics of this breed.
3. Explain the term *prolificacy*. Explain why farmers seek to improve prolificacy in a flock.
4. Suffolk and Texel rams are often used as terminal sires in the production of lambs for slaughter. Explain the term *terminal sire*. Give two reasons why these breeds are used for lamb production.
5. Explain the term *cast or draft ewes*. Why does a mountain ewe's fertility decrease after a few years in mountainous areas?
6. Name an Irish breed of sheep and explain how Teagasc improved this breed.
7. Why are crossbred ewes used to produce lambs for slaughter?
8. Explain the term *a ram is half the flock*.
9. Discuss the effect of terminal sires on weaning weight and the finishing time of lambs for slaughter.
10. Describe the criteria used in the selection of a breeding ewe and a ram in Easter lamb production.

EXAM QUESTION

Explain the breeding strategy used in a lowland sheep production system of your choice. (LC, HL, 2005)

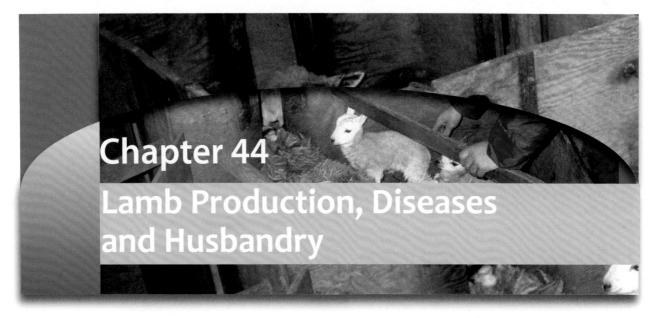

Chapter 44
Lamb Production, Diseases and Husbandry

Ewes are seasonally polyoestrous. This means that they have many oestrus cycles during a set time of year. Ewes are short-day breeders, meaning that they naturally come into oestrus during autumn as daylight decreases. The pineal gland (located in the centre of the brain) and the hormone melatonin control the onset of oestrus. As daylight hours decrease, the pineal gland is stimulated to produce melatonin. Melatonin is only produced during the hours of darkness, so as the length of night increases during autumn, the amounts of melatonin increase. This increase in the melatonin levels in ewes triggers a chain of other hormonal activities, which ultimately causes ovulation. Goats and deer are also short-day seasonal breeders.

The oestrous cycle in sheep

The length of the oestrus cycle in ewes is 17 days; thus ewes come into heat every 17 days. The average duration of oestrus or standing heat is 36 hours, with ovulation occurring during the second half of standing heat. Once fertilisation occurs the gestation period is 147 days or five months.

☰ The Sheep Breeding Year

In Ireland there are two breeding systems employed to produce lambs for slaughter: early or Easter lamb and mid-season lamb. Both of these systems are outlined in Table 44.1.

Table 44.1 A comparison of early and mid-season lamb production	
Early lamb	**Mid-season lamb**
Lambs born December–January	Lambs born March–April
Higher feed costs; concentrates required	Lower feed costs, better utilisation of grass
Cost of adjusting breeding cycle; breeding out of season	Normal breeding cycle of ewe
Lambs finished for Easter market gain better lamb prices	Mid-season lamb, lower price compared to Easter market

Flushing

If farmers want to have lambs finished for the Easter market, when they can obtain a higher price for lamb, planning for this must begin in July (see Fig 44.1 overleaf).

If farmers are aiming for mid-season lamb, breeding does not begin until the end of September or the beginning of October (see Fig 44.2 overleaf).

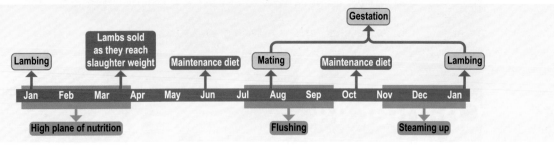

||||| Fig 44.1 Easter lamb production calendar

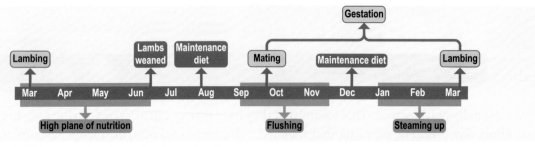

||||| Fig 44.2 Mid-season lamb production calendar

Regardless of which system is operated, the ewes are heavily stocked on good pasture before mating. Thy are then put on an improving plane of nutrition about three weeks before mating commences. This can be achieved by decreasing the stocking rate on good pasture. When mating starts the ewes should have a body condition score of 3.5. Flushing has a number of advantages:

> **Flushing**: The process by which the ewes are moved from a low plane of nutrition to a high plane of nutrition.

- It increases ovulation rate, leading to more eggs being released.
- It increases conception rates.
- It ensures better implantation of the embryos to the uterine wall.
- It increases litter size, leading to more twins and triplets.
- It ensures more regular oestrus cycles.

☰ Synchronised Breeding

Sponging

Allowing ewes to naturally come into oestrus can result in a prolonged lambing season. Therefore, some farmers choose to synchronise the oestrus cycle of ewes. During flushing, progesterone-impregnated sponges are placed in the vagina of the ewes. The sponges are removed 12 days later. All the ewes come into oestrus two days later.

A raddle with a coloured crayon is fitted to the ram before the ram joins the flock. The raddle leaves a mark on the ewes as they are mated. This allows the farmer to calculate lambing dates. The colour of the marker crayon is changed every 17 days (length of oestrus cycle of the ewe) to check for any ewes repeating. If a large number of ewes are repeating, it would be wise to check the fertility of the ram. When the breeding cycle of the ewes is synchronised, the ram to ewe ratio is reduced from 1:40 to 1:10.

||||| Fig 44.3 Sponge

||||| Fig 44.4 Raddle with ram crayons

Breeding out of season

To take full advantage of the higher lamb prices at Easter, lambs need to be born early January to allow them to be finished in time. This means that the ewe must be mated in July/August, which is before they would naturally come into oestrus (remember sheep are short-day breeders). Farmers can induce the onset of oestrus by sponging the ewes for 12 days and then injecting them with PMSG (pregnant mare serum gonadotrophin) once the sponges are removed. The ram is introduced 24 hours after the sponges are removed. All ewes should be in heat 48 hours later. The ram to ewe ratio should be 1:10.

Sponging and an injection of PMSG is a very reliable method of breeding out of season. However, some breeds can be encouraged to start ovulating six weeks earlier than normal by the sudden introduction of the ram. This is known as 'the ram effect' and is only successful with some breeds of sheep.

The ram effect

Rams produce a chemical substance called pheromones. The smell of these pheromones initiates the onset of oestrus in the ewes, with ewes ovulating four days later. This first oestrus is a 'silent heat', meaning it is not detected by the ram. This will be followed by a normal oestrus cycle 17 days later, when the ewes will be mated by the ram. The success of the ram effect relies on the ewes and rams being separated (out of sight and smell) for six weeks before mating and the rams must be at least

IIIII Fig 44.5 Ram with flock

2 km away from the ewes (that includes neighbouring rams and buck goats).

The advantages of the ram effect are that it can help synchronise breeding without sponging and help compact the lambing period. However, the ram effect is ineffective if the ewes are already coming into their oestrus cycles and also with maiden ewes, as they will not start to cycle until they are the correct weight and condition.

Mating to lambing

Once mating is completed, move the rams to a separate field. The rams will have lost some condition during the mating season and will require some extra feeding. Flushing should continue with the ewes for four weeks after mating to ensure that the embryos develop properly, as most spontaneous foetal deaths occur during the first four weeks of gestation. After this time, the ewes can return to a maintenance diet and BCS can drop back down to 3.0. In the last six to eight weeks of gestation 75 per cent of foetal growth occurs. As a result, the ewes are again placed on an increasing plane of nutrition. This feeding practice is called steaming up.

Poor nutrition in late gestation, particularly in ewes that are carrying twins or triplets, can cause pregnancy toxaemia, also known as twin lamb disease, which can be fatal to both ewes and lambs. To prevent twin lamb disease, feed each ewe 100 g of concentrates in addition to good quality hay and silage (high DMD) per day. For ewes carrying single lambs, gradually increase this feed to 500 g of concentrates per day. Ewes carrying twins should receive 750 g of concentrates per day. The concentrates should contain 15–18 per cent crude protein. Ewes carrying triplets should start steaming up 10 weeks before lambing.

Scanning

Scanning ewes is a vital procedure in determining the correct feed requirement of each ewe (see Fig 44.6 overleaf). Scanning aids the separation of ewes carrying singles from ewes carrying twins and triplets, making it easier to feed the ewes the correct amount of concentrates. It also identifies barren ewes and these can then be culled from the flock, saving farmers money on feed. Teagasc recommends scanning sheep 80 days after the ram joined the flock.

Health

Vaccinate ewes against clostridial disease four weeks before lambing. To prevent lameness due to footrot bathe ewes' feet regularly. Lameness has been identified as a contributing factor in twin lamb disease. Heavily pregnant ewes with footrot are unable to graze properly or compete with other ewes at the forage trough. As a result, they have an inadequate feed intake and this makes them more susceptible to twin lamb disease.

Steaming up increases the birth weight of the lamb and ensures good milk production in the ewe. Note that feeding the ewes too much concentrate can also be problematic, resulting in big lambs that can cause lambing difficulties.

Housing

As winter approaches, the ewes are housed indoors. Winter housing should be clean, draught-free and well-ventilated with adequate floor space and feeding space for the ewes. It can be straw bedded or slats. Table 44.2 lists the recommended space requirement for housed ewes.

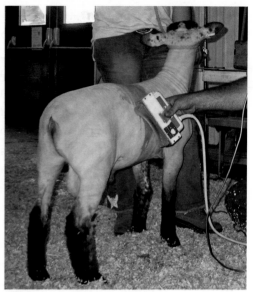

||||| Fig 44.6 Scanning sheep

Table 44.2 Floor and feeding space requirements for housed ewes				
	Floor space (m²)		Feeding space (mm)	
Ewe type	Slats	Straw	Roughage	Meal
Large (90 kg)	1.2	1.4	600	200
Medium (70 kg)	1.1	1.2	500	200
Small (50 kg)	1.0	1.1	400	175

(*Source: Teagasc*)

☰ Lambing

The ewe's behaviour changes once she commences lambing. She will search for a spot to lamb, paw at the ground, get up and lie down frequently. Leave her alone at this time, as the majority of ewes will lamb without difficulty. However, ensure an experienced person is on hand to help the ewe if she has difficulty lambing. Any ewe given assistance should receive an injection of antibodies to prevent infection.

Lambs weigh between 3 kg and 5 kg when born. Allow the ewe to lick the newborn lamb. This helps to stimulate the lamb's circulatory system and, more importantly, it helps in the bonding process between the ewe and the lamb. The lamb should get to its feet after a few minutes and start to suckle.

||||| Fig 44.7 Slatted sheep shed

It is critical that the lamb gets colostrum as it contains antibodies vital for the protection of the lamb's immune system, which is not fully developed when born. A lamb should receive at least 1 litre of colostrum in the first 24 hours. If the ewe has not produced colostrum then colostrum from a newly calved cow can be used.

Dip the navel in iodine to prevent navel and joint ill. Vaccinate lambs against clostridial diseases and orf. Dispose of the afterbirth, as it will attract predators, e.g. foxes and crows. Lambs born outside are at greater risk of suffering from hypothermia or chill. Revive chilled lambs by feeding them colostrum through a stomach tube. Warm lambs by using an infrared lamp positioned far enough from them to prevent burning.

||||| Fig 44.8 Ewe after lambing

If the chill is severe, give lambs an injection of glucose. Place the ewe and her lambs in a pen of 3.24 m² for a few days to ensure bonding between the ewe and lambs.

> **Colostrum:** The first milk secreted by mammals after giving birth. It is high in nutrients and antibodies and is essential for the survival of the newborn animal.

||||| Fig 44.9 Lamb fed with a stomach tube

||||| Fig 44.10 Ewe with a lamb

Fostering lambs

Farmers often foster lambs from multiple births onto ewes with single lambs. There are a number of methods used and one of the most common procedures involves using the birth fluids of the ewe with the single lamb. In order to do this, the farmer must be present at the birth. The lamb to be fostered is first washed to remove the scent of its own dam; its feet are temporarily tied together so that it cannot stand up. When the ewe gives birth to her lamb, the farmer removes it briefly and coats the foster lamb in the birth fluids. The foster lamb is placed in front of the ewe so that she will lick it clean.

||||| Fig 44.11 Ewe and lambs a in fostering crate

After 20 minutes the ties are removed from the foster lamb's feet and then the ewe is given her own lamb. The ewe with the lambs is observed over the next 24 hours to ensure that both lambs are thriving and that the ewe has not rejected either lamb.

An alternative to this method is to use a fostering crate. This prevents the ewe from kicking or hurting the foster lamb, while allowing the lamb access to the ewe's udder. After a few days, the lamb will have adopted the smell of the ewe and the ewe will accept the foster lamb.

Castration

During the first few days ram lambs can be castrated and their tails docked. Tail docking is carried out to prevent the build up of faeces and lessen the chances of flystrike. Castration is unnecessary if ram lambs are to be slaughtered before they are six months old, as they will only reach puberty then. Ewe lambs reach puberty between six and eight months old. Dose lambs for worms at about six weeks old.

Factors that contribute to ewe and lamb mortality

- Lambs did not get colostrum or not enough colostrum.
- Lambs and ewes were not vaccinated.
- Lambing outdoors increases the risk of chilled lambs and abandoned lambs.
- Increased risk of predators if lambing outdoors.
- Ewe not steamed up.
- Twin lamb disease.
- Lack of supervision at lambing time.
- Hypocalcaemia (milk fever).

Post-lambing

Post-lambing the ewes are kept on a high plane of nutrition to ensure good milk production. They should have hay or silage ad lib (high DMD) and concentrates, particularly for early lambing. Once grass is available in sufficient quantity, there is no need to continue feeding concentrates as good quality grass is a complete feed. However, if grass is scarce, farmers should continue to feed concentrates. Watch ewes for signs of grass tetany and provide them with a mineral lick or have Calmag dusted onto their meal.

Ewes and their lambs should be rotationally grazed rather than set stocked.

Lambs produced for the Easter market should be creep fed concentrates and sold off as they reach slaughter weight (34–40 kg). A Suffolk cross lamb will reach slaughter weight 12–14 weeks after it was born.

||||| Fig 44.12 Lambs creep feeding

Creep gates and creep feeders allow lambs to have access to pasture and concentrates but not the ewes. Teagasc estimates that lambs creep fed will be 2 kg heavier at weaning and will be ready for slaughter two weeks earlier.

Weaning

Weaning takes place between the months of June and July when the ewes and lambs are separated from each other. The ewes are put onto bare pasture and dried off in preparation for flushing, aiming for a body condition score of 3.5 for mating. At this time, check the ewes and cull any ewe with chronic health problems such as mastitis or footrot, or lambing difficulties, e.g. prolapses, poor milk production or ewes with non-functioning udders. Teagasc advises a replacement rate of 23 per cent annually.

Rearing your own replacement ewes is always better than bought-in ewes as there is less risk of disease. If farmers are planning to breed their own replacement ewes, a maternal sire like the Belclare Improver, Border Leicester or Bluefaced Leicester is used.

Some farmers will breed their best ewe lambs as this can increase potential output. Good management of these ewe lambs is required, as they will require additional feeding compared to mature ewes. Ewe lambs must be fed for growth in addition to producing their own lamb and milk production. A ewe lamb needs to be 45–50 kg at mating, with a BCS of 3.

As there is an additional workload when breeding ewe lambs, the majority of farmers wait and breed their young ewes as hoggets. A ewe hogget is a year and a half old and will weigh roughly 63–65 kg (85–90 per cent of a mature ewe's weight). Charollais rams are a popular choice for mating with ewe lambs and ewe hoggets as they produce small lambs, which lessens the risk of lambing difficulties.

☰ General Husbandry

There are routine procedures that are carried out on sheep farms in order to maintain a healthy and productive flock.

Vaccination programme

Vaccinations can be used to prevent a number of diseases in sheep. Sheep are vaccinated against clostridial diseases and orf. Vaccinations for footrot and pneumonia are also available.

Dosing

Dosing is used to prevent the build up of stomach worms, liver fluke and other internal parasites. The dose is usually in liquid or paste form and is administered at the back of the animal's tongue, either by using a dosing gun for ewes and rams or a syringe (minus the needle) for lambs.

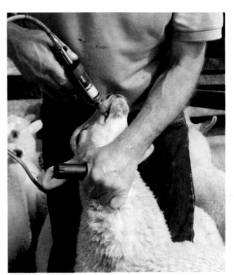

||||| Fig 44.13 Dosing sheep

Dipping

All sheep are susceptible to flystrike between the months of April and November and sheep scab between September and March (see page 353). The sheep are dipped in summer to prevent flystrike and in winter to prevent mange mite, which causes sheep scab. For dipping to be effective against sheep scab, the sheep must be in the dip for at least one minute, with the head immersed twice.

The dipping solution must be freshly prepared and done on a dry day to avoid rainwater diluting it.

||||| Fig 44.14 Sheep dipping

Due to the hazardous and toxic nature of sheep dips to the operator, risk of contamination of water sources and difficulty with the disposal of the dipping solution, many farmers choose not to dip their sheep and instead use pour-ons or sprays to prevent flystrike and mange mite. These are sprayed along the back and around the tail region of the animal. Mobile sheep showers are also available and are extremely efficient at treating large numbers of sheep.

Docking and dagging

Dagging involves the removal of wool around the tail of the sheep. Intestinal worms can cause diarrhoea. Faeces soil the wool around the tail, which attracts bluebottle flies and is known as flystrike. The flies lay their eggs in the soiled wool and when the maggots hatch they feed off the flesh of the animal. Removal of the wool around this area helps to prevent flystrike.

Foot bath, foot trimming and paring

Foot trimming and paring is necessary when the outer surface of the foot grows beyond the soft sole of the foot. This is particularly common in sheep that are housed. If the foot is not trimmed, the animal can become lame.

Footrot is caused by bacteria that inflame and infect the tissue between the digits of the foot. This leads to lameness. To prevent footrot, animals are walked through foot baths that contain a solution of copper sulfate or formalin. Treatment for footrot includes pairing of the infected foot and administering antibiotics. Keeping sheep on clean pasture, which has not been grazed in the last two weeks, helps to eliminate the bacteria.

||||| Fig 44.15 Lame sheep

Shearing

Sheep are normally sheared in June. It prevents the sheep from overheating in warm, summer weather and it aids in preventing flystrike. Wool is also a saleable product. Some farmers shear their sheep before winter housing as it gives the sheep more space.

Table 44.3 Diseases of lambs and sheep				
Disease	**Cause**	**Symptoms**	**Treatment**	**Prevention**
Twin lamb disease	• Breakdown of fat reserves in the ewe's body leads to liver failure	• Separates from flock • Staggers, tremors • Collapse and death	• Fatal disease unless caught early • Administer energy solution (glucose)	• Steaming up with concentrates as rumen's size restricted • Growing foetus limits the intake of hay and silage
Orf (zoonose)	• Virus	• Small spots on udder, ewes' teats, lips, gums, nose of young lambs and genitals of rams • Secondary infection of lesions can occur	• No treatment for virus • Treat sores with antibiotic cream	• Vaccinate ewes before lambing • Vaccinate lambs at a few weeks old

Table 44.3 Diseases of lambs and sheep cont.

Disease	Cause	Symptoms	Treatment	Prevention
Milk fever (Hypocalcaemia)	• Low levels of calcium occurs in late pregnancy or early lactation	• Similar to twin lamb disease • Listlessness, unable to stand, unconsciousness, death	• Injection of calcium borogluconate	• Dust ewes' feed with Calmag or provide mineral lick
Grass tetany (Hypomagnesaemia)	• Occurs when ewes and lambs are turned out onto lush grass low in magnesium	• Twitching, muscle spasm • Coma, death	• Injection of soluble magnesium	• Dust ewes' feed with Calmag or provide mineral lick
Nematodirus	• Roundworm lays eggs in the lamb's gut, pass out of gut onto grass; overwinter as eggs; hatch in spring after cold spell • Large numbers can hatch together; young lambs most at risk as they lack resistance	• Many lambs showing scour • Lambs stop eating, become dehydrated and die	• Dose for worms at regular intervals	• Put lambs on clean pasture that has not been grazed by lambs the previous year
Coccidosis	• Protozoa, parasite found in faeces, affects young lambs 4–8 weeks old • Parasite invades the lining of the intestines	• Lambs fail to thrive • Bloody scour • Dehydrated • In worst cases death	• Lambs have initial immunity while suckling (ewe immune) • Oral dose lambs	• A medicated creep feed gives protection
Clostridial diseases	• Variety of bacteria that cause pulpy kidney, blackleg, lamb dysentery and tetanus	• Varied, most lead to sudden death	• Treatment is difficult	• Vaccine available • Vaccinate a '7 in 1' and an '8 in 1' • Vaccinate lambs • Give ewes an annual booster
Flystrike	• Maggots of the green and bluebottle flies eat into the sheep's flesh • Flies lay their eggs in fleeces soiled with faeces	• Maggots irritate sheep; tail wags constantly followed by dark stain on wool • Sheep lying on its own	• Spray on an insecticide • Treat flesh eaten by maggots with antiseptic cream to prevent infection	• Dip sheep • Dose sheep for worms to prevent diarrhoea • Use insecticidal sprays
Sheep scab (notifiable disease)	• Mange mite feeds on skin and flesh • Extremely contagious	• Sheep irritated by mites rub against fences and gates, causing wool loss • Yellow scabs visible on skin	• Notify district veterinary office immediately • Dipping and injections administered by vet	• Winter dip sheep

☰ Wool

Wool is a complex protein fibre that grows from follicles on the sheep's skin. The fibres have scales on their surface, which make the fibres interlock. The fibres are also crimped, with many bends that give the wool fibres a natural elasticity. This crimp also adds bulk, which helps to trap air between the fibres. Therefore, wool is an excellent insulator.

Sheep produce both wool and hair fibres. However, the ratio of these fibres varies between breeds. Merino sheep produce the finest wool with a ratio of wool to hair of 25:1, while most British and Irish breeds have wool to hair ratios of 8:1.

There are two types of wool yarn: woollens and worsteds. Woollens are produced from short wool fibres and are used to produce textured products such as blankets, rugs, jackets and coats. Worsteds consist of long fibres that lie close together and are used to produce trousers and suits with a smooth finish.

Australia is the world's biggest producer of wool.

▕▏▎ Fig 44.16 Wool fibre

Summary

- ▨ Ewes are seasonally polyoestrous; they have many oestrus cycles during a set time of year.
- ▨ Ewes are short-day breeders; they come into oestrus during autumn as daylight decreases.
- ▨ In Ireland, two breeding systems are employed: early or Easter lamb and mid-season lamb.
- ▨ Flushing involves moving the ewes from a low plane of nutrition to a high plane of nutrition.
- ▨ Some advantages of flushing include: increased ovulation rate, increased conception rates and better implantation of the embryos to the uterine wall.
- ▨ Synchronised breeding involves sponging the ewes to synchronise the oestrus cycle of ewes, thus compacting lambing time.
- ▨ Breeding out of season is practised by farmers aiming to produce lamb for the Easter market.
- ▨ Breeding out of season involves sponging the ewes with progesterone and then injecting them once sponges are removed with PMSG.
- ▨ The ram effect is used to start ewes cycling six weeks earlier than normal.
- ▨ Steaming up involves placing the ewe on an increasing plane of nutrition six to eight weeks before lambing.
- ▨ Steaming up prevents twin lamb disease.
- ▨ Ewes expecting a single lamb should receive up to 500 g of concentrates per day. Ewes carrying twins should receive 750 g of concentrates per day during steaming up.
- ▨ Ensure lambs get colostrum when they are born as it contains vital antibodies. Dip their navels in iodine to prevent navel ill.

Summary

▓ Lambs' tails are docked in their first few days to prevent the build up of faeces and lessen the chances of flystrike.

▓ Lambs and ewes should be rotationally grazed when put out on grass.

▓ Lambs being produced for the Easter market should be creep fed concentrates and sold off as they reach slaughter weight (34–40 kg).

▓ Farmers should rear their own replacement ewes to prevent the entry of disease onto farms.

▓ When breeding for replacement ewes, use a maternal sire such as the Belclare Improver, the Border Leicester or the Bluefaced Leicester.

▓ Vaccinating, dosing, dipping, shearing and foot bathing are routine tasks carried out by all sheep farmers.

QUESTIONS

1 Sheep are *seasonally polyoestrous* and are described as *short-day breeders*. Explain the meaning of the highlighted terms. Describe how a short day length triggers the onset of oestrus in ewes.

2 Give approximate values for each of the following for sheep:
 (a) Weight at birth
 (b) Finishing weight (slaughter weight)
 (c) Length of gestation
 (d) Length of oestrus cycle
 (e) Duration of oestrus.

3 Define the term *flushing*. Explain how this is carried out.

4 List three advantages of flushing.

5 Why must flushing be continued for four weeks after mating?

6 Explain how farmers synchronise breeding in ewes.

7 What is the purpose of each of the following in breeding sheep?
 (a) Raddle
 (b) Pregnant mare serum gonadotrophin (PMSG)
 (c) Changing the colour of the ram crayon every 17 days.

8 Explain the meaning of the term *the ram effect*. Explain how it could be used to bring ewes into oestrus earlier than normal.

9 What is the body condition score (BCS) at mating for the ewe and the ram?

10 Why has the ram a greater BCS at mating than the ewe?

11 Describe the feeding and management of the ewe six weeks before lambing.

12 Explain the importance of each of the following before lambing:
 (a) Scanning ewes
 (b) Steaming up
 (c) Addition of Calmag to the ewe's feed.

13 Why is lameness seen as a contributing factor to twin lamb disease?

14 Describe the care of a newborn lamb.

15 A farmer has surplus lambs that need to be fostered on to a ewe with a single lamb. Advise the farmer as to the best way to foster the lamb on.

16 Describe the management and feeding of lambs and ewes between lambing and weaning.

17 Write a short note on three of the following:

(a) Dipping

(b) Dosing

(c) Foot pairing and foot baths

(d) Vaccination programmes.

18 Write a short note on four of the following diseases:

(a) Twin lamb disease

(b) Orf

(c) Sheep scab

(d) Nematodirus

(e) Coccidosis.

EXAM QUESTIONS

1 List four advantages of in-wintering of ewes. (LC, HL, 2008)

2 Discuss the factors that contribute to ewe and lamb mortality. (LC, HL, 2009)

3 Explain the advantage of each of the following in the management of a flock of sheep:

(a) Synchronised breeding

(b) Breeding out of season. (LC, HL, 2006)

4 In farm enterprises, animals are culled.

(a) What is meant by culling?

(b) Give three reasons why animals are culled. (LC, OL, 2007)

5 Describe the management of a lamb from birth to weaning. (LC, OL, 2007)

6 Explain the technique known as flushing in sheep production and give two of its advantages. (LC, HL, 2008)

7 Describe the feeding of ewes during the final 6–8 weeks of pregnancy and give reasons for the change in the feeding regime. (LC, HL, 2006)

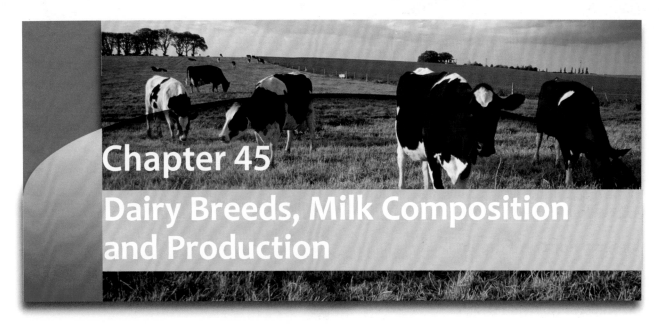

Chapter 45
Dairy Breeds, Milk Composition and Production

The dairy industry is an extremely important contributor to the Irish economy. According to the Central Statistics Office, there were 1.1 million dairy cows in Ireland in 2008. The total milk output for 2008 was 5 436 million litres of milk, with 472 million litres consumed as liquid milk.

Roughly 10 per cent of all milk produced in Ireland is processed as liquid milk; the remaining 90 per cent is converted into commodities such as butter, cheese, yoghurt and milk powder, e.g. sodium casein and whey powders. Ireland exports 80 per cent of all its dairy products to the UK, Europe and other international markets.

☰ Dairy Breeds

Holstein-Friesian

For many years, one dairy breed, the Holstein-Friesian, dominated the dairy industry in Ireland. It is the world's highest milk-producing cow, producing large milk yields but with a low milk solids content. It is a large animal with black and white markings. It originates from the Netherlands where it was bred for high milk production.

Unfortunately, breeding for high milk production led directly to a decrease in the fertility and health of the Holstein-Friesian.

||||| Fig 45.1 Holstein-Friesian

Ayrshire

The Ayrshire is a dairy breed that originates from Scotland, with red and white markings. It is known for its easy calving and longevity. Its milk has a moderate butterfat content and high protein.

||||| Fig 45.2 Ayrshire

Jersey

The Jersey is a small, light-brown breed that originates from the Channel Island of Jersey. This breed produces milk high in percentage fat and protein but a lower yield than the Holstein-Friesian. As this animal is a much smaller breed of dairy cow, it has a lower maintenance cost. Other advantages of this breed include: easy calving, high fertility and longevity and it is less prone to lameness.

||||| Fig 45.3 Jersey cow

Jersey x Holstein-Friesian

Jersey x Holstein-Friesian cows are smaller, lighter and tend to be dark brown in colour compared to the purebred Holstein-Friesian.

In trials carried out by Moorepark Dairy Production Research Centre, Teagasc found that the milk volume of this Jersey crossbred was reduced, but the yield of milk solids increased, leading to increased profit per lactation compared to purebred Holstein-Friesians.

Teagasc also noted that the Jersey crossbred cows had increased production efficiency due to higher grass intake relative to its size and compared to the purebred Holstein-Friesian.

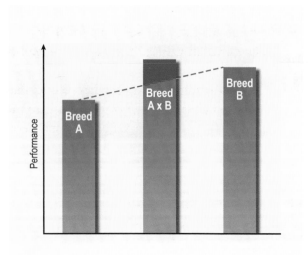

||||| Fig 45.4 Hybrid vigour or heterosis
(Source: Moorepark Dairy Production Research Centre, Teagasc)

||||| Fig 45.5 Jersey x Holstein-Friesian cow

When crossbred animals perform better than the expected average of their parents this is called hybrid vigour or heterosis. Fig 45.4 shows two purebred animals: breeds A and B. When crossed they produce the breed A x B.

The performance of all three breeds is represented in the histogram (see Fig 45.4). The line drawn between breed A and breed B represents the average of these two breeds. The shaded area on the box shows how the crossbred A x B out-performs the expected average of breeds A and B.

☰ Milk Composition and the Udder

Milk is a suspension of protein, fat and other solids in water. The composition of cow's milk is approximately 88 per cent water, 3–4 per cent butterfat and 8.6 per cent solids non-fat (SNF), which is composed of lactose (4.8%), protein 3.3 per cent and minerals. Milk is produced by specialised cells in the udder of a cow. The udder is an exocrine gland composed of four quarters that function independently of each other and delivers milk through its own teat.

The cow's udder

Fig 45.6 illustrates the structure and the support tissue of a cow's udder. The right half of the udder is separated from the left half by a membranous wall called the medial (central) suspensory ligament. This ligament is composed of strong elastic tissue that forms numerous branches that support the udder as it expands and stretches, while the udder fills with milk between milking. The inter-mammary groove marks the position of the median suspensory ligament when the udder is viewed from behind. In addition, the udder is supported also by the lateral suspensory ligaments, which extend from tendons from the pelvic bone. These ligaments are

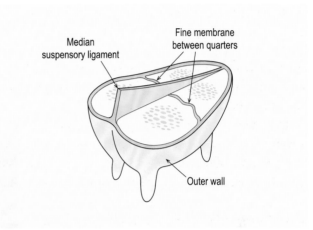

||||| Fig 45.6 Cow's udder

extremely important in supporting the udder, as a modern dairy cow's udder may weigh up to 50 kg.

The udder is further sub-divided into the rear and front quarters, which are separated by a thin wall of connective tissue.

The milk-producing tissue of the udder is called alveolus. The milk-secreting cells each have a duct that allows milk to drain out. These ducts meet to produce larger ducts, which eventually empty milk into the gland cistern that can store approximately 500 cm³ of milk. The gland cistern is connected to the teat cistern, which can hold 40 cm³ of milk. The milk exits the teat through the streak canal.

The udder has a rich blood supply. Milk synthesis requires a large amount of nutrients. For a cow to produce 1 kg of milk, it requires approximately 400–500 kg of blood to pass through the udder. Blood also carries hormones that control milk synthesis and trigger 'milk let-down'. The surface of the udder has a number of receptors that are sensitive to touch and temperature. These nerve receptors are stimulated during preparation of the cow's udder for milking and this triggers the release of oxytocin and initiates milk let-down.

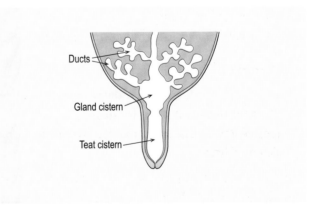

||||| Fig 45.7 Cow's udder with ducts and gland cistern

Milking

During milking, do not disrupt the normal milking routine, as disruptions can lead to a cow preventing the milk let-down process. Loud noises, unfamiliar noises, rough treatment or pain can cause the cow to release adrenaline. Adrenaline works against the hormone oxytocin by blocking its release or preventing it from reaching the udder.

Lactation and the dairy cow

The cow will start milking soon after she has given birth. The average lactation period for a dairy cow is 10 months (305 days). She is dried off for the final two months (60 days) to allow time for the tissue in the udder to repair itself, to regain body condition and to complete the development of her next calf in the uterus.

After the birth of the calf, the cow produces colostrum (also known as beestings) for the first four to five days.

Colostrum is different to normal milk in that it is much creamier and darker in colour and it has a higher percentage of protein, fat and other SNF. Most importantly, it is high in immuno-globins (antibodies).

Feeding colostrum to newborn calves is essential and has a number of benefits:

- The calf depends on antibodies in the colostrum to protect it against disease.
- The ability of the calf to absorb these antibodies is greatest in the first 24 hours.
- Colostrum is high in easily digestible nutrients.
- The high fat content has a laxative effect that helps to clean out the digestive system of the newborn calf.

Colostrum is not accepted by Irish creameries; farmers should continue to feed it to the calf until the cow starts to produce her normal milk.

A lactation curve (see Fig 45.10, page 361) plots the milk production of a dairy cow over the course of her lactation until she is dried off. Milk production increases from the start of lactation until a peak yield is reached four to six weeks after calving. A high peak yield normally results in a higher total milk yield. The total lactation yield can be estimated using the following formula:

||||| Fig 45.8 Dairy cow and calf

||||| Fig 45.9 Bottle-feeding colostrum to a newborn dairy calf

Total lactation yield (kg) = Lactation peak yield x 200 (average management)

Or

Total lactation yield (kg) = Lactation peak yield x 220 (high management)

In order for a cow to reach her potential peak yield, she must be on a high plane of nutrition. If a cow is not adequately fed, she will not reach this peak yield and as a result will have a lower total milk yield.

The peak yield will depend on the lactation number of the cow. A heifer calving for the first time will give a peak yield of 75 per cent of a mature cow's peak yield. This will increase until the fifth lactation when the cow will produce her maximum peak yield. This is due to the increase in size and development of the udder compared to that of a heifer lactating for the first time.

After a cow reaches her peak yield, her milk yield will start to decline. The rate at which her milk yield declines is known as persistence. A cow with a

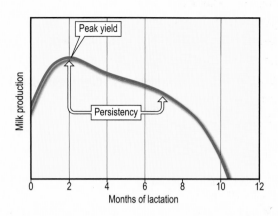

Fig 45.10 Lactation curve

higher peak yield tends to have a lower persistency. As a result, a heifer that has a lower peak yield than a mature cow will have a higher persistence. A heifer's milk yield will drop 0.2 per cent per day compared to a mature cow's milk yield, which drops to 0.3 per cent per day.

Factors affecting milk yield

Many factors affect milk yield: breed, age and body weight at calving, frequency of milking, drying off period, lactation number and feeding. Lactation number has already been covered and the influence of breed on milk yield and milk composition will be discussed in the next section.

Age

Milk yield rises with the age of the cow. This is partly due to the increase in body weight and udder size of the dairy cow. Studies have shown that recurring pregnancies and lactations can increase milk yields by 30 per cent from the first lactation to the fifth lactation.

Frequency of milking

Studies have shown that increasing the frequency of milking increases milk yield. This is because the milk secreting cells in the alveolus are working at full capacity. This can lead to a 20 per cent increase in milk yield if the herd is milked three times a day and a further 5–10 per cent increase if the herd is milked four times a day. However, the increase in milk yield has to be considered against the time and labour costs involved in milking the herd three or four times a day.

Decreasing milking frequency leads to a decrease in milk yield. Studies have shown that milking once a day cuts the milk yield by half in heifers on their first lactation and by 40 per cent in older cows.

Drying off

Dairy cows should be dried off two months (60 days) before the start of their next lactation. This drying-off period maximises milk yields in the following lactation. Studies have shown that lactation yields can be reduced by 25–40 per cent if the drying off period is less than 40–60 days.

Factors affecting milk composition

The composition of milk, percentage SNF and percentage fat can vary greatly. Some of the factors that affect the composition of milk are outlined overleaf (see Table 45.1).

Breed

Milk yield and milk composition vary greatly between breeds of dairy cows and crossbred dairy cows. Examine the table below, which compared the milk yield and milk composition of a Holstein-Friesian, Jersey and a Jersey x Holstein-Friesian.

Table 45.1 Comparison of milk yield and milk composition of dairy breeds			
Breed	Milk yield (kg)	Fat (%)	Protein (%)
Holstein-Friesian	5 651	4.12	3.49
Jersey	4 220	5.32	4.03
Jersey x Holstein-Friesian	5 272	4.77	3.88

(*Source: F. Buckley and L. Shalloo, Moorepark Dairy Production Research Centre, Teagasc*)

Animal feed

Good grassland results in increased milk, fat and protein yields. Fibre is an extremely important component of a cow's diet as the digestion of fibre results in the production of acetate and butyrate, two fatty acids that are precursors of milk fat. Nearly half the fat in milk is produced from acetate. Lack of fibre in the diet results in less acetate being produced in the rumen, which in turn decreases the concentration of fat in the milk by 2.0–2.5 per cent.

Fig 45.11 Round bale hay

Stage of lactation

The percentage fat, lactose and protein content of milk vary with the lactation stage. The percentage fat and protein is high immediately after calving, then decreases for 10–12 weeks and rises again towards the end of lactation. The percentage lactose decreases towards the end of lactation.

Stage of milking and completeness of milking

The percentage fat at the start of milking is only 1–2 per cent. This increases as milking continues, and by the end of milking percentage fat is at its highest. This is due to the fat globules being trapped in the alveolus at the start of milking. Incomplete milking also leads to a lower percentage fat content of the milk. However, any fat remaining in the udder at the end of milking will be picked up when the cow is next milked.

Milking interval

The milking interval is the time between the cows being milked. Most farms operate a 14/10-hour or a 13/11-hour interval.

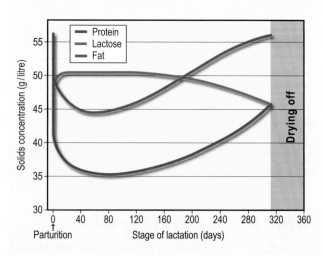

Fig 45.12 Changes in concentration of fat, protein and lactose over a lactation of a cow

The percentage fat content of milk varies between the morning and evening milking if the milking interval is unequal. In studies where milking intervals were unequal, it was found that there was an increase in milk yield but a decrease in percentage fat because of dilution after the longer interval. If cows are milked at 12-hour intervals, there was little variation in the percentage fat; however 12-hour milking intervals may not be practical on dairy farms.

Age

The fat percentage and protein contents of milk decrease with the dairy cow's age.

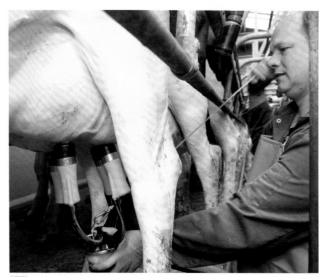

Fig 45.13 Dairy cows being milked

Disease

Infections of the udder, particularly mastitis, influence milk composition. The fat percentage, protein and lactose all decrease and the concentration of white blood cells and immunoglobulin increase.

Milk Industry in Ireland

Milk production in Ireland has undergone radical changes over the past years, with many dairy firms introducing a new payment scheme for milk. This scheme pays dairy farmers for milk based on the milk's composition. Farmers are paid for kg of protein and kg of fat, with a negative value for volume of water.

Milk-pricing system is represented by the equation A + B – C, where A represents kg of protein, B represents kg of fat and C is volume of water.

In Ireland, the demand for milk is year round. However, dairy cows will only lactate for 10 months or 305 days of the year. So how does supply meet demand? Farmers who supply liquid milk for consumption often operate both spring-calving and autumn-calving herds. This ensures that they have a constant milk supply.

The majority of dairy farmers are not supplying milk for the liquid milk market, but other milk that can be used for the production of commodities such as butter, cheese and milk powder. Here the creameries are looking for the quality of the milk rather than quantity. In addition, farmers are more likely to be paid under the new payment scheme of A + B – C. Payment is related to the amount of protein and fat in their milk and there are penalties if milk volume is large.

Fig 45.14 Milk products

The type of production dictates the breed of dairy cow used. If farmers are supplying a dairy with liquid milk, they are more likely to use a purebred Holstein-Friesian herd as they are looking for quantity of milk. Farmer supplying a creamery for milk products would select a dairy cow that would give high milk solids with low milk yields and in this case might select a crossbred Jersey.

Milk hygiene and milk testing

Before raw milk is paid for by the dairy or creamery, it undergoes a number of tests to assess the composition and hygiene quality of the milk. If the quality of the milk is outside set standards, penalties may be applied or the milk may have to be discarded. The following are a sample of tests carried out by creameries and milk processors on milk.

Total bacterial count (TBC)

Total bacterial count is an indicator of the standard of hygiene on a farm. The total number of living bacteria per ml of milk is counted. TBC must not exceed 100 000 cell/ml on a two-month geometric average. High TBC can be due to mastitis, dirty milking machinery, not changing milking machine filters or failure to properly cool milk to below 4°C.

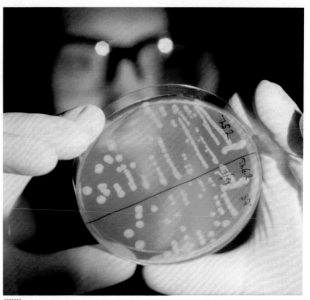

|||||| Fig 45.15 Bacterial colonies growing on an agar plate

Somatic cell count (SCC)

Somatic cell count is a test that measures the health of the udder. Somatic cells are white blood cells and they occur naturally in milk. If an udder has mastitis, the number of somatic cells increases. High SCC counts affect the processing of the milk. SCC should not exceed 400 000 per ml in a three-month geometric mean.

Temperature

Milk needs to be cooled to 4°C within 30 minutes of milking. If the milk is not cooled properly, this allows bacteria such as lactobacillus to grow, which converts lactose (milk sugar) into lactic acid. This causes the milk to go sour and to curdle. Farmers are penalised if the temperature of their milk at the collection point exceeds 6°C.

Antibiotics

Antibiotics must be absent from milk at all times as antibiotics present in milk can contribute to antibiotic resistance developing in bacteria. Antibiotics in milk also interfere with the processing of the milk. Antibiotics affect the bacteria cultures used in the production of yoghurts and cheese. As a result, cows undergo a withdrawal period if treated with antibiotics and they are milked separately so that their milk does not go into the bulk tank.

The Delvo test is carried out on all raw milk to test for the presence of antibiotics. A sample of milk is added to a purple agar containing a bacterium that is extremely sensitive to antibiotics. If there are antibiotics in the milk, they inhibit the growth of the bacteria. If the bacteria can grow, they produce an acid and this changes the agar from purple to yellow. Milk testing positive for the presence of antibiotics cannot enter the food chain and must be discarded.

Thermoduric test

Thermoduric bacteria can resist high temperatures and can survive the pasteurisation process. These bacteria can produce spores that can end up in the finished food product, where they can grow.

The test for thermoduric bacteria involves counting the number of bacteria that survive pasteurisation. Farmers are penalised if thermoduric bacteria exceed 1 000 per ml.

Sediment

Milk must be free from sediment and particles. To ensure this, it is advisable that farmers clean the udder and teats of the cows and dry them before the clusters are attached. Milk must be filtered and filters changed regularly to prevent sediment reaching the bulk tank.

Experiment 45.1

Assessment of hygiene quality of milk using resazurin

Materials
Samples of milk (raw unpasteurised milk, raw sour unpasteurised milk, fresh pasteurised milk and sour pasteurised milk), resazurin solution, water bath, test tubes, labels, pen

Method
1 Label four test tubes A, B, C and D.

2 To test tube A add 10 cm³ of raw unpasteurised milk, to B add 10 cm³ of raw sour unpasteurised milk, to C add 10 cm³ fresh pasteurised milk and finally to D add 10 cm³ of sour pasteurised milk.

3 Add 1 cm³ of resazurin to each test tube.

4 Place in a water bath at 37°C for 10 to 15 minutes.

5 Record any colour change that has occurred.

Note: Blue colour is the best quality (low bacterial numbers), followed by mauve, then pink and white. A white colour signifies very poor quality milk, indicating high bacterial numbers.

Result

Table 45.2 Results of assessment		
Test tube	**Contents**	**Colour**
A	Raw unpasteurised milk	
B	Raw sour milk	
C	Fresh pasteurised milk	
D	Sour pasteurised milk	

Experiment 45.2

To determine the butterfat content of milk

Materials

Milk sample from the start of milking and another from the end of milking, two butyrometers, concentrated sulfuric acid, amyl alcohol, centrifuge

Method

1   In a strip cup, remove a sample of milk from the start of milking and in a separate cup from the end of milking.

2   Heat both samples in a water bath until they reach 20°C.

3   Add 10 cm³ of concentrated sulfuric acid to each butyrometers. Label the butyrometers A and B.

4   Add the sample of milk from the start of milking to butyrometer A and the sample from the end of milking to butyrometer B. Pour the milk gently down the side of the butyrometer to prevent the milk mixing with the acid.

5   Add 1 cm³ of amyl alcohol to each butyrometer. Stopper and invert before placing in the centrifuge for three minutes.

6   Remove samples and heat to 65°C in a water bath. Ensure the level of the hot water covers the narrow column.

7   Read the percentage fat.

Result

The butterfat content of milk is lowest at the start of milking and is highest at the end of milking.

Husbandry and management in maintaining high hygiene standards in milking

▦ Maintain clean housing, cubicle beds, dairy parlour and holding yard.

▦ Wash cow's udder and teats.

▦ Check for mastitis (strip cup).

▦ Treat mastitis, dry cow treatment, drying off period.

▦ Teat dip after milking.

▦ Ensure fly control (prevents summer mastitis).

▦ Filter milk.

▦ Wash the bulk tank and milk line regularly.

▦ Ensure proper cooling of milk before it enters the bulk tank.

▦ Refrigerate milk at <4°C.

▥ Fig 45.16 A bulk tank is used for the storage of raw milk

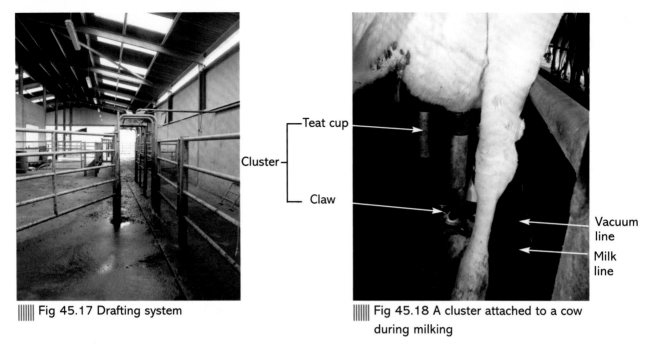

|||| Fig 45.17 Drafting system

|||| Fig 45.18 A cluster attached to a cow during milking

Dairy Parlours

The majority of dairy parlours in Ireland are herringbone parlours. Some farmers with large dairy herds use a rotary dairy parlour. The parlour can have varying levels of automation. Fig 45.17 is an automated drafting system, which can remove individual cows out of the herd. Fig 45.18 shows a cluster attached to the udder of a dairy cow.

The milking machine

The milking machine operates by using a pulsating vacuum that draws milk out of the cow's teat into the milk line. The milk is then transported via the milk line first to the receiving vessel and then through the filter and heat exchanger (which drops the temperature of the milk). It is stored in the bulk tank until it is collected by the creamery (see Fig 45.19).

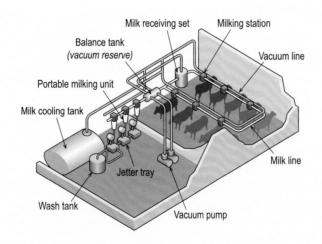

|||| Fig 45.19 Milking machine

Summary

- The Holstein-Friesian is the highest milk-producing cow, producing large milk yields with low milk solids content.
- The Jersey is a small, light-brown breed; it produces milk high in fat and protein and a lower yield.
- Jersey x Holstein-Friesian crosses exhibit hybrid vigour.
- When crossbred animals perform better than the expected average of their parents it is called heterosis or hybrid vigour.
- Milk is a suspension of protein, fat and other solids in water.
- The udder is an exocrine gland composed of four quarters, which deliver milk through their teats.
- The milk-producing tissue of the udder is called alveolus.
- The hormone oxytocin is responsible for the process of milk let-down.
- The average lactation period for a dairy cow is 10 months (305 days).
- The dairy cow is dried off for 60 days to allow time for the tissue in the udder to repair itself, to regain body condition and to complete the development of her next calf in the uterus.
- After the birth of the calf, the cow produces colostrum for the first four to five days.
- Colostrum is high in nutrients and antibodies and is essential for the survival of the newborn calf.
- In order for a cow to reach her peak milk yield, she must be on a high plane of nutrition.
- Factors that affect milk include: the cow's age, milking frequency and the drying-off period.
- Factors that affect milk composition include: the breed, animal feed, stage of lactation, stage of milking and milking interval.
- Some of the tests carried out on milk at the creamery include: total bacterial count, somatic cell count, temperature, antibiotic test, thermoduric test and a sediment test.

QUESTIONS

1 Name two dairy breeds and give two characteristics of each breed.

2 Discuss the advantages of using a Jersey Holstein-Friesian cross over a purebred Holstein-Friesian or purebred Jersey in a dairy herd.

3 Milk is composed of water, fat and SNF.
  (a) What do the letters SNF stand for?
  (b) Identify any two nutrients found in SNF.

4 Name the cells responsible for the secretion of milk in the udder.

5 Label A, B and C in the diagram of the udder (Fig 45.20).

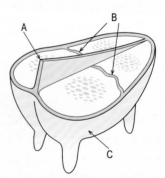

|||| Fig 45.20

QUESTIONS

6 Briefly explain how the udder produces milk. Explain the effect of oxytocin and adrenaline on the udder.

7 What is colostrum? Why is it important that a calf receives colostrum?

8 In relation to a dairy cow, state in days the length of each of the following:
(a) Lactation period
(b) Drying-off period.

9 Give three benefits of drying off a dairy cow.

10 What is a lactation curve? Draw a lactation curve for a dairy cow and identify on the diagram the peak yield and the persistence.

11 Identify two factors that affect the peak yield of a dairy cow.

12 State two factors that affect the milk yield of a dairy cow and briefly explain each factor.

13 Describe an experiment to determine the hygiene quality of a sample of milk.

14 A creamery tested a sample of milk and recorded (a) high total bacterial counts, (b) high somatic cell counts and (c) dirt particles in the milk. Give reasons for the results obtained in (a), (b) and (c) and identify how a farmer might improve the milk quality.

EXAM QUESTIONS

1 The following table shows the effect of body condition score (BCS) at calving on milk production in early lactation.

Table 45.3

Treatment	BCS	Milk yield kg/cow/day	Milk fat %	Milk fat kg/cow/day	Milk protein %	Milk protein kg/cow/day
A	2.73	25.50	3.71	0.94	3.14	0.80
B	3.00	26.50	3.81	1.01	3.18	0.84

(a) What is meant by a body condition score?
(b) What is the relationship between body condition score and milk yield in the data above?
(c) What is the total yield of fat plus protein under treatment A?
(d) State two factors, other than BCS, that may influence the percentage fat in milk. (LC, HL, 2007)

2 (a) Explain how each of the following affects milk composition: (i) breed, (ii) stage of lactation and (iii) milking interval.
(b) Outline the contrasting breeding strategies employed in two different dairy farms, one involved in liquid milk production, the other a creamery milk supplier. (LC, HL, 2009)

3 Describe how a farmer can ensure the production of high quality milk under the following headings: (a) hygiene and (b) composition. (LC, HL, 2008)

4 Suggest four reasons why dairies will not accept milk from cows that have been recently treated for mastitis. (LC, HL, 2010)

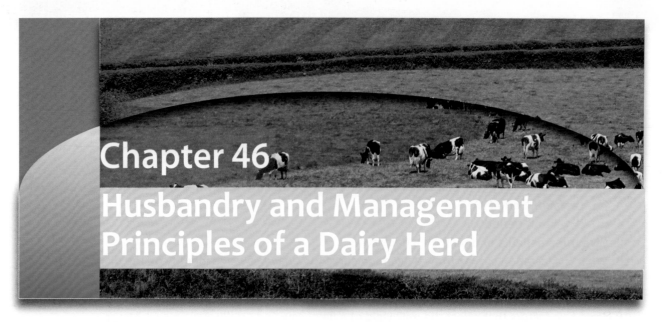

Chapter 46
Husbandry and Management Principles of a Dairy Herd

As stated in Chapter 45, dairy herds are either spring or autumn calving. Spring calving is a much more cost-effective system as farmers get the maximum utilisation out of their grassland. Therefore, milk production is seasonal in Ireland, with the bulk being produced over the spring and summer months. In order to benefit from this system, farmers plan for spring calving in mid-February.

|||||| Fig 46.1 Dairy cows grazing grass

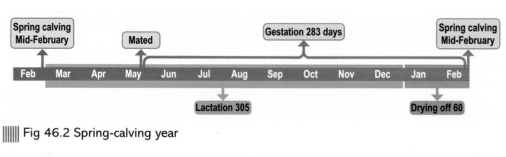

|||||| Fig 46.2 Spring-calving year

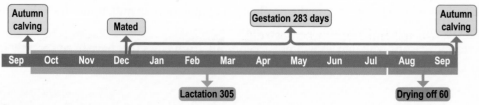

|||||| Fig 46.3 Autumn-calving year

As you can see from Figures 46.2 and 46.3, the gestation period of a dairy cow is nine and a half months or 283 days. The length of oestrus cycle in a cow is 21 days. The average duration of standing heat (cow stands to be mounted) is two to 18 hours. Regardless of which system farmers operate, they need to maintain the calving interval at 365 days to be economical.

Calving

In a spring-calving herd farmers aim to have their herd calving down in mid-February. Before calving, a cow should have a BCS in the range of 3.0 to 3.25. Low BCS before calving decreases the lactation yield of the cow. According to research by Teagasc, cows that have poor body condition scores after calving suffer fertility problems, e.g. they are unable to resume their oestrus cycles after calving, they have poor conception rates and have a greater chance of embryonic mortality.

Records of when the cow was served by the bull or AI dates help to identify those cows that are close to calving. Before a cow calves, isolate the cow from the rest of the herd and place her in a clean, dry calving pen/shed that contains handling facilities. Ensure an experienced person is on hand, who can regularly inspect the cow and identify any problems. Make available a calving jack, calving ropes and gloves in case the cow requires assistance.

The majority of calves are born in the normal presentation, i.e. with the head tucked between the two front legs. However, some calves are positioned wrongly, e.g. present backwards with their hind legs first, causing calving difficulties

If problems arise, call a vet. By following the procedures above farmers can significantly reduce cow mortality at calving.

Once the calf is born, a farmer should ensure that:

- All mucus is cleared away from the mouth and nose of the calf.
- The cow licks the calf or the calf is rubbed vigorously with straw to stimulate its circulation.
- Its navel is dipped in iodine, to prevent infection.
- It receives between 2 and 3 litres of colostrum.
- The calf is tagged for identification and traceability.

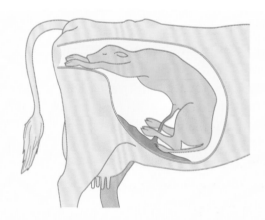

Fig 46.4 Normal presentation of a cow calving

Fig 46.5 Using a calving jack

Fig 46.6 Farmer assisting at the birth of a calf

The mortality of calves can be high in the first few weeks of life so it is important to take proper care and management. As described in Chapter 45, feeding colostrum is vital in protecting the newborn calf from disease as it provides antibodies. If for some reason the cow cannot produce colostrum, give the calf colostrum from another cow that has given birth. Feed the calf colostrum as long as it is available.

In dairy farms, the calf is removed from the cow and is usually grouped with other calves of similar age. The calves are fed milk or milk replacer either once or twice a day, at the same time each day. They are also given access to hay, concentrates and fresh water. Providing hay for the calf is important as it helps develop the rumen, something that is referred to as the 'scratch factor'.

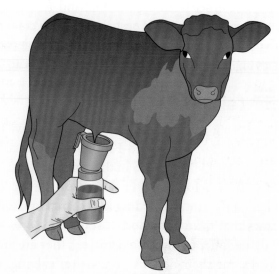

||||| Fig 46.7 Dipping a calf's navel in iodine

House the calves in well-ventilated, draught-free houses, as poor ventilation can lead to pneumonia in calves. Maintain good hygiene, especially with feeders and troughs, to prevent scour in the young calves.

||||| Fig 46.8 Cow licking her calf

||||| Fig 46.9 Young calves being bucket fed

||||| Fig 46.10 Older calves out on grass are fed milk through a feeder

||||| Fig 46.11 Tagging a calf

☰ Weaning

Calves are weaned off liquid milk or milk replacer and onto concentrates and grass at six weeks old. At this time, the calves should be eating 750 g of concentrates per day. Once out on grass, continue feeding concentrates until the calves have adjusted to their new diet. Calves are selective grazers and should be provided with high quality grass. They should graze in the leader-follower system, grazing ahead of older cows. This system of grazing has two advantages; firstly the calves have better LWG and secondly it helps to control the number of parasites (worms and flukes) to which they are exposed. By the time the calves are six months old they should be 30 per cent of their mature body weight. Calves will continue to graze grass over the summer months and into autumn.

|||||| Fig 46.12 Calves grazing

Overwintering

By the time the weanlings are housed for winter they are roughly nine months old. To ensure that they continue to put on good LWG, feed them good quality silage with a DMD of 75 per cent. If silage quality is poor, then supplement it with concentrates. Feeding kale and other catch crops over the winter months increases LWG. Dose weanlings for hoose and other worms before housing.

Management of cows in early lactation

After calving, a cow loses weight, as the cow's feed intake does not meet her energy output. The cow uses energy to produce the calf, especially in the two months before calving, when the calf is growing rapidly within the uterus. The cow requires energy to give birth to the calf and to produce milk. In order to meet these energy demands, the cow uses up some of her own energy reserves; the phrase 'milking off her back' refers to this process.

In early lactation, the cow is kept on a high plane of nutrition. This is achieved by providing the cow with good quality silage and supplementing her diet with concentrates. This ensures that the cow reaches her lactation peak and, therefore, can produce her potential lactation yield.

|||||| Fig 46.13 Holstein-Friesians strip grazing

Supplement the cow's diet with minerals to prevent milk fever and grass tetany when she is turned out to grass.

Cows are turned out to grass as early as possible and grass should be grazed rotationally using paddocks or strip grazing. If grass growth is slow, the feeding of concentrates should be maintained.

Management of cow in mid and late lactation

The first heat after calving is usually a silent heat, with only a small number of cows in standing heat. It is vital that farmers record the next normal heat cycle, 21 days later, to ensure that they can plan the start date for mating.

When a cow is in heat, she will stand and allow other cows to mount her. When this happens a cow may only stand for a few seconds and it may go unnoticed. To aid in identifying cows in standing heat many farmers use heat detection aids.

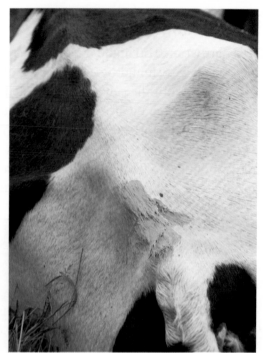

▐▌▐▌▐ Fig 46.14 Tail painting on a dairy cow

- Tail painting is a heat detection aid often used by farmers. The top of the cow's tail is painted with a bright colour. When the cow is in heat and mounted by other cows the paint rubs off. The colour of the paint can be changed to identify all cows that are cycling before mating.

- The Kamar device is another popular method. This pressure-sensitive chamber contains a dye. It is attached to the top of the tail and when the cow is mounted, the chamber bursts and the dye changes colour.

- When cows are in heat they often become very restless. Activity meters measure the activity of a cow and compare it to her activity over the previous few days. The activity meters identify cows with increased activity as being in heat.

▐▌▐▌▐ Fig 46.15 Cow activity meter

- Heifers can be extremely difficult to detect if they are cycling and coming into heat. A vasectomised bull fitted with a chin ball that contains a dye will mount and mark any cow in heat.

At the start of breeding, the BCS of the herd should be averaging around 2.9. Most farmers in Ireland use AI to inseminate their dairy herd. A stock bull may be used to mop up any cows that have not been successfully inseminated. AI is discussed in detail in the section on replacement heifers.

During mid and late lactation, the cow should be rotationally grazing grass. At this stage, it should not be necessary to supplement the cow's diet with concentrates.

In late lactation the milk yield is smaller and cows are dried off 60 days before calving. At this stage, feed cows good autumn grass or good quality silage. Place them on an increasing plane of nutrition during this time to ensure that they have regained a BCS of 3.25 before calving.

☰ Replacement Heifers and the Economic Breeding Index (EBI)

Dairy farmers regularly cull cows from their dairy herd. Dairy cows can be culled for a number of reason:

- **Health problems**: Lameness and disease (TB, brucellosis, etc.).

- **Problems with milk production**: Mastitis, high SCC, poor milk yield and poor milk quality.

- **Problems with fertility**: Decrease in fertility, difficulty getting the animal back into calf and calving problems.

- **Grading up the herd**: Improving the genetic merit of the herd, replace older cows with heifers of high genetic merit.

Rearing replacement heifers allows farmers to maintain and expand their herd size. Teagasc recommends an annual optimum replacement rate of 17 per cent for a dairy herd. If farmers replace a higher percentage of their herd, then milk production drops significantly as more mature cows are replaced with younger animals in their first, second and third lactation and these animals are only producing 75 per cent, 92 per cent and 97 per cent lactation yield respectively compared to a mature cow. Having a high proportion of animals in their first or second lactation results in a herd not reaching its full milk potential. Teagasc estimates that the cost of rearing a replacement heifer for the farmer is €15,000 when you take into account the cost of rearing the calf, labour, land and housing. Therefore, farmers should choose heifers of high genetic merit to replace their culled cows.

Farmers are encouraged to rear their own replacement heifers as this maintains a closed herd and prevents the entrance of disease. If replacement heifers are bought in there is a greater risk of disease. Therefore, farmers should quarantine and vaccinate these animals before they enter the herd.

||||| Fig 46.16 Farmer tending to heifers

Rearing replacement heifers requires good management, as the aim is to breed a replacement heifer at 15 months so that she will calve down for the first time at two years old. It is uneconomical to feed a heifer for an extra year that will calve for the first time at three years old.

Target weights for heifers

Heifers can be mated once they reach 60 per cent of their mature body weight. Table 46.1 (overleaf) lists the target weights for a purebred Holstein-Friesian and a crossbred Jersey to meet at mating (target weight for bulling) and calving.

Target weights for mating and calving vary greatly between breeds and crossbreeds. Heifers require a live weight gain (LWG) of 0.6–0.7 kg/day to reach the bulling target of 60 per cent mature body weight.

Age	% mature live weight	Holstein-Friesian	Jersey cross	Feed
Birth (Feb)		38 kg	34 kg	Colostrum, milk
6 weeks (April)		63 kg	56 kg	Milk, hay, concentrates
3 months (May)	15%	90 kg	80 kg	Grass, rotational grazing
6 months (Aug)	30%	155 kg	138 kg	Grass, rotational grazing
12 months (Feb)	50%	280 kg	250 kg	75% DMD silage/hay
15 months (May)	60% (bulling target)	330 kg	295 kg	Rotational grazing grass
21 months (Nov)	80%	490 kg	437 kg	75% DMD silage
24 months (Feb)	90% (calving target)	550 kg	490 kg	Silage and concentrates

Table 46.1 Target weights for heifers

(Source: Teagasc)

To ensure heifers reach this weight, provide them with high quality grass rotationally grazed during the summer months and good quality silage over winter. Studies at Moorepark Dairy Research Centre found that heifers overwintered on silage and kale had better LWG than those fed silage alone.

The BCS at mating for first-time heifers should be 3.25 to ensure that the heifer is cycling (coming into oestrus). If heifers are in poor condition at mating with a BCS of less than 3.0, these heifers will calve later and their milk yield will be significantly less.

Bull selection is critical for a first-time calving heifer. It is important that farmers select an easy calving bull; otherwise the calf may be too big and this can lead to calving difficulties. Mate replacement heifers with high EBI (Economic Breeding Index) sires. In the majority of cases, this is done using AI unless the farmer has a high EBI stock bull. High EBI sires improve the genetic merit of the herd and their daughters will provide high EBI replacement heifers for the future.

|||||| Fig 46.17 Holstein-Friesian bull

|||||| Fig 46.18 Jersey bull

The EBI

Teagasc and the Irish Cattle Breeding Federation (ICBF) developed the Economic Breeding Index (EBI) to accurately identify genetically superior, profitable animals and to produce genetic improvements in the average dairy production system.

EBI: A single figure profit index given in euros of profit per lactation for the animal's progeny compared to an average dairy cow.

The EBI helps farmers to identify sire and dam lines that would be most profitable in their dairy herd. It was introduced in 2001 and it is composed of five sub-indexes that contain information on a wide range of traits. An animal's EBI is calculated by adding the value of the EBI sub-indexes together.

1   **Production index**: Focuses on milk production.

2   **Fertility index**: Focuses on calving interval and survival.

3   **Calving index**: Focuses on calving difficulty, gestation and calf mortality.

4   **Beef index**: Focuses on carcass weight and conformation.

5   **Health index**: Focuses on lameness, udders and health.

These five sub-indexes allow farmers to address particular issues within their own herd.

The EBI allows for the selection of cows with high milk solids and good fertility and that require less feed to produce, thus giving a more efficient and productive dairy cow. When farmers are selecting a sire to cross with their dairy herd, it is important to use a top quality bull with a high EBI. These sires can be chosen from the ICBF Active Bull List®.

The EBI is constantly undergoing developments to accurately identify genetically superior animals. To achieve this objective a new technique called **genomic selection** was launched in Ireland in 2009. Genomic selection identifies the DNA or genes responsible for the yield of milk solids and fertility, therefore allowing a calf's DNA to be analysed at birth so that the genetic merit of the calf can be predicted. Currently this technology is only available for the analysis of Holstein-Friesians but it is hoped to expand this technology to other breeds.

☰ Diseases of Dairy Cows and Calves

In this section, we examine some diseases that are prominent in dairy herds. A more comprehensive account of diseases of cattle is examined at the end of Chapter 48.

The first disease examined is mastitis, an infection of the cow's udder. There are different types of mastitis and three of them are described in Table 46.2 (overleaf). Mastitis is a contagious disease and is spread during milking through the operator's hands and the milking machine.

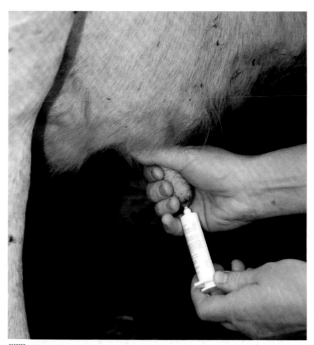

||||| Fig 46.19 A vet administering dry cow treatment, a long-lasting antibiotic used to treat and prevent bacterial infections in the udder

||||| Fig 46.20 The teats of the udder are disinfected after milking to prevent mastitis

	Table 46.2 Diseases of dairy cows			
Disease	Cause	Symptoms	Treatment	Prevention
Clinical mastitis	• Variety of bacteria	• Inflammation of the udder, affecting one or more quarters • Visible changes in milk, clots • Milk may be more watery	• Antibiotics • Milk from the cow is withheld from the bulk tank	• Dry cow treatment during drying off • Ensure milking machine works correctly as faulty machines damage teats • Change milk liners regularly • Use teat disinfectant after milking; dirt on udder or teat increases infection; strip teat regularly to check for mastitis • Ensure clean and dry bedding in winter housing calving shed • Cull chronically infected cows
Sub-clinical mastitis	• Variety of bacteria	• No obvious change in milk, may be some inflammation of the udder • Only clear indication is a high somatic cell count	• Treat cows with sub-clinical mastitis with a long lasting dry cow treatment that helps to regenerate tissue and prevent new infection • Treatment during drying off ensures no milk loss during the lactation period	• Same as above
Summer mastitis	• Variety of bacteria, spread by flies	• Seen in dry cows and heifers in July to September • Udder swells • Foul-smelling discharge from affected udder • Severely affected cows may abort	• Early detection vital; look for flies constantly around a single teat • Irrigation of infected quarter • Administer antibiotics	• Treat sores and wounds on animal • Control flies with pour-on or spot-on • Use long lasting dry cow treatment • Apply Stockholm tar as a physical barrier

Scour

One of the biggest causes of mortality in calves is scour. There are two different types of scour: nutritional and infectious. Infectious scour can be caused by viruses, protozoa and a variety of bacteria.

	Table 46.3 Diseases of calves			
Disease	**Cause**	**Symptoms**	**Treatment**	**Prevention**
Nutritional scour	• Fed too much milk • Irregular feeding times • Milk ball develops in calf's stomach, can develop into infectious scour	• Diarrhoea • Dehydration, weak • Not life-threatening unless it develops into infectious scour	• Take off milk immediately • Feed calf water with glucose and electrolytes • Feed weak calves with a stomach tube • Feed fluid for 3–5 days and gradually put calf back on milk or milk replacer	• Good feeding routine • Make gradual changes to the calf's diet
Infectious scour	• Bacteria • Viruses • Protozoa	• High temperature • Foul-smelling diarrhoea • Dehydration • Listlessness • Hypothermia • Shock followed by death	• Take off milk, feed fluid replacement • Identify causative agent, treat with antibiotics if bacterial • Consult vet • If calf's temperature drops below 37°C place it under infrared lamp • Isolate infected animal	• Calf houses, buckets and bedding must be clean and disinfected • Maintain good hygiene • Ensure calf gets adequate colostrum at birth
Navel/Joint ill	• Bacteria, initial infection starts in the navel and then spreads to the joints • Usually affects calves less than one week old	• **Navel ill**: Navel is swollen and painful; thick pus may ooze • High temperature • **Joint ill**: Swollen, stiff, painful joints • Death in severe cases	• Treat with antibiotics and painkillers • Vet is required to remove abscesses if they develop	• Dip navel in iodine after birth • Calve in a clean environment • Ensure calf receives adequate intake of colostrum
Viral pneumonia	• Initial infection is by a virus followed by a secondary infection by bacteria due to weakened immune system caused by the first infection	• Rise in temperature • Discharge from the nose and eyes, rapid breathing, coughing • Calf lies down a lot • Weight loss, loss of appetite • Death in severe cases	• Isolate calf • Vet required • Treat bacterial infection with antibiotics	• Well-ventilated, warm, dry and draught-free housing essential • Avoid overcrowding • Ensure calf receives adequate intake of colostrum • Vaccine available
Ringworm	• Fungal infection (zoonose)	• Circular patches of hair loss develop into grey, crusty scabs on the animal's head, neck and flank	• Apply a topical medicine to infected skin • Animals recover in a few weeks	• Clean and disinfect housing as spores survive on walls of buildings • Vaccine available

Summary

- The gestation period of a dairy cow is nine and a half months or 283 days.
- The length of oestrus cycle in a cow is 21 days.
- The average duration of standing heat is two to 18 hours.
- Before calving a cow should have a BCS in the range of 3.0 to 3.25.
- Before a cow calves isolate her from the rest of the herd. Ensure an experienced person is on hand.
- Feed the calf the following feeds: colostrum, milk/milk replacer, hay and concentrates, grass and concentrates.
- When the calves are let out onto grass they should graze grass in the leader-follower system, grazing ahead of older cows.
- Weanlings are housed for winter when they are roughly nine months old, and fed good quality silage with a DMD of 75 per cent.
- After calving, a cow will milk off her back, as the amount of feed she consumes does not meet her energy demands.
- Farmers use heat detection aids and tail painting to detect when the cow starts to go back into oestrus cycling.
- Cows are culled from the dairy herd due to health problems or fertility problems or to grade up the herd.
- Rearing replacement heifers requires good management, as the aim is to breed a replacement heifer at 15 months so that she will calve down for the first time at two years old.
- Heifers can be mated once they reach 60 per cent of their mature body weight.
- The Economic Breeding Index was developed by Teagasc and the Irish Cattle Breeding Federation to identify genetically superior, profitable animals and to bring about genetic improvements within the average dairy production system.
- The EBI is a single figure profit index given in euros of profit per lactation for the animal's progeny compared to an average dairy cow.
- The EBI allows for the selection of cows with high milk solids and good fertility and that require less feed to produce this, giving a more efficient and productive dairy cow.
- Genomic selection identifies the DNA or genes responsible for the yield of milk solids and fertility; therefore allowing a calf's DNA to be analysed at birth so that the genetic merit of the calf can be predicted.
- Mastitis is a bacterial infection of the cow's udder.
- One of the biggest causes of mortality in calves is scour.

QUESTIONS

1 In relation to a dairy cow, state the length of each of the following:
   (a) Gestation in days
   (b) Length of oestrus cycle
   (c) Duration of oestrus.

QUESTIONS

2 Describe the feeding programme for a calf from birth to weaning.

3 What is the ideal body condition score for a cow before calving?

4 Describe the importance of body condition score (BCS) at the time of calving.

5 Outline precautions a farmer can take to reduce cow and calf mortality at calving.

6 Identify the importance of each of the following in the diet of a calf: (a) colostrum, (b) hay and (c) the provision of concentrates when the calf first goes out on grass.

7 Describe a suitable feed for overwintering of weanlings.

8 For a spring-calving herd, describe the feeding practices for a dairy cow in early lactation.

9 Dairy farmers use heat detection aids to identify cows in oestrus. Give an example of a heat detection aid and briefly describe how it works.

10 Give two reasons why dairy farmers might cull a cow from their dairy herd.

11 What is the recommended replacement rate in a dairy herd? Give reasons for your answer.

12 Give reasons why it is important to have a heifer at a BCS of 3.25 before mating.

13 Identify one reason why dairy farmers are encouraged to rear their own replacement heifers.

14 Dairy farmers are encouraged to use easy calving bulls on first-time heifers. Give a reason for this.

15 What are the target weights for a replacement Holstein-Friesian heifer at (a) mating and (b) calving?

16 What is the ideal BCS of a replacement heifer at calving and why?

17 What is EBI and how is it calculated?

18 Discuss the benefits of using a high quality EBI bull on a dairy farm.

19 Distinguish between nutritional scour in calves and infectious scour in calves. Describe how you would treat a calf with scour. How can scour be prevented in the calving shed?

20 Give a scientific explanation for each of the following:
   (a) A high incidence of mastitis in dry cows during the month of August.
   (b) The use of crossbred Jerseys in a dairy herd supplying milk to a creamery.
   (c) The feeding of colostrum to a newborn calf.
   (d) The practice of including calcined magnesite in the diet of lactating cows in early spring.

EXAM QUESTIONS

1 Outline precautions taken to reduce mortality at calving time in a dairy herd. (LC, HL, 2007)

2 Discuss the rearing of replacement heifers on a dairy farm under the following headings:
   (a) Growth targets
   (b) Breeding policy. (LC, HL, 2002)

3 What is mastitis? State one symptom of mastitis. Describe two ways of preventing mastitis in dairy cattle. (LC, OL, 2009)

4 Describe the feeding programme for a calf from birth to weaning in a spring-calving dairy herd. (LC, HL, 2008)

Chapter 47

Beef Production in Ireland

☰ Beef Production in Ireland

In 2008, Ireland was the largest exporter of beef to Europe and the fourth largest exporter of beef in the world, according to Ireland's food and drinks industry. In 2009, the value of the beef exported was estimated at €1.4 billion, with the UK market worth €660 million.

||||| Fig 47.1 Beef cattle

Beef animals are also exported as live cattle. Bord Bia recorded a total of 286 000 live cattle exported in 2009 and estimate the value of this to be worth €157 million. The main markets in Europe for Irish beef are the Netherlands, Italy, Spain and the UK. Ireland also exports beef to Russia and Morocco.

Beef production in Ireland uses a grass-based system, which makes it considerably cheaper to produce a beef animal in comparison to using a grain-based system. However, it takes two years to have a beef animal ready for slaughter on high production farms; it requires two and a half years on other farms. Ireland utilises a number of beef production systems including:

1   Calf to beef in two years
2   Suckler herd
3   Bull beef production
4   Heifer beef production
5   Culled cow finishing.

This section deals with the production of beef from a calf in two years. The production of beef from a suckler herd is discussed in Chapter 48, along with the diseases of cattle.

Beef Breeds in Ireland

Beef breeds can be divided into two categories: British beef breeds and Continental beef breeds.

British beef breeds

Aberdeen Angus

The Aberdeen Angus breed originates from Scotland and is renowned for its easy calving. Therefore, it is used as a sire for heifers in both the beef and dairy herds. Compared to other beef breeds Aberdeen Angus has a low growth rate and finishing weight. However, Aberdeen Angus breed societies have been improving the growth rate of this breed.

The Aberdeen Angus has a black coat and skin, is naturally polled, and of small to medium size. It is an early-maturing breed that produces a lean carcass.

Hereford

The Hereford breed originates from Herefordshire in England. It was first introduced into Ireland towards the end of the 1700s. This breed is easily recognisable with its deep-red coat, white face and underside, giving it the name 'whiteheads'. Some of the characteristics of this breed include: good conformation, well-muscled, strong legs and feet, early maturing and easy calving. They have a growth rate intermediate between the Aberdeen Angus and the Continental breeds. Herefords are commonly used as a beef sire on dairy and suckler herds to produce calves for beef production.

Continental beef breeds

Belgian Blue

The Belgian Blue breed originates from the southern part of Belgium. It usually has a whitish-blue coat but can sometimes have a black and white coat. It is a double-muscled beef breed, with a higher growth rate than a Charolais. Belgian Blues have a high kill out percentage and produce a high percentage of lean meat on the carcass. When a Belgian Blue bull is mated with a normal cow, the calf produced will have some of the double muscle.

Fig 47.2 Aberdeen Angus bull

Fig 47.3 Hereford cows

Fig 47.4 Belgian Blue bull

The major disadvantage with this breed is that the double muscle causes calving problems. When a purebred Blue bull is mated with a purebred Blue cow, the calf is usually delivered by caesarean.

Charolais

Charolais are the most popular beef breed in Ireland according to the CMMS (Cattle Movement Monitoring System). The Charolais is a French breed first imported into Ireland in 1964. It is white or cream in colour with a fast growth rate, good conformation and a lean carcass. There is a risk of calving difficulties due to the blocky conformation and high birth weight of the calf. Therefore, it is recommended not to use a Charolais bull on a heifer.

Fig 47.5 Charolais suckler cow

Limousin

The second most popular beef breed in Ireland – the Limousin – originates from France. Limousin cattle are recognised by their reddish-brown coat and their long slender bodies. They have a high muscle to bone ratio, good conformation and high fertility and are easy calving. They have a lower growth rate than other Continental breeds.

Simmental

The Simmental breeds originate from the Simmen Valley in Switzerland. It has a red and white spotted coat usually with a white face. There are two types of Simmental: a beef breed bred for beef production and a dual-purpose breed bred for milk and beef

Fig 47.6 Limousin beef bull

production. The dual-purpose breed is a popular choice for suckler herds because of their beef and milk traits. The growth rate of a Simmental is less than that of a Charolais.

☰ Growth, Maturity and Slaughter Weight of Beef Animals

In America, beef animals can be brought from birth to finishing weight for slaughter in roughly one year. This type of farming is extremely intensive, with the animals fed on a high plane of nutrition. In Ireland, beef production requires two years to get a calf from birth to finishing weight for slaughter. This is because our farming is based on grassland and grass is a much cheaper feed for cattle than the concentrate-based feeding system employed in America.

Fig 47.7 shows the deposition of fat and muscle from the birth of the animal until it is four years old. A young animal puts on fat very slowly at the start. The rate of muscle deposition decreases as the animal reaches maturity. In contrast, the amount of fat that is deposited from the age of two years and older increases. This fat is subcutaneous (under the skin of the animal) and lies in the thoracic cavity. It is trimmed from the carcass after the animal is slaughtered. Bone growth has a smaller relative growth rate than either fat or muscle.

The weight at which fat deposition increases depends on the breed of the animal. British beef breeds are early-maturing beef breeds, as they start putting down fat at lower live weights than Continental breeds.

Continental breeds are later maturing, with high growth rates, larger sizes and finish at higher live weights without laying down fat. Therefore, Continental beef breeds have grown in popularity in Ireland. Table 47.1 gives the average finishing weight of British and Continental steers.

Continental breeds require high levels of feeding to match their high growth rates while British beef breeds require moderate feeding levels.

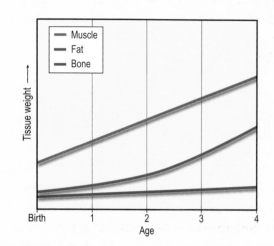

|||||| Fig 47.7 Tissue growth relative to age

Table 47.1 Finishing weight of British and Continental beef breeds	
Beef breed	Finishing weights for steers
British beef breeds	
Aberdeen Angus	500 kg
Hereford	530 kg
Continental breeds	
Belgian Blue	700 kg
Charolais	700 kg
Simmental	680 kg
Limousin	650 kg

(*Source: Teagasc*)

Calf to Beef in Two Years

Traditionally the calves for this type of beef production are male, with some female calves coming from a dairy herd.

Dairy farmers will cross some of their herd with a beef bull to improve the conformation of the resulting progeny. These calves are sold to beef farmers. This system of beef production requires the purchase of calves every year, and rearing these animals to their finishing weight at two years old.

Unless the beef farmer buys calves directly from the dairy farmer there is a risk of buying-in disease.

|||||| Fig 47.8 Holstein cross calves

≣ Year 1

Buying a calf

When buying a calf from a mart or a dairy farmer the beef farmer should:

1   Buy a healthy calf that is one to two weeks old.

2   Examine the calf carefully, to ensure that there is no discharge from the eyes, mouth or nose; check that the navel is not swollen; inspect the rear of the animal for signs of scour.

3   Ensure that the calf is bright, alert and has a shiny coat.

The breed of calf has a big impact on the conformation of the animal, e.g. beef crossed calves have better conformation than purebred dairy calves. Also important for the conformation is the type of bull that is crossed with the dairy dam, whether it is a British beef bull or a Continental beef bull, as this determines whether the animal will be early or late maturing and affects the animal's finishing weight.

The calf's sex determines the growth rate of the animal. Male animals have better growth rates than females. Heifers are slaughtered at lighter live weights than steers or bulls.

|||||| Fig 47.9 Calves in a mart pen

Management of calves

Place the calves in a clean, dry pen in a shed with good ventilation. Allow them to rest and recover from the stress of transportation.

The stomachs of young calves are extremely sensitive and do not take stress or sudden changes in diet well. After about two to three hours, feed each calf 2 litres of warm electrolyte solution. Do not give the calf milk or milk replacer on arrival as its stomach may not digest it properly and this could lead to scour.

Table 47.2 is a feeding schedule for bought-in calves.

|||||| Fig 47.10 Beef calf licking its lips after a bucket of milk replacer

		Table 47.2 Feeding schedule for bought-in calves	
Day	**Time**	**Feeding schedules**	**Concentrates**
1	pm	Ad lib warm electrolyte solution	Nil
2	am	2 L warm milk replacer	Nil
	pm	2 L warm electrolyte solution	Nil
3	am	2 L warm milk replacer	Handful
	pm	2 L warm electrolyte solution	
4	am	2 L warm milk replacer	Ad lib
	pm	2 L warm milk replacer	

(Source: Teagasc)

Give the calves fresh concentrates every day and, to prevent scour, keep all the buckets clean. Allow the calves access to fresh hay. Feed them milk replacer and concentrates until they are weaned off milk and are each consuming 2 kg of concentrates per day. Feeding concentrates is much cheaper than feeding milk replacer; grass is the cheapest of all feeds.

Target weights for calf to beef production

Teagasc has produced a table of target weights that beef farmers will aim to meet in order to finish the calves at two years. Table 47.3 gives target weights for a purebred dairy calf (Friesian) and a Continental crossed dairy calf (Charolais x Friesian). Target weights and growth rates depend on the Continental breed used.

	Table 47.3 Production target weights for Friesian and Continental x Friesian		
	Friesian	**Charolais x Friesian**	**Time of year**
Slaughter age (months)	24 months Kg ADG*	25 months Kg ADG	Year 1
Born: 0 months	40	50	Feb/March
Turn out to grass: 3 months	100 0.8	100 0.8	April
Winter housing: 9 months	220 0.5	230 0.5	November
			Year 2
Turn out: 13 months	300 0.9	310 1.0	March/April
Housed: 20 months	470 0.86	500 1.0	November
Slaughtered: 24/25 months	600	680	

ADG* = *Average daily gain*
Note the above target weights apply to Charolais only; growth rates of other Continental breeds will vary.

(Source: Teagasc)

Management of calves out on grass

Turn out spring-born calves onto grass once the weather is warm and there is enough grass for the calves to eat. Feed them concentrates for a few weeks after turn-out to prevent any setback while they adjust to their new diet. Calves should graze good quality grass rotationally in a leader-follower system. The calves graze first followed by older stock (yearlings and finishing stock); this prevents the calves being exposed to large numbers of parasites before they have built up some resistance. It also ensures that the calves get the leafy grass.

Dose the calves to control hoose (lungworm) and stomach worms during this time. The average live weight gain during the summer months while the calf is out on grass is 0.8 kg/day.

|||||| Fig 47.11 Charolais calves out on grass

Turn in to winter housing

Weanlings are housed around November in Ireland. Low soil temperatures restrict grass growth at this time of year. In addition, heavy stock (beef yearling) left grazing over winter will poach the land. Poaching reduces grass growth the following spring and bare patches of soil are easily colonised by weeds.

Before housing, dose the weanlings for stomach worms and for liver fluke and treat for lice.

The most common type of winter housing in Ireland is the slatted shed. Weanlings should have 1.4 m² of floor space per animal. Group any underweight weanlings together and feed them extra concentrates. Ensure good ventilation and that all animals have access to clean water.

When the weanlings are housed during the winter months, there is a decrease in

|||||| Fig 47.12 Cattle in winter housing being fed hay

their live weight gain as they are moved from a high plane of nutrition (grass) to a lower plane of nutrition (silage). This decrease is called a store period, as illustrated in Fig 47.13. During this time, the animal's frame grows, but it puts on very little muscle. Beef farmers aim for a live weight gain between 0.5 kg/day to 0.7 kg/day. The target weight for steers is 220 kg; for heifers it is less.

For a lighter weanling, the aim is for a live weight gain of 0.7 kg/day. Farmers need to feed good quality silage with a DMD of 73 per cent or greater. If the quality of silage is average or poor, then farmers must supplement the diet of the weanlings with concentrates in order to achieve the same live weight gain.

Table 47.4 indicates the amounts of concentrate required for a live weight gain of 0.7 kg/day when feeding silage of excellent, average and poor quality.

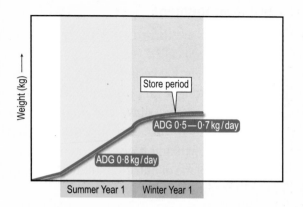

 Fig 47.13 Store period winter year 1

Table 47.4 Optimum concentration input (kg/head/day) for Continental steers gaining 0.7 kg live weight gain/day when offered different quality silage			
	Silage quality		
	Excellent 73% DMD	Average 69% DMD	Poor 62% DMD
Concentrates kg/day	0	1.5	2.75
Silage kg/day	27	23	19

Feeding excellent quality silage reduces feeding costs as target weights can be reached without feeding concentrates. Dusting a mineral and vitamin mix onto the silage prevents mineral deficiencies such as grass tetany.

 Fig 47.14 Limousin beef cattle eating hay

≡ Year 2

Yearling management

When the animals are turned out onto grass in their second year they are called yearlings. A steer should weigh approximately 300 kg and a heifer 275 kg. Back on grass, the live weight gain per day of the yearlings is much higher than a yearling kept on a continuous high plane of nutrition. Such growth is called compensatory growth and it occurs when an animal returns to a high plane of nutrition following a period of restricted feeding (see Fig 47.15).

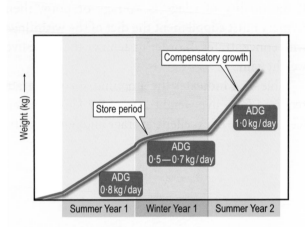

Compensatory growth: The increase in growth rate that occurs following a period of restricted feeding.

||||| Fig 47.15 Compensatory growth

The compensatory growth effect is used to our advantage in Ireland as it occurs when grass supply increases naturally during the summer months. The yearlings rotationally graze grass for the summer. Yearlings are not as susceptible to stomach and intestinal worms as calves, so dosing may not be necessary in the second year.

Winter housing second year

The yearlings are housed weighing 470 kg. Each animal should have between 2 and 2.3 m² in the slatted house. Before housing the animals are treated for stomach worms, liver fluke and lice. Cattle of similar weight, sex and breed are penned together. This allows for better feed management.

Feeding the yearlings high quality silage and concentrates ensures that the beef animals reach their finishing weight and maintain their 1.0 kg live weight gain per day.

Teagasc Grange Research Centre recommends feeding 4.0 kg per day of concentrates with 75 per cent DMD silage in order to finish the steers.

The level of feed is dictated by a number of factors including the sex and the breed of the animal. British crossed beef breeds will finish at lighter weights (600 kg) as they are early maturing compared to the Continental breeds that will finish at heavier weights (700 kg).

≡ EU Beef Classification Scheme

The EU classification scheme is a grading scheme for beef throughout Europe. It assesses the slaughtered carcass under the following criteria:

1   **Conformation**: The shape and width of the carcass and its muscle development is visually assessed. Particular attention is placed on the width and shape of the shoulders, the width of the carcass along the back and the width and roundness of the hindquarters. Conformation is divided into five classes E, U, R, O, P. The letter E represents the best conformation while the letter P represents the worst. The category of P is further subdivided into P+, P and P-, describing declining conformation. A category E animal would be a double-muscled beef animal with excellent carcass quality, while animals in the P category would have very poor conformation, e.g. Holstein-Friesians.

2 **Fat**: There is a visual assessment of the degree of fat cover on the carcass and in the thoracic cavity. There are five fat classes, with 1 indicating the least amount of fat and 5 indicating the greatest amount of fat. The fat class of 4 is divided into 4L (low fat) and 4H (high fat). Consumer demand is for lean meat; therefore the ideal fat score is 3. Penalties may be applied to carcasses with higher fat scores.

3 **Sex**: Carcasses are also classified by sex and are coded as follows:

  ▨ A is a young bull.

  ▨ B is a stock bull.

  ▨ C is a steer.

  ▨ D is a cow.

  ▨ E is a heifer.

Fig 47.16 Beef carcasses

Table 47.5 Beef classification grid							
Conformation	E	U	R	0	P+	P	P-
Fat score 1							
2		①					
3							
4L				②			
4H							
5							

1 Only double-muscled purebred continental animals are classified in this range.

2 Most Irish beef animals score in this range when they are classified after slaughter.

Summary

- Beef production in Ireland is a grass-based system.
- Aberdeen Angus and Hereford cattle are British beef breeds; they are early maturing and start to put down fat at lower live weights.
- Belgian Blue, Charolais, Limousin and Simmental are Continental beef breeds; they are late maturing and have high growth rates and finish at higher live weights.
- In Ireland, beef production requires two years to get a calf from birth to finishing weight for slaughter.
- Continental breeds require high levels of feeding to match their high growth rates.
- In calf to beef in two years, the calves for this type of beef production are male and some female calves that have come from a dairy herd.
- When buying a calf for beef, purchase a healthy male beef crossed calf. This calf will have good conformation and a better growth rate than a purebred dairy calf.
- Feed a bought calf the following feeds: electrolyte solution, milk/milk replacer, concentrates and hay.
- Turn out spring-born calves onto grass once the weather is warm and there is enough grass for the calves to eat.
- Feed concentrates to calves for a few weeks after turn-out to prevent any setback.
- Graze calves using the leader-follower system; this prevents the calves being exposed to large numbers of parasites before they have built up some resistance.
- Before housing, dose the weanlings for stomach worms and for liver fluke and treat for lice.
- Feeding excellent quality silage reduces feeding costs as target weights are reached without feeding concentrates.
- Dusting a mineral and vitamin mix onto the silage prevents mineral deficiencies such as grass tetany.
- Compensatory growth is the increase in growth rate that occurs following a period of restricted feeding.
- British crossed beef breeds finish at 600 kg and Continental breeds finish at 700 kg.
- EUROP is a grading scheme used for beef throughout Europe.
- Conformation, fat and the sex of the animal determine the carcass's grade under EUROP.

QUESTIONS

1 List the characteristics of each of the following beef breeds:
   (a) Aberdeen Angus
   (b) Charolais
   (c) Limousin
   (d) Belgian Blue.
2 The Simmental is a dual-purpose breed of cattle. Explain the meaning of the term *dual-purpose*.
3 In the last 30 years, the number of Continental beef breeds has increased steadily in Ireland. Give two reasons for the growing popularity of Continental beef breeds over British beef breeds.
4 Explain the difference between an early maturing breed and late maturing breed. Give an example of each type of breed.

QUESTIONS

5 List three criteria a farmer should consider when buying a calf.

6 Describe the management of a newly purchased calf.

7 List the target weights for a Charolais crossed calf:
   (a) Turn out to grass at three months
   (b) Turn in to winter housing
   (c) Turn out summer year 2
   (d) Slaughter at 24 months.

8 Describe the feeding and management of a calf when turned out on grass in year 1.

9 Why is dosing calves important?

10 When weanlings are put into winter housing they undergo a *store period*. When returned to grass the following spring these animals have increased live weight gains and the animal is described as undergoing *compensatory growth*.
   (a) Explain the meaning of the highlighted terms.
   (b) Describe the feeding of a weanling in winter housing.
   (c) State the ADG (average daily gain) for (i) a weanling in winter housing and (ii) a yearling out on grass.
   (d) Draw a growth curve for a beef animal showing (i) store period and (ii) compensatory growth.

11 Which criteria are used to grade a carcass using the EUROP beef classification system?

12 How does conformation affect the grading of beef carcasses?

EXAM QUESTIONS

1 Calves are often grazed in the leader-follower system.
   (a) What is the leader-follower system of grazing?
   (b) Give two reasons why calves are grazed in this way.
   (c) Cattle are housed for the winter in November. What is the ideal target weight for spring-born calves being housed for their first winter?
   (d) What measures can farmers take to ensure that underweight calves make an improved weight gain indoors? (LC, OL, 2009)

2 Beef animals are housed indoors during the winter months.
   (a) List three housing requirements for weanlings housed in their first winter.
   (b) Why are most beef animals slaughtered at 2 years old? (LC, OL, 2009)

3 List the target weights for the efficient production of spring-born beef animals at the following stages of growth.
   (a) At housing for the first winter
   (b) At the start of grazing for the second summer
   (c) At slaughter at 24 months. (LC, HL, 2005)

4 Write notes on the 'leader-follower' grazing system when used in a calf to beef enterprise. (LC, HL, 2005)

5 Describe the management facilities necessary to maximise the growth rate of beef weanlings when housed indoors during their first winter. (LC, HL, 2002)

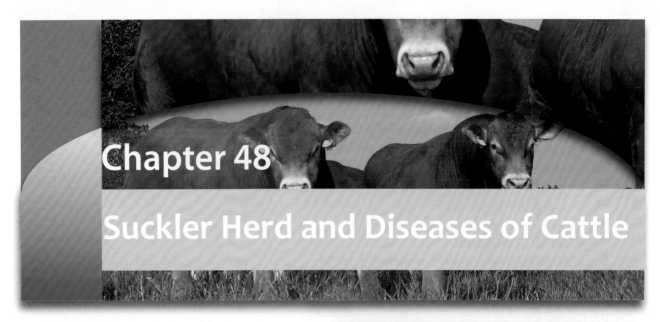

Chapter 48

Suckler Herd and Diseases of Cattle

In contrast to calf to beef in two years, the feeding of the suckler calf is carried out by the suckler dam. Therefore, calves in a suckler herd have a greater live weight gain than calves to beef in two years.

In Ireland, most suckler herds are spring calving. Under this method, the suckler cow gives birth around February or March. This allows for the maximum utilisation of grass and thus reduces feed costs compared to an autumn-calving suckler herd.

A productive and efficient suckler herd requires high levels of management. The first step to ensuring this is the careful selection of a suckler dam.

||||| Fig 48.1 Calf suckling cow

The Ideal Suckler Cow

The ideal suckler cow is a 50% dairy x 50% Continental beef animal possessing a good milk yield and good conformation. This animal displays hybrid vigour and has a number of advantages over a purebred beef dam. Crossbred suckler dams:

- Have higher fertility.
- Have lower calf mortality.
- Have a longer reproductive life (lowers replacement rate).
- Have higher milk yields, which gives high growth rate in calves, resulting in heavier weaned calves.
- Have a shorter calving interval.
- Produce a hardier calf.

Even though dairy genes are desirable in a suckler dam, a purebred Holstein-Friesian is unsuitable for single suckling. It produces too much milk for one calf and causes scour. In addition, a Holstein-Friesian has poor conformation, which would result in a poor carcass grade.

The most popular suckler dam is a Holstein-Friesian crossed with a Limousin or a Simmental due to high growth rates, good conformation, high lean-meat content of the carcass and heavier carcass weights.

||||| Fig 48.2 Limousin suckler calves

☰ Calving

The care and management of calves is similar to that described for calves produced in the dairy herd. The main difference is that calves are not removed from the dam. Calves suckle the dam until they are weaned. Weaning occurs around September to October for a spring-born suckler calf.

Target weight for suckler calves

Calves from a suckler herd have higher growth rates than calves raised in the beef system. This is largely due to the calf's consumption of milk from the dam. Table 48.1 shows the growth rate of a bull calf over seven months to weaning compared to a calf to beef in two years.

Table 48.1 Growth rate of bull calf from suckler herd compared to calf to beef in 2 years			
System	Birth weight	Weaning weight	ADG from birth to weaning
Suckler herd	45 kg	300 kg	1.2 kg/day
Calf to beef	40 kg	230 kg	0.8 kg/day

Management of suckler herds out on grass

The suckler herd should graze grass rotationally, using either a paddock or a strip-grazing system. The suckler dam must be given good quality pasture to ensure good milk production for her calf. Initially, when the calf goes out on grass, it depends solely on the milk from its dam. However, as time goes by it will start to eat some grass. As calves are selective grazers, they should be allowed to creep graze ahead of the herd. Use a creep gate that allows the calf access to the grass but prevents the cow. Calves can also be given access to concentrates using this method.

||||| Fig 48.3 Hereford cow and calf; note the creep feeder for calves in the background

During this time, the suckler cow comes back into heat. To identify cows coming back into heat, use heat detection aids, e.g. tail painting, or a vasectomised bull. Then, put the cows back into calf by either using a high quality stock bull or AI.

Turn in to winter housing

Calves are frequently separated from the dams when the animals are going into winter housing. The feeding and management of the suckler weanling is similar to that described in Chapter 47, 'Calf to Beef in 2 Years' (see page 385).

Reproductive efficiency and calving interval for a suckler herd

The reproductive efficiency and calving interval have a huge effect on the productivity and profitability of a suckler herd.

> The **reproductive efficiency** of a suckler herd is the number of calves weaned per 100 cows served.

In a suckler herd, the aim is to produce one calf per cow per year. To ensure that a suckler herd meets this target, follow these steps.

First, the cow or heifer must be at the correct BCS of 2.5 at mating.

Second, heat detection is vital, as it takes longer for a suckler cow to come back into heat than a dairy cow. Suckling and the calf's presence inhibit the onset of oestrus in the cow. To encourage the cow to start oestrus cycling, farmers generally restrict the calf's access to its dam once the calf is 30 days old. This is labour intensive, but the cow will come into heat quicker than a cow with unrestricted access to her calf.

Cows that have poor fertility or fail to come back into calf should be culled. Replacements for the suckler herd must be bred from cows and bulls of high genetic merit. Use a Hereford or an Aberdeen Angus bull on maiden heifers to prevent calving difficulties. Calving problems increase the risk of cow and calf mortality and decrease reproductive performance, which lead to infection of the uterus and the birth canal and poor conception rates, caused by damage.

Calving interval

A calving interval is another key factor in maintaining an efficient suckler herd.

> **Calving interval:** The time that has elapsed between successive calvings.

The calving interval in a suckler herd should be kept at 365 days. Suckler farmers aim for compact calving, with 90 per cent of calves born within 10 weeks. To ensure this, heat detection and restricting access to the calf from day 30 is vital.

The importance of AI in suckler herds

The use of AI is an important factor in the breeding of suckler herds. This gives farmers a wide choice of bulls of superior genetic merit, all of which will have been performance and progeny tested. The use of a superior bull can bring about improvements in the genetic merit of the herd. Bulls can be chosen with beef characteristics to produce calves for slaughter, or with maternal characteristics for the breeding of replacement heifers for the suckler herd.

When a farmer is selecting a bull to use on a heifer, it is important to check the **index of calving difficulty**. A number of factors contribute to calving difficulties:

- Breed of the bull
- Breed of the cow
- Age of the heifer or cow
- Sex of the calf
- Calf birth weight
- Body condition score of cow at calving.

There are significant differences between bulls within each breed and between breeds of bulls for calving difficulty. The calving index is from 1 to 5. A low calving index figure indicates easy calving, while a high calving index indicates calving difficulties. Table 48.2 lists examples of the differences between breeds of bulls for calving difficulties. An AI catalogue will give an accurate index for each individual bull.

Table 48.2 Index of calving difficulties for different beef breeds	
Breed	**Calving difficulty index**
Aberdeen Angus	2.3
Belgian Blue	4.5
Charolais	4.5
Hereford	1.8
Limousin	3.8
Simmental	4.2

☰ Other Types of Beef Production

Bull beef production

The production of beef from young bulls is on the increase in Ireland. Bulls have a better FCR (food conversion ratio), which means that they are better at converting feed into live weight gain. Bulls have a live weight gain of 1.5 kg and greater per day compared to steers of 1.3 kg per day.

Bulls are uncastrated and produce testosterone which increases weight gain, resulting in an 8 per cent higher live weight gain compared to castrated males (steers). This results in greater carcass weight at slaughter.

|||| Fig 48.4 Young Limousin bulls

At slaughter, bulls have more lean meat on their carcass than steers and attain better conformation scores on grading.

This type of bull production requires high levels of management with the aim of finishing the animal and having it ready for slaughter at 15–16 months old.

Bulls must be housed in small groups, preferably not in the same house as heifers. They must be handled with care due to their aggressive nature. There are specific guidelines for the slaughter of bulls, as stress before slaughter can darken the colour of the meat, making it difficult to market.

Heifer beef production

Heifer beef production usually involves beef crossed heifers from the dairy herd. Some may be used as replacements for suckler herds; others will be finished off in 19–22 months and slaughtered. British beef crossed heifers will finish earlier than Continental crossed heifers.

The management of heifers is similar to steers, requiring similar feeding and grazing. However, steers have a 10 per cent higher growth rate than heifers; the average ADG for steers in their second year is 1.3 kg/day compared to 0.9 kg/day for heifers. Heifers will finish at lighter weights compared to steers and will have a lower kill out percentage than steers. There is a risk of purchasing in-calf heifers with this system.

> An **in-calf heifer** is a young female that is expecting a calf. In heifer beef production, farmers want to fatten up heifers for slaughter and not for the production of calves.

|||||| Fig 48.5 Limousin heifers

Cull cow finishing

With up to one-fifth of the cows being replaced in some dairy herds annually, culled cows, if finished to the correct target weight, can be a source of additional income for dairy farmers. However, the culled cow must be well fleshed with a BCS of 3.5 to attain a conformation score of P+ and a fat score of 3L or 4L (low fat) after slaughter. The aim of this type of production is to maximise the value of the carcass. Culled cows can be finished off on grass or indoors on silage and concentrates; the target is a growth rate of 0.75 kg/day.

≡ General Husbandry for a Suckler Herd

Castration

Male calves not intended for breeding should be castrated at eight to 12 weeks old. First, the calf is immobilised. Castration is carried out using a burdizzo, which crushes the spermatic cord. This cuts off the blood supply to the testes. As a result, the testes die and shrivel up.

A castrated male is called a steer or a bullock. Castrated animals are easier to handle than bulls. Steers are unable to serve heifers in heat.

Dehorning a calf

Dehorning is done to prevent injury to other animals and to anyone handling the calf. In addition, non-pedigree calves destined to be sold must be dehorned, as it is illegal to sell animals with horns at the marts.

The calf is dehorned using a gas or electrical dehorning iron. If the calf is over two weeks old, a vet must anaesthetise the calf. The calf is placed in a dehorning crate; the hair around the horn bud is clipped. The dehorner is heated up and placed on the horn buds for about five seconds. The dehorner causes the tissue around and under the horn bud to die; it prevents horn growth and the horn bud falls off.

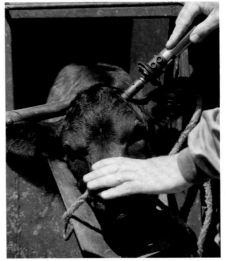

||||| Fig 48.6 A calf is dehorned

Tagging a calf

It is a legal requirement to tag newborn calves within 20 days of birth to ensure stock traceability. Two plastic tags are applied, one to each ear. The calf is then registered with the Calf Registration Agency.

Dosing

Large numbers of parasites set back calves' growth. Therefore, dose calves routinely, as they are susceptible to stomach and intestinal worms and liver fluke. In summer, dose calves for stomach worms and hoose, and when turned in to winter housing. After housing, dose calves for liver fluke.

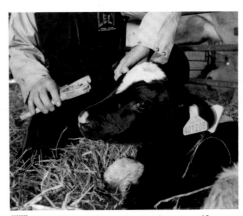

||||| Fig 48.7 A farmer tagging a calf

TB and brucellosis testing

TB and brucellosis are notifiable diseases. Since Ireland's declaration to be brucellosis free in 2009, herds need only be tested every 24 months, unless animals are being moved.

An eradication programme is in operation to control bovine tuberculosis. Herds must be regularly tested for reactors.

||||| Fig 48.8 A vet checking the result of a TB test, using callipers

<table>
<tr><td colspan="5" align="center">**Table 48.3 Diseases of cattle**</td></tr>
<tr><th>Disease</th><th>Cause</th><th>Symptoms</th><th>Treatment</th><th>Prevention</th></tr>
<tr>
<td>**Contagious abortion**</td>
<td>● Bacteria: Brucella abortus (zoonose)
● Notifiable disease; Ireland declared brucellosis free in July 2009</td>
<td>● Causes abortion or premature calving between the 5th and 8th months of gestation</td>
<td>● Cull infected cow
● Foetus and placenta sent to district vet office
● Disinfect all areas</td>
<td>● Maintain a closed herd
● Rear own replacement heifers
● Vaccinate heifers
● Purchase cattle from reliable sources
● Quarantine all bought-in stock</td>
</tr>
<tr>
<td>**Lameness**</td>
<td>● Numerous causes including bacterial infection of the hoof, overgrown hoof
● Swollen joints</td>
<td>● Cow constantly rests sore leg, limps
● Not feeding
● Failure to thrive</td>
<td>● Pare the hoof
● Treat with antibiotics for bacterial infection
● Dip hooves in disinfectant</td>
<td>● Routine hoof care
● Maintain good hygiene</td>
</tr>
<tr>
<td>**Liver fluke**</td>
<td>● Flatworm, endoparasite</td>
<td>● Failure to thrive
● Reduced milk production in dairy cattle, lower FCR in beef cattle
● Diagnosed by faecal examination for fluke eggs</td>
<td>● Dose cattle</td>
<td>● Dose animals regularly
● Drain land, fence off wet areas
● Keep vulnerable stock like calves away from wet areas
● Treat dairy cows when drying off</td>
</tr>
<tr>
<td>**Hoose**</td>
<td>● Nematode Dictyocaulus</td>
<td>● Young calves are susceptible to hoose
● Causes coughing and failure to thrive in calves</td>
<td>● Dose calves</td>
<td>● Good grassland management
● Graze dairy calves in leader-follower system</td>
</tr>
<tr>
<td>**Stomach worms**</td>
<td>● Nematode Ostertagia
● Cooperia</td>
<td>● Young calves are susceptible to stomach worms
● Causes scouring and failure to thrive</td>
<td>● Dose calves</td>
<td>● Good grassland management
● Graze dairy calves in the leader-follower system</td>
</tr>
</table>

See also bovine tuberculosis on page 57, grass tetany and milk fever on page 353, and mastitis on page 378.

Summary

- Calves in a suckler herd have a greater live weight gain than calves in calf to beef in two years.
- Most suckler herds in Ireland are spring-calving herds. This allows for the maximum utilisation of grass and reduces feed costs.
- The ideal suckler cow is a 50% dairy x 50% Continental beef animal possessing a good milk yield and good conformation.
- The most popular suckler dam is a Holstein-Friesian crossed with either a Limousin or a Simmental due to high growth rates, good conformation, and high lean-meat content on the carcass.
- In the suckler herd, the calf suckles the dam until it is weaned.
- The suckler herd should graze grass rotationally, using either a paddock or a strip-grazing system.
- Calves should creep graze ahead of the herd, using a creep gate which allows the calf access to better grass or to concentrates.
- Use heat detection aids, e.g. tail painting, or a vasectomised bull to identify cows coming back into heat.
- The reproductive efficiency of a suckler herd is defined as the number of calves weaned per 100 cows served.
- It takes longer for a suckler cow to come back into heat, as suckling and the calf's presence slows the onset of oestrus in the cow.
- Replacements for the suckler herd must be bred from cows and bulls of high genetic merit.
- Use a Hereford or an Aberdeen Angus bull on maiden heifers to prevent calving difficulties.
- A calving interval is the time elapsing between successive calving.
- Bull beef production is popular as bulls have a better FCR (food conversion ratio) and have greater carcass weights at slaughter.
- Heifer beef production uses beef crossed heifers from the dairy herd.
- Cull cow finishing are normally culled cows from dairy herds that are finished off and slaughtered.
- Castrate male calves not intended for breeding at eight to 12 weeks old.
- Dehorning prevents injury to other animals and to anyone handling the calf.
- Tagging a calf is a legal requirement for traceability of stock.
- Dose calves for stomach and intestinal worms, liver fluke and hoose.
- Test herds every 24 months for brucellosis. Test herds regularly for reactors.

QUESTIONS

1 Outline the characteristics of an ideal suckler dam.
2 Why is a purebred Holstein-Friesian unsuitable as a suckler cow?
3 A calf from a suckler herd is at a heavier live weight at weaning than a calf in the calf to beef system. Give a reason for this.
4 Describe the grazing management of a suckler herd out on grass.
5 Define reproductive efficiency and calving interval.
6 Calving difficulty can lead to high economic losses. Outline ways in which a farmer can prevent calving difficulties.
7 Explain the importance of restricting the cow's access to her calf once the calf is 30 days old.
8 Describe the importance of using AI in a suckler herd.
9 Using Table 48.2 on page 397 showing the index of calving difficulties, identify two sires that should not be used on a maiden heifer.
10 List the advantages and disadvantages of bull beef production.
11 Describe the importance of each of the following in a suckler herd:
 (a) Castration
 (b) Dosing
 (c) Dehorning the calf.

EXAM QUESTIONS

1 In a beef suckler system, describe the management practices necessary to achieve high levels of production. (LC, HL, 2007)
2 Two criteria used to measure the breeding management of a suckler herd are: (i) reproductive efficiency and (ii) calving interval. Explain the above terms and outline how they can be optimised in a spring-calving suckler herd. (LC, HL, 2008)
3 Account for the importance attached to the index of calving difficulty in AI sire catalogues. (LC, HL, 2010)
4 Highlight the main difference between bull beef production and heifer beef production. (LC, HL, 2010)

Glossary

A

abiotic factors The non-living factors in a habitat.

abomasum The fourth chamber of the ruminant stomach, which secretes gastric juices to break down protein and aid the final stage of digestion.

active immunity Acquired when the body is infected by bacteria or a virus. The body produces antibodies to fight the infection, which will persist to provide protection against the disease in the future.

active transport The movement of a substance from an area of low concentration to an area of high concentration against a concentration gradient; this movement requires energy.

allele An alternative form of the same gene.

anaerobic respiration Respiration that occurs in the absence of oxygen.

arteriole A small branch of an artery.

artificial selection A process by which humans breed plants and animals to ensure certain desirable traits.

autrophic An organism that makes its own food.

available water capacity The amount of water between the field capacity and permanent wilting point that is available for absorption by plant roots. Available water capacity = Field capacity – Permanent wilting point.

B

biochemical oxygen demand (BOD) The amount of dissolved oxygen needed to break down organic material in a 1 litre water sample.

biodiversity All living organisms within an ecosystem; this includes plants, animals and micro-organisms.

biotic factors The living factors in a habitat.

body condition scoring (BCS) BCS of cattle, sheep and pigs allows the animal produced to be assessed for the level of fat reserves an animal has at various production stages.

C

calving interval The time elapsed between successive calvings.

carnivore An animal that feeds on the flesh of other animals.

cast or draft ewe A ewe whose fertility has declined due to the harsh conditions experienced in mountainous areas. It is sold to a lowland farmer, where once on an improved plane of nutrition will continue to produce lambs for many years.

catch crops Fast-growing crops grown between two main crops when land would otherwise lie idle.

cation exchange The ability of soil particles (clay and humus) to attract, retain and release cations.

cation exchange capacity The quantity of cations that a soil absorbs. It can also be described as the capacity of a soil to exchange cations between the soil surfaces and the soil solution (water).

cementation in soil The binding together of soil particles; silt and sand particles are cemented together in aggregates during flocculation by clay particles.

chromosomes Chromosomes are composed of DNA and protein and are only visible during cell division.

colostrum The first milk secreted by mammals after giving birth. It is high in nutrients and antibodies and is essential for the survival of the newborn animal.

compensatory growth The increase in growth rate that occurs following a period of restricted feeding.

complete metamorphosis An insect life cycle where each stage of the cycle is physically different to the previous stage: Egg – larva – pupa – adult.

compound fertiliser Any fertiliser that contains two or more nutrient elements. Compound fertilisers are often produced by the combination of two or more straight fertilisers.

conformation The shape of an animal and the distribution of fat and muscle around its body.

contagious diseases Diseases easily transmitted by contact through bodily fluids, or through contamination of buildings, clothing or vectors.

crossbreeding Mating animals or plants from two different breeds, varieties or species.

D

diploid A cell is diploid or 2n when it has a full set of chromosomes.

diffusion The movement of a substance from an area of high concentration to an area of low concentration along a concentration gradient.

dominant gene Expressed in the phenotype when present in the genotype and normally represented by a capital letter.

dry matter (DM) The matter remaining in a sample of food after the water has been removed.

dry matter digestibility (DMD) The amount (percentage) of dry matter that can be digested by an animal.

dry matter intake (DMI) The amount of feed an animal consumes, excluding its water content.

E

Economic Breeding Index (EBI) A single figure profit index given in euro of profit per lactation for an animal's progeny compared to an average dairy cow.

ectoparasite An external parasitic organism that lives on the skin or exterior of the body.

edaphic factors Factors relating to the soil, soil pH, soil temperature and drainage.

endoparasite A parasitic organism that lives in the internal organs of an animal.

ensiling The process of storing grass or another crop in a silo, clamp or pit for preservation as silage.

eutrophication The enrichment of a habitat or environment with nutrients.

F

fertiliser An inorganic, manufactured material that may contain one or more of the essential elements required for crop growth.

field capacity The amount of water in a soil after the gravitational water has drained away.

flag leaf The uppermost leaf on a stem.

flocculation The clustering together of soil particles to create larger structures called floccules.

food conversion ratio (FCR) A measure of an animal's efficiency in converting a mass of food into body mass or live weight. It is expressed as a ratio of the food consumed in comparison to the live weight gained.

freemartin condition Occurs in mixed sex twin calves (one heifer calf and one bull calf). In the uterus, hormones from the male twin pass to the female twin. The male hormones masculinise the female and the result is called a freemartin. The female calf will be infertile and cannot be used for breeding. Her genitals will be smaller. This is a common outcome in cattle where mixed sex twin calves are born. It also occurs in sheep and pigs but is not as common.

fungicide A chemical that kills or inhibits the growth of fungi.

G

gamete Sex cells (sperm and egg). Gametes are haploid (see below).

gene A part of a chromosome that contains information to produce a protein.

genotype The genes present in the organism whether they are expressed or not.

geotropism A plant's growth response to gravity.

gilt A female pig that has not yet had a litter.

H

habitat The place where a plant or animal lives.

haploid A cell is haploid or n when it has half a set of chromosomes. Gametes are haploid.

heading dates The heading date of a grass species is the time when the ear emerges on the grass plant. Grass species are categorised as early, intermediate and late heading.

heading out When half the grass plants have produced seed heads.

herbicide A chemical that kills plants or inhibits their growth.

herbivore An animal that feeds on plant material.

hermaphrodite An organism that contains both male and female reproductive organs.

heterosis The advantage in performance of crossbred animals above the mid-parent mean of the two parent breeds.

heterotrophic An organism that cannot make its own food and relies on food made by other organisms.

heterozygous The alleles present in the genotype are not the same. The organism has one dominant and one recessive gene. Commonly known as a hybrid.

homozygous The alleles present in the genotype are the same, e.g. TT. True breeding.

humification The process by which soil organic matter is converted to humus.

humus The dark-coloured, decomposed plant and animal matter found in soil. It is rich in nutrients and contributes to soil structure.

hybrid vigour The increased productivity displayed by offspring from genetically different parents.

hygroscopic A substance that can absorb moisture from the atmosphere.

hygroscopic water Water that forms a thin film around a soil particle and is held on the surface of the particle by force of attraction. It cannot be removed from the soil and is unavailable to plants.

I

immunity The ability of an organism to resist disease through: the production of antibodies and white blood cells in response to exposure to the disease, inoculation against the disease, or the transfer of antibodies from a mother to her young.

inbreeding The mating of closely related animals that increases the chances of the offspring being affected by undesirable recessive traits.

incomplete dominance Occurs when two alleles are equally dominant and when both occur together in the genotype; the resulting phenotype is a blend of the two.

incomplete metamorphosis An insect life cycle where the immature insect (nymph) undergoes a series of moults. The nymph looks similar to the adult: Egg – nymph – adult.

infectious diseases Diseases caused by micro-organisms (bacteria, fungi or viruses) or other agents that enter the body of an organism.

inflorescence The fixed arrangement of spikelets on the stem.

ion exchange This process takes place in soil where ions are attracted to soil particles and held on the surface of these particles. This is known as adsorption. The clay soil particles contain ions of their own and release these particles in exchange.

L

Law of Independent Assortment States that during gamete formation, members of a pair of alleles segregate and move into the gametes independently of any other pair of alleles.

leaching Soluble matter, such as minerals, dissolves in water filtering through soil and is carried downward. The leached minerals may accumulate at a lower horizon.

livestock unit (LU) A measurement of livestock grazing. One livestock unit (LU) is equivalent to one dairy cow or one suckler cow. It can be used to determine how much grazing and winter fodder is needed on a farm. One livestock unit requires 12 tonnes of herbage annually. This value can be used to determine the total quantity of herbage required on the farm for the herd.

loam A soil that contains equal amounts of sand, silt and clay.

lodging (of a cereal) The tendency of cereal crops to bend over, so that they lie more or less flat on the ground. This makes it impossible to harvest the crop and reduces the yield.

M

maintenance diet The amount of feed that allows an animal to maintain a constant body weight.

manure An organic material that consists of the wastes of plants and animals.

Mendel's Law of Segregation When gametes are formed only one allele from a pair of alleles is carried in the gamete.

metabolisable energy The energy from feed that an animal can convert into LWG, milk and wool and is measured in MU/kg.

metamorphosis A process of development in insects.

milk pricing system Represented by the equation A + B − C where A represents kg of protein, B represents kg of fat and C is volume of water.

multiple alleles When a characteristic is controlled by two or more alleles, the alleles are called multiple alleles.

N

notifiable disease A disease which must be reported to the district veterinary office if it is infectious and highly contagious.

O

omasum The third chamber of the ruminant stomach which squeezes food and reabsorbs water and liquids.

omnivore An animal that feeds on both plant and animal material.

osmosis The movement of water across a semipermeable membrane from an area of high water concentration to an area of low water concentration.

P

parasite An organism that lives on another host organism. The parasite usually benefits at the expense of the host and may cause damage to the host.

passive immunity Short-term immunity acquired by a young animal through the mother's milk in the days following birth or across the placenta.

pathogen A micro-organism that causes a disease.

performance testing The evaluation of a bull's performance by comparing its weight gain and food conversion ratio with other bulls kept under similar feed and housing conditions.

peristalsis Food entering the oesophagus is moved along to the stomach by muscular contractions that have a rhythmic, wave-like motion.

permanent wilting point The point at which no more capillary water can be removed from a soil by plant roots. Plants will die from drought if the soil in which they are growing reaches its permanent wilting point.

pesticide A chemical used to kill pests, particularly insects or rodents.

pH A measure of the concentration of the hydrogen ions in a solution. It can also be expressed as the negative log of the hydrogen ion concentration: $-\log_{10}[H^+]$

phenotype Outward appearance of the organism.

phototropism A plant's growth response to light.

pig dentition

I: $\frac{3}{3}$ C: $\frac{1}{1}$ P: $\frac{4}{4}$ M: $\frac{3}{3}$

podzolisation Occurs in acidic pH conditions where minerals such as iron and aluminium are leached from the A horizon, leaving it bleached in colour. They accumulate in the B horizon, forming an iron pan that is impermeable to water.

pollination The transfer of pollen from the anther of one flower to the stigma of another flower of the same species.

polyploidy A cell that contains more than two sets of chromosomes, e.g. triploid (3n), tetraploid (4n), octoploid (8n).

production diet The extra amount of feed required to produce 1 kg of LWG, 1 litre of milk, 1 kg of wool, or to produce a calf or lamb.

progeny testing The evaluation of the performance of a bull's offspring compared to other bulls' offspring under similar feed and housing conditions.

R

recessive gene Expressed only when an individual has no dominant gene present; usually represented with a lower-case letter.

reproductive efficiency The reproductive efficiency of a suckler herd is the number of calves weaned per 100 cows served.

respiration

Glucose + Oxygen → Carbon dioxide + Water + Energy

$C_6H_{12}O_6 + 6O_2 \rightarrow 6CO_2 + 6H_2O +$ Energy

reticulum The second chamber of the ruminant stomach which regurgitates partially digested material back to the mouth for further chewing.

rumen The first chamber of the ruminant stomach which contains microbes that break down cellulose anaerobically.

ruminant animal Has a four-chambered stomach which is modified and adapted for the digestion of cellulose.

ruminant dentition (cow, sheep)

I: $\frac{0}{3}$ C: $\frac{0}{1}$ P: $\frac{3}{3}$ M: $\frac{3}{3}$

S

saprophyte An organism that breaks down dead and decaying organic matter.

seasonally polyoestrous (sheep) Having many oestrous cycles during a set time of year.

selective reabsorption The process by which the body reabsorbs certain molecules for use in the body by active transport.

separation in soil Soil aggregates are broken up within the soil. Large cracks may develop in the soil and this damages its overall structure.

sex-linkage (X-linkage) A gene that is found on the X chromosome but there is no copy on the Y chromosome.

soil biomass The total mass of living material in a habitat.

soil profile A vertical section through the soil from ground level to bedrock, showing all of the soil horizons.

soil texture A measure of the proportion of different-sized mineral particles (sand, silt and clay) that are found in a soil sample.

straight (simple) fertiliser Contains only one of the essential elements.

symbiotic relationship This occurs when two different species have a close relationship that benefits both organisms.

T

tillering The development of side shoots in a plant.

topping Mowing grass to a height of 5–7 cm. It is carried out post grazing to remove any remaining grass. Topping cuts grass to the correct post-grazing height and encourages tillering. It can also be used to control weeds.

translocation The movement of sugars produced in the leaves to other regions of the plant.

transpiration The loss of water by evaporation from the leaves.

tropism A plant's growth response to an external stimulus.

V

venule A small branch of a vein.

vertebrate An animal that has a backbone or spinal column.

volatilisation A process where ammonium ions are converted to ammonia gas, which is then lost to the atmosphere.

Z

zoonose A disease that can pass from animals to humans.

zoospore A mobile spore; each spore has two flagella that help the spore to move.

Index